WHEN THE ASHES BURN

Local police thought George Picket was little more than a serial complainer, but as Chairman of the Chelmsford Allotment Society, the summer's run-in with a wayward group of youths had begun to reach ever more serious heights. Then one late October evening a single match lights a trail of suburban death and destruction, whose dreadful hidden consequences reach far beyond the innocent allotment plots.

Freelance reporter Jack Latimer takes up Picket's case, completely unaware of the millennial nightmare the Chairman's tale will unearth. A severed head, a badly bungled drugs deal, a dead hangman's grandson and the menace of juvenile crime are just some of the elements Jack will encounter in reporting a story which threatens to destroy not only his career, but his very life, too.

When the Ashes Burn is a chilling, truly horrifying psychological thriller from a highly talented young British novelist.

WHEN THE ASHES BURN

Phil Lovesey

HarperCollins*Publishers*

This novel is entirely a work of fiction. The names, characters and incidents portrayed in it are the work of the author's imagination. Any resemblance to actual persons, living or dead, events or localities is entirely coincidental.

Collins Crime
An imprint of HarperCollins*Publishers*
77–85 Fulham Palace Road, London W6 8JB

First published by Collins Crime 2000

1 3 5 7 9 10 8 6 4 2

A catalogue record for this book is available from the British Library

ISBN 0 00 232680 9

Typeset in Meridien and Bodoni by Palimpsest Book Production Limited, Polmont, Stirlingshire

Printed and bound in Great Britain by Caledonian International Book Manufacturing Ltd, Glasgow

For Luc – for fourteen years

PART 1

PREPARING THE GROUND

1

His hands shook for three reasons.

It was cold.

It was his first ever cigarette.

He was scared witless.

The faintest smell of October's creosote was quickly smothered by the acrid fug of the embered Marlboro. Daft choice, Marlboros, far too strong for a novice, a first-timer like him. But he wasn't to know. He had no knowledge about cigarettes, was simply glad to have found a corner shop far enough from home in which the owner wouldn't recognize him, just sell him the things, no questions asked. In case anything went wrong.

In case anyone caught him.

He tried to smother a cough. Got to keep quiet, small, invisible. Out there in the freezing black, crouched below the cobwebbed glass, entombed in the wooden shed. Isolated.

Damn! Out went the cigarette. Another match, a second shaking attempt to relight it. How his mother would have shrunk with shame to have seen him there, a secret inhaler. But it simply *had* to be this way, hidden by the night. Everything was so much more convenient, fated almost. As if it had all been leading to this one snatched chance, this golden nicotinic opportunity.

But there was so little room for error. He'd get into a lot of trouble if he was discovered, cramped inside the allotment shed.

From somewhere in the distance came the muted thud of premature pyrotechnics, the muffled boom of an expensive firework detonating in the late-October sky. Plenty more of those to come, he mused, a hundred thousand celebratory rockets were no doubt set to screech skywards as the millennium approached. Encroached. Smothered him.

But for now, he was more concerned about the matter literally in hand. He'd reached the rather appalling conclusion that for the cigarette to stay alight, he'd be required to actually take a puff. Insert the thing. Draw the smoke in, watch the glowing tip fire briefly in the stifling gloom.

So he did. Because he *had* to.

Done. Just the one puff, smoke filling his cheeks, throat closing to forbid further progress to the virgin-pink of his unblemished lungs. Then, just as quickly exhaling, feeling the warm exhaust swirl angrily round his cold head, stinging both eyes, as if enraged by his halt to its natural bronchial pathway, a job half-done.

But done.

He rose giddily to his feet, leaving the rest of the pack on a tiny slanting shelf heavy with grimy bottles of tomato-feed, blood and bone meal fertilizers. He didn't want another cigarette, ever. He would run the hottest bath when he got back home, scrub the offending pollution from his body – bliss. He sneaked a peak through the tiny, cracked window, his dark adapted eye making out other allotment sheds standing like silent sentries guarding their sleeping owners' patches of lovingly tended ground.

Now he paused to listen, not trusting his eyes alone. It simply wouldn't do to be spotted, remembered leaving by some late-night dog-walker ambling home on the pathway bordering the site.

No one. Just the distant swish of occasional traffic. Perfect.

He dropped the still smouldering cigarette on the tinder-dry shed floor, making no attempt to heel it out. Simply watching for a moment as it lay dangerously abandoned beside a brittle pile of yellowing newspapers.

Then left for home.

2

Jack Latimer smiled wearily at the pretty young Asian girl waiting for him just beyond the ticket barrier.

'C.F.,' he said, drawing level, planting a kiss on her flawless cheek. 'I'm thirty-six years old. I think I can just about manage to make my way over to Liverpool Street on my own.'

She beamed back. 'Just call it devotion to the job,' she replied, voice competing with the throbbing hum of idling engines. 'Plus it gets me out of the office for a day.'

A group of back-packers blundered past, Swedish tourists, blonde and noisy, keen to savour the best of the capital waiting outside Euston's bustling concourse.

'A day?' Jack said, stifling a yawn. 'Can't really say I'm in the mood for a trip to the tower in an open-topped bus, C.F.'

'Nottingham didn't go so well, then?'

He sighed, taking her arm and steering her towards the crammed tube escalators. 'Complete balls-up. The guy just never showed. The address didn't match, or the phone numbers. Two days out and all I've come back with is a fair to middling hangover, and a used ticket to see the Robin Hood Experience.'

'Used? You must have been drunk.'

'You're right, I don't remember a thing.'

Which wasn't quite truthful. Wasn't anywhere near truthful. The tired freelance journalist remembered nearly every moment of the promising story which had turned to dust as he spent the best part of forty-eight hours touring Nottingham and its suburbs for leads which simply never appeared.

OK, it hadn't been the most promising of potential stories,

dramatic certainly, but riddled with dangerous implausibility. A police contact had told Jack that they'd just nicked a quartet of Essex villains in Devon a few days before their intended crime spree began. Apparently the plan involved automated banking machines and small amounts of Semtex explosive. Further questioning revealed the unlucky foursome had purchased the sandy-coloured putty from a middleman in Nottingham, thought to be selling arms and explosives from a renegade former IRA cell operating in the Midlands area.

Given a few names and addresses, Jack had set off to delve a little deeper into a story that had so far eluded the overstretched resources at the Serious Crimes and Anti-Terrorism Unit.

It was a chance story – a gamble. A hundred-to-one shot that he'd find anyone willing to name names, point fingers. The result and cost to Latimer Associates so far – two days out of the office for its one and only reporter, and roughly three hundred in travel and expenses down the pan.

He smiled at C.F. as she sat opposite him on the crowded Central Line train, glad she'd made the effort to come and meet him, fully understanding the lure of a day out in the big city as opposed to taking the occasional phone call in a shabby office above a kebab shop opposite Chelmsford's decrepit bus station.

She was making faces at him now, poking out her tongue and rolling her eyes as others in the crammed carriage looked away, returned to paperbacks and early editions of the evening papers. He felt himself loosening up, aped a finger up his nose, forefinger bent, as if he'd sunk three inches of digit into his left nostril. Then began grinding it around, knowing she still loved that, briefly remembering the mix of childish intrigue and collusive mischief which had greeted the sight fifteen years earlier, when as a quiet six-year-old she'd blushed, then giggled at Daddy's strange new friend.

And as his friendship with Anwar Patel strengthened, she came to call him 'Uncle Jack', looking forward to his visits, his instinctive childish lunacy. He called her C.F., Coffee-Face, acronyming her soft brown complexion into their special

6

secret name, one she had grown to cherish. But only from Jack. At twenty-one Veema Patel had matured into a headstrong young woman whose soft dark eyes were not to be confused with the confident individual underneath. Her last boyfriend had made the unfortunate mistake of saying Jack's nickname was overtly racist. She dumped him the same night.

'So what's the next move?' she asked her boss as they sat over coffees in Liverpool Street Station. 'Wait for more contacts from Nottingham?'

He frowned. 'I think it's a dead one, C.F. Another for the Maybe One Day file.'

'If there's room. It's starting to bulge in there, Jack.'

'And whose bloody fault is that?' he replied sharply, instantly regretting it, seeing the tiny recoil as her head jumped fractionally back. Jesus, he was tired, and barking at C.F. just made matters worse. Truth was, as always, she was right. Saleable freelance stories were getting thinner and thinner as both broadsheets and tabloids filled their pages with as much cheap millennium fodder as the public seemed to be able to lap up. Nine weeks to the big moment, and all Jack's standby outlets were wallowing in millennium supplements and Y2K double-page spreads which sat garishly on the pages he'd once had a fair chance of sliding a juicy exposé on to. Times had been worse for Jack and C.F. – but not that much. Small though the business was – just the two of them and a hundred square feet of Chelmsford's least salubrious office space – overheads would soon start tumbling into overdrafts. He'd already secretly cut his own salary in order that C.F. had something of a Christmas bonus to look forward to, but there was no denying that after the Nottingham cock-up, Latimer Associates badly needed something newsworthy and saleable.

He put far too much sticky brown sugar into his coffee. 'Anything else arrived while I was searching for the merry men up north?'

'Nothing much,' she replied, still watching him warily.

'Look, I'm sorry I snapped.'

'It's OK.'

'I'm just, you know . . .'

'Tired.'

'Yeah.'

C.F. waited until they'd rushed and rumbled through Romford until she told him about her persistent caller.

'There was something,' she said, sensing from the way his leg jumped that he was desperate for a cigarette. She'd known him too long, and wished he wouldn't, wished he'd chuck the damn things away for real – not just for her benefit. Because she knew *why* he did that, pretended to crush a half-smoked pack, feigned a little too much disgust at himself whenever he lit up – he didn't want to remind her of her father. It was Jack's best shot at being sensitive, done for the right reasons, but hopelessly misjudged. C.F. would far rather he'd have simply carried on puffing away at his twenty a day, because the present pantomime merely reminded her of a father whose blackened sticky lungs were gradually taking him away from her, cough by agonizing cough.

'Something?' he replied.

'Nothing to do with the Nottingham business. A local thing.'

Warning bells began tolling inside Jack's head. He'd had his fill of 'local' stories, depressing bits of half-news eagerly given by excited Chelmsfordians keen to see their son, daughter, nephew, niece, dog in the papers. And inevitably, when times were tough, Latimer Associates reluctantly took such pieces, relying on Jack's journalistic talents to embellish them into something the *Essex Chronicle* might part with a hundred quid for.

He tried massaging some life into his dry face, fingers working the flesh to the gentle rocking of the speeding coaches. So this was it, back from a potential fifteen-hundred payday, for a cheap and cheerful piece of local tat. Still, it was all news, as his old editor used to say. All worthy of accurate reporting. He tried to smile, but couldn't. He'd really wanted Nottingham to come good.

'A very persistent man,' C.F. continued. 'Must have rung five or six times at least.'

'It's your sexy telephone voice,' he replied, watching the barren Essex flatlands fly by outside, the same feeling creeping into his belly whenever he returned – what in God's name was he doing in Chelmsford? *Really* doing? How did a once aspiring, talented young journalist end up above a kebab shop in an undistinguished little town? And as always, the nearer the train got, the more complex the answers became. Amy, his ex-wife still lived there, enjoying the quiet security of the four-bedroom detached house he'd so easily walked away from four years earlier. A terrible day which still haunted him, time failing to heal the wounds, erase the memories. The temper again, his refusal to abandon principles, embrace a little forgiveness and understanding. For he hadn't just walked from a wife, but a son as well – Alex, the thirteen-year-old pride and joy he now only got to hug every other weekend.

How different it must have once appeared on the outside. Jack and Amy Latimer, the perfect media couple, him a reporter, her a radio agony aunt, one son – the ideal picture of suburban happiness to all but those who stepped inside, heard the rows, witnessed the vitriol, watched as the ideal loving little family tore itself apart.

So, much as he despised the town, Jack couldn't face leaving. After the divorce, when logically the entire western world beckoned as his potential oyster, he'd moved less than three miles into a one-bedroomed flat, realizing he loved his son far more than he loathed Chelmsford.

As a trembling father holding a trusting bundle wrapped in a warm hospital towel, Jack had made a whispered promise into the soft sleeping face – that he'd be there for Alex, always. And, regardless of his temper, occasional lapses in human diplomacy, anyone who really knew Jack Latimer knew him to be a man of his word. Though, in truth, the nobility of the sentiment had cost him dear to date. For as others had learnt to their emotional cost, teaching the benefits of flexibility to a man of principles could prove to be a highly frustrating experience.

C.F.'s voice hauled him back to the here and now. 'He's really keen to see you. Won't tell me a thing. Says he wants to speak to you personally.'

'Who?'

'George Picket's his name.' She paused, remembering. 'There was something about the voice, Jack. He spoke almost in a whisper, as though . . .'

'What?' he said, watching as she frowned, dismissed whatever she was going to say.

'I talked to DS Samson about him. Just a hunch, you know, in case he was a phone pervert.'

'I follow,' Jack replied, glad she'd had the sense to turn to his old friend Kenny Samson. Not that C.F. couldn't handle herself when he went away, and the smitten Greek owners of Kebab Korner wouldn't fight to the death if anyone came looking for her – but sometimes he just felt uncomfortable about leaving her there, responsible, somehow. He'd made a fair few enemies over the years, investigative journalism tends to court them as potential paydays, and it hadn't been unknown for postal threats to reach his office floor. Trouble was, sooner or later, most of Jack's 'potential paydays' walked out of prison, and sometimes made attempts to find the weasel who'd exposed their particular scam. It was another reason he preferred Chelmsford, always travelled second class on trains and only drove pre-booked hire cars – professional anonymity. 'And?'

'He laughed when I told him about Picket. Said he was just a sort of serial complainer, always walking into New Street to have a go about something or other. He said you were going to love him.'

'I hate him already,' Jack replied, as the train swept under the first of three bridges, signalling its imminent arrival in Jack's reluctant home town. 'I'm going to wish I was back in Nottingham doing bugger-all, aren't I? Couldn't you have steered this Picket guy in the *Chronicle*'s direction?'

'He said they were a lazy bunch of donkeys.'

He smiled, relieved to be less than two minutes from a cigarette. 'Well, C.F., at least our Mr Picket sounds like a fair judge of character. We'll look him up when we get back. Who knows, he could turn out to be a bigger payday than Nottingham, eh?'

'Sure,' she said, anxious to sound equally keen, unwilling

10

to admit she wouldn't be heartbroken never to speak to George Picket again. For although she'd never thought of herself in any way psychic or intuitive, something about the flat reserved voice on the phone had quite chilled her to the bone.

3

Dave Higgs hugged himself closer into his young lover's back. It was gone two in the morning, and despite the athletic sex – almost too demanding for an old queen his age – champagne and brandy chasers, he still couldn't sleep. Fear kept him awake, a stomach-churning dread which filtered its way effortlessly into his nightmares when his eyelids occasionally shut and sealed him from the real world.

He stroked the broad muscular back, kissed the soft nape of the neck, gently rousing the younger man from his deep, oblivious sleep.

'We have to talk,' he whispered urgently.

The young man groaned, turned to face him, tried to smother his lips with a dry kiss.

Higgs drew back. 'Talk,' he repeated, moving the strong wandering hand from his groin to his chest.

'OK,' came the sleepy reply, laced with cheek. 'Afterwards.'

'Now. It's very important.'

The younger man pulled away, sighing slightly. 'Not now. Not again.'

'I have to know.'

'I can't tell you anything, Dave. I love you too much.'

'Love isn't going to keep us alive if this goes wrong,' Higgs hissed. 'I'm so fucking worried. I can't sleep for worrying.'

'You're always worried.'

'Because I know what my brother's like,' Higgs replied, fervently hoping the boy would drop the chivalrous-lover act. For God's sake, didn't he understand the danger they were in? Didn't he, more than anyone, realize the damage his brother meted out for offences far less serious than this one? And if the psychotic bastard ever discovered what the two of them had done, no amount of love in the known universe would save them. They'd be found in pieces, a stark warning to others that in the Higgs family blood wasn't thicker than water, piss, or any other bodily fluid. 'He'll kill us. It's that simple. I have to know what you did.'

'The less you know the better.'

'For fuck's sake . . . !'

'Don't get all angry.'

Higgs got out of bed, ran shaking fingers through his greying ponytail. 'How can I put this in words you'll understand,' he said, voice trembling with emotion. 'I really appreciated you helping me . . .'

'No problem.'

'Shut up and listen!'

'Sorry.'

'And now I want you to help me again. Tell me what you did, so at least I can put things right.'

The young man smiled back. 'What you don't know can't hurt you. I tell you, and you'll worry even more.'

Higgs sat at the edge of the bed, head in his hands. 'I don't know how much more of this I can fucking take. I really don't.'

Large rough hands began clumsily massaging his shoulders. 'But I did it for you,' his lover replied. 'So you wouldn't worry any more. You went all . . . all sort of stupid. Crying an' that. I just wanted to help. That's why I did it. I was only taking the problem away. So you wouldn't cry any more. Crying's horrible. Sad. I didn't like you sad.'

Higgs took a deep breath, realizing the conversation was headed in the same endless frustrating circle of the past two weeks, and that maybe, just maybe, there was a twisted kind of sense in what the young boy said. Perhaps it *was* better he didn't know the precise details. Perhaps the boy, for all his misplaced optimism, was right, and that ignorance in this instance, was a kind of fearful bliss.

He'd get no more from the boy that night, and while instinct told him to try harder, batter down the defences with desperate rage and bullying, cowardice took over. The same yellow streak which had allowed his lover out into the night on the fateful day in question. Because he'd been right about that one – Higgs had been glad at the time that the problem walked with him. It was only later, hours later, as he lay waiting for familiar footsteps to return, that he thought to guess at his brother's reactions if he'd known what was happening.

They made love, Higgs lying back while his lover went to work with his tongue, but finding no peace in the physical sensations, knowing all the while that if Martin had the merest inkling of what had happened, they'd both be dead.

He finally drifted into restless sleep at five in the morning, cursing the cowardice which had placed both their lives in such imminent danger.

When he woke at ten, the flat was empty, and he was left alone for another day wondering if this one would be his last.

4

It was just past eleven in the morning and a weak winter's sun was fighting a losing battle to penetrate the thick grey sky. In the thin quarter-of-a-mile strip which housed the Chelmsford Avenues Allotments, George Picket had been shovelling a pile of soggy grey ashes into a wet heap for half an hour before Bill Kent arrived to tend his own rectangular patch of dew-damp earth. The seventy-two-year-old made his way cautiously over to the Chairman's former shed.

'Terrible thing, George,' he said, watching as Picket flung a charred piece of former timber on to the pile. 'Heard the commotion on Wednesday night, wondered what all the sirens were about.'

'Fire engines,' Picket replied grimly. 'Took two of them to put the blaze out. Damn thing went up like a tinderbox.'

'I'm sorry, George, really. Disgusting, it is.'

Picket leant against his spade, ignoring the rheumatic pains which shot through his shoulder. He was sweating under his coat, despite the cold. 'I told them,' he said. 'Told them all – police, the lot. Told them something like this was going to happen. And now it has. They've gone and burnt down my shed.'

'Gone too far in my book, George.'

'For too damn long, Bill.'

'What do the police say now?'

'Nothing,' Picket said bitterly. 'They reckon without proof, they can't bring charges. Bunch of lazy incompetent fools, if you ask me. Little wonder the damn country's going to rack and ruin.'

Kent stared back, frowning. 'But we both know the little

sods who did it. The same little yobbos who've been terrorizing us all summer.'

Picket returned to the spadework, voice shrinking back barely above his trademark whisper, controlled, simmering 'Lost count of the number of times I've been up to New Street since May, Bill. Twenty, thirty, maybe more. And each time it's the same lecture about "under-resourced manpower" or "insufficient evidence". Plus there's the fact that they can't do anything about the young hoodlums until they turn fourteen. Law's an ass.'

'So until then, they just let them burn down our property?'

'That's about the measure of it, yes.'

'And dig up our vegetables?' Kent pressed, recalling a gruelling summer under siege by a five-strong gang of wayward children. 'Throw their excrement around, abuse us, break into our sheds, smoke their drugs, leave their disgusting contraceptives for us to find? And the police still won't do a thing?'

'Nothing,' Picket replied, massaging his aching back. At sixty-one, his hard-worked joints sometimes made him feel fifteen years older, but the digging was a therapy of sorts – mental therapy, working a fraction of his rage to the surface, dispensing it through physical effort. For in his mind he was digging their graves, five six-foot-deep holes, in which he'd roughly shove their broken bodies. No coffins, no last rites. Just the worms for company, beetles to devour their eyes.

'It's not right, George,' Kent told the Chairman. 'And it's getting worse. How many more sheds are they going to burn before someone does something?'

Picket stopped, wiped the cold sweat from his brow, stood tall over the spade. 'Know what some cocky young sergeant told me?'

'No idea.'

'That we should mount some sort of undercover surveillance operation. Get one of those video camera things, record them next time they're on allotment property.'

Kent thought about it for a moment. In all honesty, it didn't sound like such a bad idea, but one look at the Chairman's face told him to keep his opinion to himself. He'd long since learned that for all George Picket's apparently quiet demeanour, the polite facade occasionally gave way to a volatile temper, stinging rebuffs and sarcastic retribution. Maybe now wasn't the time to concur with such a plan. He opted for what he supposed was the correct response. 'Sounds like they want us to do their job for them,' he said quietly.

'Exactly what I told them,' Picket replied coldly. 'Bunch of workshy liberals. All it takes is for someone in authority to instil a bit of respect into these little thugs. Parents aren't going to do it, schools are too goddamned afraid to raise a hand to them, is it any wonder they run wild?' He rammed the spade into the ashes with real venom. 'Children are animals, Bill, savages. Born that way. Just the nature of things. They need to be trained, disciplined, taught how to behave in society.'

'The velvet glove, iron fist,' Kent added, secretly terrified his own shed would soon end up the same way as the Chairman's. It had been broken into three times already since July, windows smashed, compost bags emptied, tools stolen, germinating seeds stamped and scattered. And now this, the latest outrage – arson – and the police reluctant to stop those responsible.

It had started on a Sunday afternoon in late June. Kent had been first to hear the commotion, a chorus of abusive kids, some on bikes, boys and girls, racing round the allotments like animals. One or two other holders soon joined him, watching in disbelief as the five-strong gang began tearing down raspberry canes, ripping young runner beans from their netting, riding their bikes over months of careful tending.

They'd watched in stunned silence, too shocked by the scene, frozen. The two largest boys on bikes were getting closer, laughing, playing to the horrified audience, uncon-cerned at the mayhem.

Then the Chairman arrived, running quickly across the path that led from the bottom of Second Avenue alongside the allotment strip. The others watched as George Picket rounded on the youngsters, roaring in fury, yet only receiv-ing more abuse by way of return – obscene gestures, filthy

17

language, more hysterical laughter, before they eventually rode away, the two girls clinging to the elder boys' waists, a much younger lad pedalling like fury to keep up behind. In moments they were away down the path, then out of sight, cutting up Fifth Avenue, laughter receding.

But that night, the real damage began. Windows had been broken in the sentry-box sheds, plants destroyed. It was the beginning of an extraordinary summer for the Avenues allotment holders, never knowing when they returned to their carefully tended plots what new acts of pointless vandalism awaited them.

As Chairman, Picket had been to the Borough Council, police and local newspapers to complain – always to be met by the same wall of indifference, yet more excuses for buck-passing inactivity. And all the while, the siege continued.

Police told Picket that they most likely knew who the young culprits were – he'd had enough chances to give them a reasonable description after all. They promised to send an officer to 'have a word' with them. Which only seemed to make matters worse. The gang now had a focus point – George Picket – and set about daubing appallingly misspelt slogans on his own, larger shed. He'd almost lost count of the number of times he'd had to sand the black marker-pen and spray-paint away – *Pikets a cunt!* – in two-foot-high letters appearing overnight more times than he could remember.

And although the Chairman was reluctant to admit it, the undercover spying operation was an option he'd already secretly tried, lying in wait as the night enfolded him, hoping the little sods would turn up at any moment, keen to leap out, crack their heads together and take his belt to them, just as he'd done to his own son.

For George Picket knew well the power of punishment, the ability of even the simplest-minded individual to respond to the threat of more pain. Fear was the greatest corrector. Inflicting stinging damage *did* bring pleasure to the inflictor – the pleasure of dispensing justice, building a higher moral code, righting the wayward individual. For George Picket, it seemed searingly obvious that if a great deal more pain was dished out earlier, then it would save a hell of a lot of suffering later.

Despite his repeated pleas to New Street Police Station, he was steadfastly denied the known names and addresses of the children making his life such a misery. Indeed, after the fourth request in writing he was summoned by a station superintendent to be given a patronizing lecture about the dangers of vigilantes, coupled with the less than convincing promise that the police would 'double their efforts to contain the problem'. But as Picket acidly pointed out, double nothing's nothing.

Bill Kent began helping the Chairman shovel ashes into a series of green garden sacks. 'Make good fertilizer, anyhow, George,' he tried. 'And I take it you were insured.'

'Cold comfort,' Picket replied. 'I put a new shed up, and it's an invitation to burn it down again.'

'Could be bait, though, couldn't it?' Kent added cautiously. 'Set a trap for them.' Then realized what he'd just said, and backtracked. 'But I suppose we'd be back to doing the police's job.'

'Exactly.'

They shovelled in heavy silence for several minutes, filling three sacks.

'So what are we going to do?' Kent asked finally.

Picket leant on his shovel, glad he'd had the foresight to keep his most precious tools the short distance across the path back in his own home. Not that that was sacred any more, either. He heard them – always at night, while the rest of the town slept on unawares. But not *them*. They'd found him, knew where he lived, came to torment him while he slept, foul-mouthed abuse from unseen assailants, over and over, until he cracked, raced downstairs, hurled open the front door . . . to nothing, just the mocking silence of the night.

Sometimes it would take him a full hour in the morning to regain his composure, sitting quite still in the kitchen as dawn filtered through the ageing glass, the only movement practised circles from his wrists as he polished his black leather shoes, eyes fixed firmly to his own darkly distorted reflection, jaw aching from the tension, planning, always planning . . .

'I'm going to try the papers again,' Picket suddenly announced. 'See if they'll back me, now there's been a fire. For God's sake, there's enough inconsequential nonsense in there to make this the front page.'

'The *Essex Chronicle*?' Kent replied. 'They didn't want to know, did they? Full of millennium stuff week after week.'

'Going to try a different tack, Bill. Miss Baxter told me about some freelance chap on Duke Street. Always on the lookout for stories, apparently. If I get him involved, maybe it'll carry more weight.'

'Freelance journalist? On Duke Street?'

'Apparently.'

'Whereabouts?'

Picket paused, scanned the nearby path, senses alerted in case *they* returned like criminals to the scene of the crime. 'Above a kebab shop.'

'Hardly Pulitzer, is it?'

Picket met the quip with a menacing stare. 'Any other suggestions, Mr Kent?'

Kent quickly shook his head and began tying up the green plastic sacks.

5

It wasn't easy being Alex Latimer.

Not simply for being what he was, a rather insecure thirteen-year-old, but also for *who* he was – son of 'Agony' Amy Latimer, star of Phoenix Radio's evening telephone problem show, and popular sniggering favourite of Alex's classmates and contemporaries. Sexual items discussed on the show inevitably caused him the most distress, as jeering pupils at the grant-maintained Hector Rudge High School for Boys repeated almost word for word his mother's well-meaning advice on any number of topics from masturbation, impotence, sexually transmitted diseases, erection problems and almost every night, it seemed, female orgasms.

And sometimes, the crude asides weren't solely from the other boys. Masters, too, had been known to make the occasional stinging quip regarding his mother's profession, leaving Alex to feel the painful reddening of a threatening blush as his classmates cheered and roared their approval.

Perhaps, he'd often wondered, things might have been different if he'd had an older brother at the school, a larger boy, carrying the scars of a fearful reputation, a muscled playground monster who'd protect his soft-skinned younger brother. But as an only child, Alex could only dream of such a champion. In reality he had no one, whatever friends he had soon drifted away when they saw the other boys coming, leaving Alex to stand and take it alone.

Only once had he felt so frightened and enraged that he'd tried to fight back – a pathetically short and undignified struggle which had resulted in a split lip, bruised back, and both boys in conference with the unamused headmaster and parents after school. Only Alex's dad wasn't there. Alex's dad was 'away' on yet another newspaper story. And worse, when listeners to Phoneix Radio tuned in later that night, they were greeted by a shocked Amy Latimer saying she was devoting the evening's agony hour to the appalling subject of playground bullying, since that very afternoon her own dear son had become the target of 'insignificant, cowardly yobs'.

The very next day, he had another black eye for her troubles. Only this time he didn't complain to staff, just took the thump, went home, told his shocked mother it was a delayed memento from the first occasion. But he'd learned a valuable lesson. Keep everything inside. Keep it all buttoned up. And whilst he understood his mother's concern, he had no wish for any more of his life to be made a public soap opera on her programme.

So whenever she asked how he was, he'd always reply – OK. Alex was always 'OK'.

Money was never really a problem in the Latimer household, his mother earned a tidy sum, and his father gave what he could; so when Alex asked for a top-of-the-range Pentium computer, he got one. Then excitedly discovered a new world as he sat alone in the house, whiling the evenings away while his mother blathered to Essex's sexually pained population. A world of exotic, brightly coloured landscapes, where he was king, making decisions, questing for great trophies, using his considerable intellect to solve cryptic puzzles and defeat heinous foes, his fingers flying over the keyboard, CD-ROM buzzing and swooshing softly until his mother returned.

And gradually, the grubby complications of the real world began to matter less, replaced by smoother landscapes, virtual armies awaiting his orders, obedient, faithful.

The termly reports began getting worse, as subject master after subject master declared Alex 'must try harder' or 'seems to have lost interest'. Again, more lectures from his mother, another bout of kitchen-table soul-searching, Alex feeling slight pangs of guilt as he watched her frown, unable to accept that he was always 'OK'.

His father, too, was, in his own way, equally ineffective, treating him as if he was still nine, still the same young

22

boy he'd sat down and explained he was leaving to on that ghastly day four years ago. And Alex well remembered that Sunday afternoon, the shock of a world disintegrating, his father chain-smoking, his mother standing in the kitchen, staring out at the garden, holding herself, while the man who'd always promised him he'd be there no matter what now told him he was leaving, that it was, 'For the good of all of us. You do understand, don't you, Alex?' And he'd nodded, numb. Then watched frozen as his dad left the room, the house heavy with an awful silence.

And whilst not quite in the same crude celebrity-status band as his mother, nonetheless his father's antics had attracted a fair deal of attention at the Hector Rudge High School for Boys, too. A local paper had run a large piece on the man following Jack Latimer's successful exposé of a child vice ring in Cambridge, comparing the man's journalistic tactics with Indiana Jones, praising him as Chelmsford's hitherto unsung hero.

Shortly after the piece, Alex's concerned English master had suggested he might like to take an interest in the school's own rather dismal magazine, quickly leading to more gleeful playground rumours that young Latimer was about to find the Ark of the Holy Covenant in the boys' toilets. Alex declined the well-meaning offer.

If Alex was always 'OK' with his mother, then he was equally 'fine' with his dad. He stayed over in the cramped flat every other weekend when his father was around, mostly watching television, missing the electronic therapy of Zelda – his favourite PC game.

Conversations would almost inevitably run:

'You OK, then, Alex?'

'Fine.'

'Mother allright?'

'Fine.'

'School?'

'Fine.'

Until his dad would announce the pre-planned entertainment spectacle for the next two days – bowling, perhaps, then a meal at McDonald's. Cinema occasionally. All 'fine' by Alex. What more could he say? He knew his dad was trying, but how do you tell your father that you're just not interested any more? That nothing in the real world ever really matters. That you simply haven't got what it takes to be the hero he wants you to be. Friends aren't important. Girls are frightening. Games are where it's at. Games inspire real loyalty, real trust. Games don't promise to be there forever – then leave.

He knew his father wouldn't understand. The big local hero wouldn't accept Alex for what he was. Twice he'd tried to persuade Alex to take karate classes, the first a knee-jerk response to the bullying incident which had infuriated his mother; the second a much more elaborate affair, with books, clothing and two Bruce Lee videos he'd been forced to watch as his dad explained the technical virtuosity of the action sequences.

'Fine,' Alex had said afterwards, eyes locked with his father's, waiting until the older man broke away, mumbled something about 'it only being an idea'.

Alex had two choices when he left school. To head out quickly, jogging the mile and a half home, beating the jeering crowds out of the gates. Or to loiter, hang around on some spurious pretext, lurk by the caretaker's office, offer to help stand chairs on desks, sweep broken chalks from the classroom floors.

Much depended on the school's timetable, when the older boys were away at games, or when they rushed the gates at the first clang of the school bell.

Today was a Friday, so he hung back, knowing that something else entirely waited for him outside. Something he really didn't want to see him running for freedom, home and the lure of the computer like a frightened rabbit. Besides, he wasn't going home that Friday. The man who waited outside, smoking and leaning against yet another hired car, was his father.

Alex gave it the full fifteen minutes before walking outside, a weekend bag packed by his mother slung loosely over his narrow shoulders. He watched his dad quickly heel out a half-smoked fag as he approached. Cold light drizzle filled the air, and already the light was beginning to fade.

'You're always the last out of that place,' Jack said, reaching over to hug his son, feeling the boy stiffen slightly. 'Hop in the car, it's freezing.'

He did.

'You OK?' Jack asked.

'Fine.'

Jack's grip on the steering wheel momentarily tightened as he realized it was probably going to be another long weekend.

6

Monday morning, and Jack was back in the office at just after nine. Or, more precisely, what he liked to refer to as the 'ground floor of the Latimer media empire' – the Kebab Korner – sitting at a window table, drinking another coffee on the slate, watching as Thebus wiped tables. Alfredo, father to the gloomy young man, wandered over, a salad knife dripping sliced iceberg lettuce in his fat brown hand. He eased himself into the fixed white bucket-seat opposite Jack.

'So,' he announced, waving the gleaming wet knife in Thebus's direction. 'What am I to do about my boy, eh, Jack? Look at him. The body of a young god, a face as long as a donkey's dick.'

'Let me guess,' Jack replied. 'Girl problems.'

Alfredo's eyes shot to the greasy ceiling. 'My Thebus? Never. He has more of the fanny than ten men need. No, he wants to travel.' He almost spat out the word. 'I say – no. He say – yes. I say – no, again. And so it goes. Round and bloody round. What he want to travel for, eh? Tell me, Jack.'

Jack shot a look at the mournful young man. 'Best ask him, surely?'

'I do. He say, to see the world, Papa. I say – toosh – get a bloody video, David bloody Attenborough. He show all you need to know, right here. Then work hard, find nice girl. One day, all this be yours!' He waved both hands in an expansive gesture which seemed to dwarf the narrow café.

Jack lit up, passed one to Alfredo. 'Truth is, I'm not the one to ask.'

'Was 'matter, Jack? You look down, my friend. Someone pissed in your socks this morning? You tell me. Alfredo put extra chillis on their kebabs. Leave them stuck to the shitter for rest of the month.' He roared with laughter, then broke into a cross-eyed mime approximating his intended victim's facial distress. 'You tell me, Jack.'

Jack exhaled, remembering a weekend spent trying but failing to find any common ground between him and Alex. 'I guess,' he said slowly, 'I'm just no expert on the whole father – son thing.'

'You have trouble with your Alex? What's the matter? He's a nice boy. Very quiet. Very polite. Just like his mother – very sensible. I hear her last week. All these men, their problems with not getting it up. It's so sad. She say they need this mental therapy, you know? I say, send them to Alfredo, my kebabs will stiffen their peckers real good. Just ask my wife. Married for thirty years, and we still boom-boom every night.'

Jack smiled. 'Red meat, eh?'

Alfredo nodded proudly.

'I guess the thing with Alex is that I just want him to . . .'

'What?'

'Loosen up, I suppose,' Jack replied. 'You know, tell me what he's into. So we can enjoy a few good times together before he decides he wants to bugger off and see the world, too.'

'But, Jack, he's only young.'

'I know,' he said, stubbing out the cigarette. 'Problem is, sometimes I think I'm getting too old.' He stood, walked past the long refrigerated counter towards the back of the shop, fully intending to march straight upstairs, open up the office, see to the post and start the day. However, after doing so, he found himself idling the morning away, reluctant to start, still feeling the disappointment of Nottingham, trying to figure out how to kick-start the story once more.

Besides, he was always lousy on Mondays. Although Jack was reluctant to admit it, he had an occasional lazy streak, sometimes needing C.F.'s gentle chiding and hyper-efficient organizational skills to plan his day. And on Mondays she took her father for his weekly outpatient's appointment at the cancer clinic. Which also preyed on his mind. His old friend Anwar, never so much as sucked on an unlit cigarette, yet still contracted lung cancer. And Jesus, how many fags had he smoked in the guy's presence over the last few years? How guilty was he of passively blackening Anwar's lungs?

Sighing, he turned to Clint, his three-foot-high cactus, and silent green succulent companion of the last twenty years. It was a dull life, sitting on a windowsill in Chelmsford, but at least it ran without complication. He watered it, watched the liquid drain into the spongy brown soil. 'Kids,' he said quietly. 'Who'd have 'em?'

He went back downstairs, splashed his face in the cob-webbed concrete toilet shared by both businesses, began rubbing some life back into the eyes looking out at his from the mirror. Then remembered how attractive Amy had looked the previous evening when he'd dropped Alex back home. Something about the sparkle in her eyes, a new haircut. Then feeling slightly deflated when she told him she was seeing someone 'new' later that night. What was that all about? Jesus, it wasn't as if he was jealous, for God's sake. They'd been divorced four years. But she did look good.

He splashed more water over his face, tried to wash hers from his mind.

There was a surprise waiting for him when he got back upstairs. A stranger with his back to him, sitting in C.F.'s chair opposite Jack's empty desk, admiring Clint.

'Cleistocactus strausii,' he said, rising and turning. 'Fine specimen. Normally only grow to about two feet.'

Jack stood quite still, trying to size the tall, well-dressed, elegantly thin-faced man. Early sixties, he guessed, mentally weighing him at around thirteen stone, the dark woollen overcoat hanging over deceptively broad shoulders. Then he noticed the strange contrast of rough muscular hands, host to immaculately cleaned, short, thick nails. And lastly, the shoes, black leather turned almost patent by fanatical polishing.

'We go back a bit, Clint and I,' Jack said, uncertain if he was facing a fellow cactus lover, or a hired hit man come to dispense some rough justice in the name of a former news item bent on revenging the interfering hack. He certainly had the face – blank, expressionless, as if no excuse on heaven or earth would deter the clenched fists from their ignoble duty.

'Had it long?'

'Close on twenty years,' Jack said cautiously, taking a quick glance behind him for another figure lurking with a cosh or something similar. Instinct told him the man before him was unlikely to dispense the damage himself. He had the air of one who gave orders, not received them.

'Any flowers?'

'Occasionally. Mr . . . ?'

'Picket,' the stranger replied, without taking his eyes off the ancient succulent. 'George Picket. Chairman of the Chelmsford Avenues Allotment Society.'

A wave of relief broke over Jack. Picket – the guy who'd been hassling C.F. last week. Some sort of local gardening chairman. Which explained the Latin knowledge, the manner.

'Should try liquid tomato fertilizers, Mr Latimer. Use as the makers direct. High potassium content encourages the blooms. Cerise, aren't they, on these chaps?'

'Couldn't tell you, Mr Picket. Never seen one myself.'

'I expect you're wondering why I'm here?'

Jack sat behind his desk.

'Door was open, just sat myself down. Not offended, are you?'

'Truth is, Mr Picket, I guess I was sort of expecting you.'

The wiry eyebrows raised slightly. 'Oh?'

'Your calls last week to my secretary. She said you were most persistent.'

Picket nodded, then suddenly said, 'Audrey Baxter.'

'Sorry?'

'Recommended you. Said you put a nice piece together about her troubles.'

'Troubles?' Jack repeated, trying not to frown, trying to place a face and story with the name. Nothing.

'Refused a refund on a fifty-pound dress with a tear in it,' Picket replied authoritatively. 'Got a picture of herself holding the thing up on page six of the *Chronicle*. About two years back. Your name quoted underneath the head-line.'

Jack's brain tried painfully to engage reverse gear, sorting through the debris of the past two years' stories sold. Miss Baxter? A dress? The search still came up blank. Nothing trawled from mental filing cabinet overloaded with local trivia.

'She was frightfully pleased with the article,' Picket went on, finally making eye contact, his own semi-shot hazels addressing Jack's pale-blues. 'Got a full apology, a new frock and a voucher for twenty-five pounds.'

'I'm glad. Really. And this Miss . . .'

'Baxter. Audrey.'

'Recommended me to you?'

Picket nodded.

Jack opened a window, letting out the stale aroma of coffee and cigarettes, welcoming in blue clouds of billowing diesel from the bus station opposite. 'And now you have some problem along similar lines, Mr Picket?'

'I'm at war, Mr Latimer,' Picket responded

Now was probably the best time to slip away and run like the devil, Jack thought, while he still hadn't seen the twelve-inch breadknife the old crazy was no doubt hiding under his coat. Or a kebab slicer – maybe he'd crept in and stolen one from downstairs while he was in the toilet. What was it his old mate DS Kenny Samson had told C.F.? That he was going to have 'fun' with this guy Picket?

Jack went with his feelings, decided to give the man a chance. It was a Monday morning, the in-tray was empty, Nottingham had turned out to be crock, and something about the guy was beginning to worm its way in. His composure, almost too composed, too rigid.

'At war?' he said, reaching into a drawer and pulling out the least tatty notepad Latimer Associates currently owned. Which was a grand choice of two. 'Who with, Mr Picket?'

'Some vile little layabouts who've made it their mission to terrorize, vandalize and brutalize innocent people and their property.'

'And where might this be, Mr Picket?' Jack asked calmly,

remembering what Kenny Samson had told him about dealing with potential maniacs – listen to them, befriend them,
don't patronize them, then get help quick.

'Chelmsford Avenues Allotments.'

Jack's mind fought to find the scene, coming up another
blank.

Picket correctly read the hesitation. 'Thin strip of eighty-
two plots alongside the cycleway which runs at the bottom of
First, Second, Third and Fourth Avenues. Just off Broomfield
Road, north side of the town.'

'Yep. Got you now,' Jack replied, picturing the tiny coffin-
like sheds, smoking compost heaps, bird-scarers made from
margarine lids and twine, and the half-dozen or so bending
figures tending to their plots. A scene frozen in time from
the mid-thirties when food shortages drove suburban man
to cultivate slug-ridden vegetables in small terraced plots for
consumption in his small terraced home.

Years ago, he'd sometimes stop on his way to taking his
son Alex to the nearby park and watch as a quietly intent
little tribe of self-sufficiency buffs wrestled with raspberry
canes and cloches, wondering whether their habit was born
out of pleasure or necessity.

Not that Jack was anything other than the fairest of fair-
weather gardeners, and for that reason he secretly admired
Picket and his ilk. They were, it seemed to the GM-food-
consuming reporter, the last guardians of a fast-dying knowledge, final bastions of the practices, phrases and techniques
which once went a long way to feeding the nation. Indeed,
he'd been so fired up chatting to one elderly weeder a few
years back that he'd even thought about growing some runner beans and tomatoes in the back garden himself. However,
early optimism was swiftly defeated by slugs, blackfly and the
proximity of Tescos.

'I've been to the police,' Picket continued in reserved tones.
'Told them what would happen. Told them a dozen times,
Mr Latimer. They think I'm some sort of joke. Some kind
of moaning minnie. I know the things they say behind my
back – the insulting gestures they make.'

'Perhaps we'd better start at the beginning,' Jack offered,

sensing Picket's cold containment could obscure any real life in the story. 'Would you like a coffee?'

Picket shook his head, cleared his throat, took several moments to order events, then began the telling, starting with the earliest encounters with the five screaming youths, progressing throughout what he described as 'the summer of fear', before finishing with the most saleable news item – the burning down of his own shed.

'Arson?' Jack replied, circling the word on his pad. He'd have to phone Kenny at New Street to verify the irate Chairman's version, but if it came out that the boys in blue had ignored Picket's pleas for intervention then perhaps he had the beginnings of a story – and not just for local consumption.

For as Picket had been talking, Jack had been appraising the man, watching the gaunt haunted face, realizing that however trivial the matter seemed to outsiders, George Picket genuinely believed he was in some sort of conflict with five children – the 'uncouth, undisciplined youth of today'. And with the millennium less than nine weeks away, coupled with an increasing number of Sunday broadsheets desperate to take submissions to fill a forest's worth of lifestyle supplements, maybe this seemingly innocuous clash of the old and the new had national newsworthy aspirations. A damn big maybe, though.

Jack found his mind wandering at the thought of a broadsheet payday, began crafting the opening few paragraphs of a double-page spread. Headline – 'I told them this would happen!' Picture – Picket standing enraged over the charred remains of his shed. Subhead – 'Tiny tearaways beyond the arm of the uncaring law in suburban war with terrified allotment holders.' Or something similar. Then the copy itself, detailing a society unravelling as it hurtles towards the great new beginning, a cultural clash which underpinned the death of the old ways and the disrespectful emergence of the new. The kids themselves – symbols of malevolent change, harbingers of tomorrow's potential chaos, society torn in two by a generation of techno-inadequates fed on computer violence whilst starved of parental control.

What editor would be able to refuse such a pitch?

Plenty, Jack realized, his thoughts turning towards Alex once more, another cog in the machine of the computer brainwashed generation. Still, at least his own boy seemed content to fight his battles and air his adolescent angst on a monitor. Thank the Lord he wasn't out getting his kicks messing with real peoples' lives.

But there was something else missing. The whole thing was still too flimsy, needed another angle, something more involving, with the Chairman himself, perhaps. Sixteen years firstly in the thick of, then latterly on the fringes of the reporting game had taught Jack that news was more about people than issues. *Ergo* charities enlisting celebrities to champion their causes. And if Picket was going to champion his, Jack needed to know a lot more about the man, unearth some kind of newsworthy nugget beyond his chairmanship.

'You know for sure these kids burnt down your shed, Mr Picket?' he asked, feeling his head begin to clear a little.

'Has to be them, doesn't it?' came the icy reply. 'Too much of a coincidence otherwise.'

'You saw them?'

'Didn't need to.' The Chairman was suppressing annoyance at not being believed.

'Could it have been an accident?'

'Accident?'

'Just asking.'

'No.'

'Deliberate arson, then?'

'They knew it was my shed, Mr Latimer. They've already covered it in filthy abuse. Many times. And even if, as you suggest, it was some sort of "accident" then I'm damn sure they were the perpetrators. Other users have found old cigarette butts in their sheds. Together with used prophylactics.'

The term caught Jack off-guard.

'Condoms, Mr Latimer. They may look like young kids, but believe me, these children are little more than animals.'

'And there's five of them, you say?'

'To my knowledge.'

'Always the same five?'

33

'During the day, yes. Can't say at night, never been out and caught them.'

Jack shifted a little in his chair, raising his voice to compete with a nearby departing bus and an incoming train thundering over the railway bridge just a few yards from the office. 'You don't suppose the night-time disturbances could be put down to . . . perhaps . . . other kids. Older kids?'

Picket paused, ran his tongue over his tight top lip. 'Never. I hear them sometimes. Recognize the voices.'

'And no one can put a name to them, knows them from the local community?'

The Chairman smiled for the first time. 'Community,' he said, savouring the term sarcastically. 'Isn't that some sort of utopian dream, Mr Latimer?' Then added. 'There's a few council developments nearby. Our guess is that they come from there. But we'd be pilloried for saying so in public. Ridiculous, isn't it? We've ushered in an age of liberal political correctness that stifles the middle classes and lets the lower classes run wild.'

'And the upper classes?'

'Have always said what the hell they want to, and damn the consequences.'

Jack excused the right-wing rhetoric, put it down to a man at the end of his tether.

'And you say the police won't do a thing?'

'Nothing. Say without evidence, there's no inquiry. Ridiculous. Kids these days run rings round law and order. Whole system treats them like little angels.' He shot Jack a look of pure scorn. 'Most probably give them a two-week trip to Disneyland if they could be bothered to find them.'

'And what would you do to them, Mr Picket?' Jack asked, pen poised, waiting for first real quote of the piece.

Picket stared back, unwilling to be drawn. 'Will you look into it, Mr Latimer?'

'Why me?' Jack asked. 'Why not go direct to the *Chronicle*, the *Weekly Reporter*?'

'Tried it, half a dozen times or more over the last few months. None of them want to know. Trash-rags, the lot of them.' He stood, proffered a hand. 'Miss Baxter said you

34

were good. I trust her judgement. Just get our story on to the front page, Mr Latimer. People have got to know what we're facing. These hooligans must be stopped.'

'I'll try,' Jack replied, shaking Picket's powerful paw. 'But I'll need to speak to you again. I'll do a little sniffing around, see what I can find out, then come and visit the allotments for myself, get a photo, that kind of thing.'

'Whatever's necessary. Good day to you, Mr Latimer.' He turned and left the room.

Jack watched from the first-floor window as Picket walked away down the street. He seemed to be shuffling, limping slightly, but proudly, upright against the whipping wind, head-first into the cold stinging gusts like a gnarled figure-head on an ancient, storm-tossed galleon.

Turning back to his desk, Jack heard a warning grumble from his ravenously hungry stomach. He thought about running another sandwich on to the Kebab Korner's tab, then decided against it, opting for a call to DS Kenny Samson at New Street first.

7

'So Mr Latimer's going to tell our side of things, is he?'

Picket nodded, anxious not to spill his tea. The thin bone china cup was scaldingly hot. 'Least he seemed to take me seriously, Audrey. About the only blighter who has.'

Audrey Baxter smiled, allowing a comfortable silence to settle between them. A lifelong spinster at fifty-three, she was grateful for the Chairman's visits, glad an individual as important as George Picket saw her company as anything worth cultivating. She shifted slightly, smoothing down the knee-length brown skirt she'd only just had time to change into after he'd rung from town to invite himself over.

Picket immediately registered the innocuous gesture, filing it into his masturbatory imagination for later use. Tonight, probably. Or maybe the moment he finished his tea and strolled the hundred yards back to his house. A celebratory bout of self-abuse. And why not? He deserved it. It had been a most productive morning so far.

And sadly, for all Audrey's suppressed romantic optimism, the onanistic act was all Picket ever really used her for. She wasn't a bad looker in his limited opinion. Bit bony perhaps, neck showing signs of life's wear and tear, but always making the effort, smelling of catalogue cosmetics and showing the tiniest smudge of pale lipstick on pearly front teeth.

It had been this way for a while now, Picket using the woman for his gratuitous pleasure. And heavens, he had the intelligence to see the woman was clearly infatuated. So why not confine her obvious lust to a circumstance which suited him so?

Once a week or thereabouts, when his erotic memory of

36

Audrey began to fade, or mutate into one of the sluts from his magazines, Picket would give her a call, stop by on some shabbily invented pretext – Could she take minutes at the next Allotment Society meeting? Would she vet the new membership applications? (Picket had over a dozen such Chairman-like excuses at his command.) Or he'd take tea with her while restocking his imagination with fresh images ready to be defiled at his leisure.

For nothing was taboo in the Chairman's bedroom – save for other people. God only knew how many times he had thrashed away on the single creaking bed, his thin face contorted by the very effort of his imagined multi-orificed ravaging of Miss Baxter.

And once the highly practised ritual was over – that was it. Get up, get on with life. That was what Picket so appreciated about masturbation. He controlled every aspect of the procedure, from first limp fumblings to tissue disposal after. No one to hug afterwards, no insignificant small talk to manufacture, no thanks to be given for allowing him the sacred internal privilege of actual sex.

Audrey Baxter, ostensibly a quiet, well-spoken woman of independent means living on Second Avenue, Chelmsford, Essex, was George Picket's perfect woman – an eager mental love-slave whom he never had to wake up with.

Unlike his ex-wife. The once-proud Jane Picket. Whore. The cheap tart who never understood that George had to live with his elderly, widowed mother, couldn't simply abandon her because he'd married. A disgusting, insatiable woman who soon bored of their silent lovemaking. George had really tried, there in his dead father's house, ensuring his new wife was never sufficiently aroused to let any orgasmic wails filter through the bedroom walls where his arthritic mother sat painfully knitting into the small hours.

Restless Jane – who after three years living with George and 'Mum', grabbed lustfully at the first opportunity with a local builder who'd come to put an extension on the back of the house, a conservatory for his mother to knit out the last of her days. But there was some consolation – the astonished look on her face when he pushed her. The glorious memory of his wife's tumbling, unfaithful body colliding with the stairs. The sight of her, still – dead – at the bottom. A life extinguished by the minutest of assistance, a simple push when she was least expecting it.

Much worse was the death of his mother, two months later.

So George lost two women in less than a year, but kept two things also. The house on Fourth Avenue and a two-year-old son. Mikey Picket. Life became intolerably harder for them both. Made worse by what was to follow.

'It frightens me, Mr Picket,' Audrey announced, offering her guest a sweetmeal digestive. 'I just don't see things getting any better. Children these days, well, they aren't like we were, are they? All that foul language, for instance.'

'Dreadful,' Picket replied, expertly committing Audrey's pained, puzzled expression to memory. 'But times change, we must remember that.'

'Ah, but do you remember?' Audrey pressed, innocently warming to the theme. 'Those children in America? Started shooting schoolteachers and friends in broad daylight?'

'The price we pay for all our liberal excesses,' Picket softly replied. 'I hear they've even banned the cane at Eton now. Human rights issue, apparently.'

'Well, I'm not sure that I . . .' Audrey found herself hesitating. She'd been beaten as a child herself, strapped by the Sisters of Mercy for the tiniest of misdemeanours, and well remembered the tearful indignity of offering an upturned palm in anticipation of the fiery lick of the strap. 'Perhaps not all children need . . .'

'Perhaps,' he quietly suggested. 'That's half the problem.'

'Oh?'

'Decent folk such as yourself going too soft on them.' Picket bit carefully into the biscuit. 'We're not born civilized, Miss Baxter. We need to be created that way. Shaped, formed, disciplined by our elders and betters. Politeness, manners, respect. It all has to be learnt.'

'Oh, I agree, it's just . . .'

'Take my son, for example,' Picket continued. 'And don't forget, I brought that boy up alone. But I had a moral duty to do it properly, Miss Baxter. Turn him into an upstanding young man. And to this day, I have no regrets sticking the boy when he'd transgressed the rules of human decency and acceptable behaviour. No regrets at all.'

Audrey watched as Picket's eyes seemed to glaze over. They worried her sometimes, those eyes, the way they appeared to lock on to her face, digesting every fleshy nuance and wrinkle, divorced from the animated face surrounding them, absorbed, perhaps, in their own agenda.

The mouth below continued. 'I used to make him wait for it, too. Always on a Sunday afternoon, after we'd finished putting away from lunch. Quiet as a mouse, he'd be, while we ate, just having the smallest mouthfuls. Because he had a healthy respect for me and fear for the stick. Used to cry with the pain sometimes, Miss Baxter, plead with me to stop. But I stuck to the task, as a loving father would. Thanks me for it now, mind.'

'How is . . . your son?' Audrey inquired. Picket hadn't ever furnished her with a name, despite her many attempts to prise it from him. Then again, she was forced to admit, that was part of the Chairman's allure – the mystery.

'He's fine.'

'I'm glad.'

'Doing well for himself. Got a lovely wife and family in Cambridge. Still with the same company. Architects. Renovation, mostly. Restores derelict country manor houses to their former glory. Rewarding career.'

'Must be.'

'In spite of everything.'

Audrey was intrigued. What lurked behind this simple statement? In spite of . . . what? She looked up, alarmed and flattered to see Picket studying her face intently once more. Her throat dried a little. 'More tea?' It was all she could think of to say.

'Thank you, I will.'

She refilled his cup, hand shaking slightly.

Picket took the drink. 'Most polite of you to offer. Sign of good breeding.'

'Thank you, Mr Picket.' His last words had unwittingly

touched something deep inside. Breeding – with all its animalistic interpretations, grunting livestock, sweating fetlocks and pink, glistening afterbirth. Not that she nursed any conscious desires to breed herself, a double hysterectomy having closed the reproductive door fifteen years previously. However, the distant prospect of lovemaking, with all its intimate embraces, still had the sensual power to thrill. It was a growing desire she'd silently cultivated for some time, ever since the Chairman had first shown her how to rotovate the overgrown rectangle of weed-infested earth a dying uncle had bequeathed her in his will.

Many times, Audrey had tried to rationalize the attraction. The strong quiet voice, perhaps, military bearing, powerful hands – or simply the underlying enigma of the man, a combination of fierce opinion cloaked in obsessive politeness, charm, and the mystery of a past never fully volunteered or explained. What made him that way? What events had transpired to have shaped the George Picket who now sat studying her so intently? The son he barely mentioned, yet disciplined so harshly? The boy's mother? Why had the Chairman never mentioned her? He lived alone, she knew that much, in a house which time and technology seemed to have forgotten, as if his life had been frozen from the late-fifties. Yet, slowly, Audrey hoped she was chipping away at his austere exterior. Gradually he was letting slip a few precious crumbs from the table of his past. The way he beat his son, for instance. How many other people knew that? Audrey felt certain she was somehow being taken into his confidence, blessed with such revelations. She felt curiously honoured – and he did keep looking at her in *that* way, didn't he?

The allotment. It still made her smile. All the Baxters, mournfully, greedily gathered at the solicitor's as the last wishes of the deceased were sombrely disclosed.

'And to my dear niece Audrey,' the legal man had intoned. 'I leave my allotment, that she may know the perennial pleasures of its cultivation.'

Which had to be a joke, surely? One last prank from beyond the grave, Uncle Michael, six foot underground, leaving her her own funeral-plot-sized piece of earth. The other Baxters stifled giggles and gave their most sympathetic smiles, well satisfied with their more conventional inheritances.

But they didn't know Audrey. After giving it some thought, she gave it a shot. Besides, she had no real need of any money from dear Uncle Michael. Mother and Father had left her well provided for. In truth, she was very much a lady of leisure since their deaths. She lived frugally, but comfortably, managing on the interest from shrewd share investments made by her father during his lifetime as one of the city's high-rollers. First off, she'd bought the house in Second Avenue, then contented herself to indulge in whatever whims she could afford after paying for the weekly shop and bills.

She'd chosen Chelmsford because Uncle Michael already lived there. He was the one who'd first spotted the house up for sale, less than fifty yards from the allotment he lovingly tended. He was widowed, a pensioner, glad of her occasional company while digging piles of muddy vegetables, gathering soft summer fruits and endlessly weeding.

And, like Picket, he'd often stop by for tea and a chat afterwards, slurping noisily from her only mug, leaving earthy fingerprints around the rim and handle.

'Great bunch down there,' he'd say wistfully. 'All ages. Not just old farts like myself. You ought to try it, Aud. Council's got some spare plots going towards the back. Grow your own. Can't get much better than what you tend yourself.'

A sad irony indeed, she'd pondered, that he'd died choking on a particularly stubborn piece of organically tendered carrot.

But Audrey, not being one to dwell on such unfortunate details, decided she was now a landowner, and three weeks after the will she stood in Cramphons selecting cabbage seeds.

That same afternoon, she met the Chairman for the very first time, instantly struck by his appropriate dignity and vegetable wisdom.

'Of course,' he'd said, as they strolled across to her uncle's former patch. 'It'll need a bit of seeing to. Not that Michael was to blame. I suppose it all got a bit much for him in the end. Hasn't been touched for close on six months. Although I've

41

removed the remaining carrot stock, Miss Baxter. Didn't think you'd want such an unwelcome reminder of the tragedy.'

'Very kind. Thank you.'

'One tries. He was a good man.'

They stood surveying the dismal dark-grey mud bordered with overgrown grass.

'That shed,' Audrey asked, pointing to the decrepit wooden hut at the far end of the twenty-yard strip. 'Bit small, isn't it?'

Picket smiled. 'Simply for tools and fertilizers, Miss Baxter. And of course, they're not all as small as Michael's . . . sorry, yours.' He motioned towards a far larger construction standing proud amongst its smaller, shabbier companions. '*Chez moi*,' he proudly added.

'Gosh,' Audrey feigned. She already knew whose the hut was. Uncle Michael had kept her well informed of allotment politics.

'Space for a couple of deck chairs in there,' Picket added. 'Calor Gas stove, all my tools, seed-trays and more besides.' His eyes locked on to hers. 'Even a wireless, Miss Baxter. Radio Four, of course.'

'Naturally.'

Then had begun the first of five consecutive afternoons as the pair of them set to righting Michael Baxter's old allotment, occasionally wandering over to Picket's shed for a brew and a chat, gently probing each other's past and present, both perhaps equally struck with the similarity of their local loneliness.

She, of course, returned home each evening to a Radox bath, wondering if the elegantly untouchable Mr Picket (never 'George' – she'd tried it once and received a sharply admonishing glare for over-familiarity) could in any way replace the membership of the three local lonely hearts clubs she belonged to.

While, two streets and a swift stroll away, Picket chose to unwind by mentally introducing Michael's unknowing niece to the unbridled joys of anal sex for the first time.

'Well,' Picket said, rising. 'Mustn't waste the day, Miss Baxter.' He'd seen enough, committed every inch of her face to memory.

Audrey tried her best not to look reluctant at his leaving. 'I've nothing planned, Mr Picket, if you . . .' She tailed off, mouth running too fast for her brain to invent an appropriate reason for his staying.

'Kind,' Picket replied. 'But needs must. I'm expecting a call from that Latimer chappy anytime. Says he's going to arrange a formal interview with me. Photographs, the lot.' He walked into the immaculately clean but spartan kitchen and deposited his cup and saucer on the empty steel drainer. Turning, he saw something he wished he hadn't. The idiot woman had only gone and bought a damn microwave! His head began to tighten – a familiar feeling, one he'd learnt over the years to accept rather than fight. He'd let her know what he felt about the onward march of technology another day. Stupid bitch!

She stood behind him in the doorway, playing, he guessed, for time. Damn woman was like a love-sick puppy, made him feel trapped. For he was well aware of her true intentions. Every woman's intentions. It wasn't simply a damn good seeing-to they were after, regardless of the doe-eyed come-on. It was babies. Kids. Filth. She wanted his sperm to make more of them, have one growing inside her, bursting from her genitals, screaming, a ghastly little . . .

'Mr Picket?'

'I have to go.'

'Just exactly how long is the Chairman's reign of office?'

'The one year,' he curtly replied, walking quickly towards the front door.

She was by him, close. 'And have you enjoyed your year?'

'I have. And the four before that.'

'You're always Chairman, aren't you, Mr Picket?' She tried to appear impressed rather than sycophantic. But failed.

'Put it this way,' he replied, without turning to face her. 'Do you know anyone who'd dare oppose me?'

Audrey watched him leave, before returning to hold the still-warm cup he'd left in the kitchen, silently admitting that although she'd never dare oppose him, she wouldn't be averse to perhaps one day standing against him.

8

By the time C.F. walked quietly through the door at just gone two, Jack was fast considering a late liquid lunch followed by an early trip back to the flat. DS Kenny Samson was out on a call, so unable to furnish Jack with any details regarding the alleged allotment arson, while all leads to the Nottingham Semtex story were as dry and dead as the six cigarette butts littering his ashtray.

He looked up, yawned and stretched. 'Had a visitor this morning,' he announced.

She nodded, looked troubled.

He pressed on. 'Your man Picket. Quite a character. Probably make for an interesting piece in himself. Wants me to check on some young kids who've been terrorizing the good green-fingered members of the Chelmsford Avenues Allotment Society.'

She sat. He watched.

'A horse walks into a bar,' he tried.

'Sorry?'

'A joke, C.F. The barman says, "Why the long face?"' Still nothing. Her stillness worried him. Then he remembered the morning's business, the regular cancer outpatient's appointment. 'How's your dad?' he asked, feeling his stomach tighten.

She looked away, paused for a moment to stare at the hapless shoppers waiting for buses in the cold concrete station opposite. Then said, 'He's got secondaries.'

His stomach turned. In an instant he was by her side, crouching, arm round her shoulder, pulling her towards him. The side of her neck felt damp with tears. 'Oh, Jesus, I'm so sorry,' he whispered.

She pulled away, sniffed, reached for a tissue from her coat pocket. 'He says he's going to make it to January the first.'

'Yeah. I'm sure he will,' Jack murmured. 'And besides, surely there's something they can –'

'No,' she said simply. 'They give him between two and three months.'

He stood, pinched the bridge of his nose. 'Go home, C.F.,' he said. 'There's nothing to do here. Please.'

She cleared her throat. 'I'd rather be here, Jack. Home's too . . .' She tailed off, unable to finish.

'Sure,' Jack replied, wishing for all the world that the specialists had got it wrong, unable to reconcile the happy friend and proud father Anwar was with the ghastly prognosis. A horribly loaded silence filled the room, merely magnifying sounds emanating from the street below.

'I'm so sorry,' he said once more.

Mounting the New Street Police Station steps two at a time, Jack realized with some shame that he was almost glad to get out of the office. He'd finally managed to persuade C.F. to take a taxi home, watching in stony silence as the maroon minicab drove away down Duke Street, realizing that perhaps it was one of the characteristics of old hacks that years spent over-dramatizing the banal denied them a real response to genuine human tragedy. Life and its many crises were easier to deal with if you had no previous connection to the recipient, and could use a thesaurus of sensational journalism to describe events. He could *report* Anwar's struggle with cancer, write five hundred pithy, heart-warming words on the subject, but to comment, offer something beyond cheap prose – just seemed out of his reach, all spontaneity eaten away, lost in a void he feared was home to the real Jack Latimer. His ex, Amy, had often accused him of the same, a steadfast refusal to immerse himself in emotional reality, running scared from the hardest truths, finding solace in uncovering and reporting the problems of others.

'Evening, Dougy,' he said to the uniformed desk sergeant. 'He in?'

The big man nodded, silently pointing with a biro to the

door behind his shoulder. Jack swept through into a small corridor, then right down another, until finally arriving at the dimly lit office belonging to DI Black, DI Mason, and DS Kenny Samson.

He didn't bother knocking on the slightly open door.

Kenny Samson looked up from a desk strewn with disorderly paperwork. 'Ah,' he said, stifling a yawn. 'The wanderer returns. Any joy in Nottingham?'

'Damn-all,' Jack replied to the original provider of the gangland Semtex tip. 'If it's going on up there, then it's a well-run operation. I got no further than your colleagues in the Midlands Serious Crimes Squad.'

'Give it a few months,' Samson advised. 'Probably too much heat on at the moment. All the villains off sunning themselves somewhere exotic until the situation cools.'

'Maybe.' Jack slumped in an empty chair, glad he and Kenny were alone. It was getting dark outside, the heavy grey sky dropping in tones by the minute. He felt shattered, drained by the day, memories of George Picket seemingly weeks away rather than hours.

The sandy-haired detective put down his pen, a large grin on a face which gave vivid testimony to weekends spent as a fly-half for the Essex Police Rugby Squad. 'Know why I so love seeing you, Jack?'

The reporter stared blankly back.

'Because no matter what sort of a day I've had, I know all I have to do is take one look at you, and I begin to feel better. You know the saying – there's always someone worse off than you? Well, it's you, Jack.'

'Glad I can be of service to the thin blue line,' Jack replied sourly. 'You ever have much to do with a fellow called George Picket?'

Samson frowned. 'The old guy? Same bloke who's been ringing C.F. while you were on a jolly up north? She told me. Wanted to know if he was the type to start asking about the colour of her underwear.'

'And?'

Samson lit up. Jack refused the offered Marlboro Light. He watched the detective exhale, trying to ignore the wasted image of Anwar Patel forming itself in the blue-grey smoke above Samson's head. 'I'll be frank, Jack. The man's got something of a reputation as a pain in the arse. Always coming in and hassling Uniform about some kids goofing around his allotment.'

Jack nodded. 'Only this time the "goofing" may have got a little more personal, Kenny. He woke up last week to see two fire engines putting out his shed.'

'Someone torched it?'

'The kids, he reckons.'

Samson mulled it over. 'Uniform should have a report about it. Wouldn't really cross my desk.'

'He says you lot couldn't give a toss about what's been happening down there.'

The broken-nosed DS held up a hand. 'Hang on, Jack. I don't know who's been pissing in your pool lately, but don't go bundling CID into Uniform matters. From what I know, Picket's a time-waster. Always in here, crapping on about something or other. Every station in the country's got one.'

'Only this one's come running to me because he doesn't feel listened to.'

'Well, maybe he cried wolf once too often, Jack. As I say, it's not my patch.'

Jack found his gaze settling on the reassuring Samson family portrait standing on a cluttered window ledge just behind the confused detective. Mr and Mrs Samson and their three picture-perfect children. He was godfather to Nathan, the youngest; Amy the proud godmother. 'You ever heard of something called Zelda?' he heard himself saying.

'You what?'

'Zelda.'

'Sounds like a new-age dealer to me. Try the known boozers tonight.'

'No. No.' Jack shook his head. 'It's a kids' thing. Something Alex is really into. Like a TV programme or something.'

Samson snapped his fingers. 'Got you. Zelda. Yeah, my boy used to be into it. It's one of those computer games. Sort of Dungeons and Dragons thing. Little green man has to fight wizards and warlocks, search out the golden chalice or something. Why, what's the problem?'

'Nothing. Listen, Kenny, I need names.'

'Zelda's all I know, mate. You'd have to speak to Nathan –'

'No. Forget bloody Zelda. These kids who've been giving Picket the runaround. He says officers have been dispatched to talk to them, calm things down a bit.'

'Hang on a mo,' Samson replied, reaching for the phone and pressing an internal extension. There followed a short conversation during which Jack watched his friend scribbling on a pad, before noticing it had begun to rain outside. The large clock on the wall said four-fifteen, and the first of the streetlights had flickered on, casting a pink glow on the grey office walls.

He thought about C.F., hoping she'd made it back home by now, seeing her in his mind's eye in the back of the cab, staring vacantly out of the rain-strewn window, watching a world full of cancer-free people drifting back to their own warm houses.

More than anything he wanted to be with her then, providing assurances as 'Uncle Jack' had done so naturally in the past, telling jokes and stroking her hair to soothe the pain when she'd first fallen off her bike, helping her revise as her sixteen-year-old brain struggled to cram for the forthcoming GCSEs she'd so easily pass.

Old memories of a happier Jack, before the redundancy, before he and Anwar had stood together with enraged colleagues facing police riot shields and drawn batons outside Fortress Wapping, yelling at the injustice of the move, despairing of their inadequacy to change chaotic decisions taken by faceless bureaucrats who slept soundly while Jack and his like screamed useless objections into the night.

The old Jack Latimer – promising staff reporter, happily married with a chuckling son. Friends with most of the building. Especially friendly with the fast-talking, hard-drinking, eternally-smoking guys in the print-rooms. All smoking except Anwar Patel; small, thin, twenty years older than Jack, but always treating him as an equal, and with the brightest brown eyes he'd ever seen. Good times – Anwar and he sat together in the small hours, passionately planning their next Indian banquet as the vast rollers roared and swished and spewed out hundreds of miles of freshly inked newsprint just above their heads. And all the time Anwar's steadily blackening lungs falling victim to the cancer caused by the exhaled smoke of others. Jack's included.

Samson replaced the phone, rubbed the flattened bridge of his bulbous nose between forefinger and thumb. 'So what's your angle on this Picket business, Jack?'

'A story.'

'With police incompetence heavy on the agenda, right?'

'Jesus, Kenny, I don't know the full facts yet. It could all come to nothing – just an old guy hassled by some young kids.'

'Or?' Samson asked carefully.

'Maybe it's about children running riot, not giving a flying fuck about what they do, and to whom.'

'And police neglecting to take the old sod seriously?'

Jack sighed. 'I just want to talk to the kids involved.' He looked Samson in the eye. 'We're probably talking about any number of things, parental failure, dysfunctional families, systems with their hands tied, anything. All I know is that I've got an outraged allotment chairman looking to me to raise the issue, and a three-hundred-pound trip to Nottingham to cover. Your tip, I believe, Detective Sergeant Samson.'

Samson blushed a little, stubbed out the cigarette. 'All right, keep a lid on it, will you?' He passed the notepaper over to the intent reporter. 'Williams, the division's juvenile officer, says the gang leader's most probably a nasty piece of work going by the name of Mark Cannon. Thirteen.'

Jack took the paper, relieved to see there was also an address supplied. 'Form?'

'As long as both our arms tied together. Petty theft, truancy, TWOKing . . .'

'In English, Kenny.'

'Taking Without Owner's Consent,' Samson supplied. 'Joy-riding.'

'At thirteen?'

'As long as their feet reach the pedals, Jack. Traffic have

hauled kids as young as seven from the driver's side of stolen motors.'

'And this is his address, is it?' Jack asked, pointing at the handwritten scrawl.

Samson nodded, lowered his voice. 'Same old story, Jack. You didn't get it from me. Apparently he's a right little hard-nut, reckons himself to be a player like his older brother. Lives with him. Bloke called Steve Cannon, local dealer, in and out of HMP Chelmsford more times than a concerned social worker. Possession, mostly.'

'Looks like young Mark's heading the same way. Any info about the others? Picket mentions two other lads, one much younger, plus a couple of girls.'

'*Nada*,' Samson replied. 'Could be any of a hundred young wannabe crims hanging round the place.'

'But Cannon's a cert?'

'As good as. Williams has been round, apparently, had a word. Kid told him to go forth and multiply.'

'Cocky.'

'And clever. He knows the form – we can't touch him till he turns fourteen. Up till then it's all Juvenile Detention Orders, curfews, damn-all. He's laughing his socks off . . . for the moment.'

Jack stood, pocketed the note. 'Appreciate the favour, Kenny,' he said, managing a half-smile. 'Any chance I can have a word with this Williams guy?'

'The juve officer? Sure. I'll take you down to him. And Jack?'

'What?'

Samson leant back in the chair, rubbed his solid, expansive stomach. 'Favour for a favour. When are you going to invite me round for another one of your home-made curries?'

Jack mulled it over. 'Wednesday? About eight?'

'I'll bring the Tiger Beer.'

'And something else, if your Nathan doesn't mind?'

'Such as?'

'The Zelda game thing.'

Samson frowned. 'You got a PC then, have you?'

'I'll get one.'

'So you can play kids' games of an evening?' His face broke into its broad familiar smile. 'You're a sad man, Jack Latimer. You should get out more.'

'Thanks, Kenny, but if that's like the rest of your tips recently, I'll ignore it.'

9

There was one more call to make before he headed back to the empty flat. Although it pained him to admit it, he had a problem. And as most of Essex seemed to come to his ex-wife whenever they had problems, Jack found himself asking why didn't he? Pride, inevitably. But there was another agenda that dark early winter's evening. His last sight of her, standing in the doorway the previous night, more glamorous than he could remember, smiling cheekily at him, face alive, telling him she was seeing someone 'new' later on.

Who, for Christ's sake? And why was it still bothering him, twenty-four hours after the event? The unsettling day, C.F.'s awful news, a feeling that perhaps life was simply too damn short to hold grudges? Or maybe something else entirely – maybe taking the lift to the third floor was simply the starting point for something he'd been thinking about for a long time, mulling over as he waited in bars, train stations, hired cars, always waiting . . .

He walked out into the small corridor, then through the swing doors embossed with 'Phoenix FM' stickers. Jack had his own acronym for the FM part, but as a steadfast Radio Four man chose to keep his opinion to himself.

Lily Jones sat on reception, typing, glancing up at him.

'Evening, Lily,' he said brightly, pride forbidding him from looking as downcast as he felt. 'Amy in for the evening hatches, matches and dispatches session?'

Lily sighed, made an unnecessary show of consulting the clock – four-forty-five – *Amy Jordan's Agony Hour* wouldn't start till three minutes after seven. But they both knew she'd be preparing at her desk in the open-plan office behind another set of logo'd swing doors to the left. 'I'll just try her,' she said, reaching for the phone.

'I bet that's what all the guys say,' Jack replied sweetly.

Amy had once confided in Jack that the matriarchal Lily had always harboured deep suspicions about her one-time husband. Something about his eyes being 'too shifty'. He wondered what Lily had made of it when it was Amy who'd had the affair which was to ruin the marriage.

'She's in the boardroom,' Lily added frostily, while the muted strains of Cliff's 'Devil Woman' pumped out from unseen speakers.

He made his way slowly through the open-plan to the closed door at the far end, ignoring the quiet interest of other figures trying to look busy as he passed by. He entered without knocking, going over his first line, the opening gambit, throat drying a little.

Amy Latimer had her back towards the door, looking out of the window at the gradually emptying pedestrian precinct below. He closed the door silently behind him, ears acutely trained to every sound in the room, mind telling him to stay calm, be cool.

'I've got this problem,' he said, straining to sound casual.

The small bob-cut blonde with large, emerald-green eyes turned, smiled. 'Try me.'

'I got divorced four years ago, but for last twenty-four hours I can't seem to get my wife out of my mind.'

'Your ex-wife.'

'My ex-wife.'

She came and kissed him lightly on the cheek. 'And would this have anything to do with the fact that I saw someone else last night?'

He sighed, sat. 'Am I that obvious?'

'No, no. I mean, for you, Jack, this is something else. Rationalizing your feelings and confronting them. I'm impressed. What the hell's happened?'

'Can I smoke in here?'

She slid open a large pane of tinted double-glazed glass. Cooling air washed over Jack's forehead. 'Anwar's got secondaries. He's dying, Amy.'

53

'God.'

'And I got to thinking how unfair it is.'

'So where do I fit in?'

He closed his eyes. 'I don't know.'

'Come on, Jack, you were doing so well. Now you're clamming up on me.'

He took another drag, began turning the packet on the polished wooden table. 'I don't know that Alex gets enough out of his time with me. Gets *anything* out of his time with me.'

'You've asked him?'

'You know Alex – he's always "fine".'

'"Okay" – he's "okay" with me.'

'I'm worried, you know.'

'I'm surprised.'

'Sometimes . . .' But he couldn't continue. It was too raw, too close, a gradually growing admission which would leave him too exposed.

'What?'

He looked into the face he'd forgotten waking up with. 'What's he like then? This new bloke?'

'Gorgeous. Absolutely lovely.'

Jack stood, missed the gleam in her eye. 'I'll let you get on. Just ignore me.'

'It's been one of those days, right?'

'Bang on. Don't really know why I came here.'

She walked back to the door with him. 'I think you do, Jack. I think you just can't say it.'

'Never marry an analyst, right?'

'Or divorce her.'

He felt himself colour slightly as he stared into her eyes a fraction longer than necessary. 'Well, good luck with this new bloke, then.'

'Thanks.'

'Shan't keep you. We all have to move on.'

'If you say so.'

A thought occurred during the uncomfortable silence, surging its way up through the confusing array of past and present emotions. Jack clung to it like a lifeline. 'Listen, what kind of computer does Alex have?'

She frowned, thrown. 'Just a standard PC, I think. Pentium thing. Ask him.'

'No,' he replied, feeling stronger, less vulnerable by the moment. 'Pentium, that's fine. Thanks.'

'I don't get to know what for?'

'It's a surprise.' But he'd already turned and missed the look of slight disappointment on her face when he added, 'For Alex.'

10

'Steve about?'

The thin-faced, ginger-haired youth squinted back at the stranger on his doorstep. Then shook his head.

Jack sighed, made a show of looking at his watch. 'Said to meet me here by two.'

A disinterested shrug accompanied a dog barking somewhere down the terraced street.

'Any idea what time he'll be back?'

'Nah.'

Jack pushed a little further. 'You're Mark, aren't you? Steve's kid brother.'

'What's it to you?'

'He's told me about you.'

'So?'

Jack felt the narrowed steel-blue eyes giving him a suspicious once-over. Williams, the New Street juvenile officer, had warned Jack what to expect – principally the door slamming in his face. Mark Cannon, at only thirteen, had been on the circuit long enough to smell authority faster than a great-white homing in on a single drop of spilt blood in a calm sea. As a result, Jack had opted for well-worn shoes and clothes, hadn't shaved, and spent the short walk across town preparing himself as an actor might – getting into character, a dope-smoker looking for resin. It was a well-practised technique, Jack learning from the best reporters as a youngster that it was only by really throwing oneself into a role that the investigative hack could pull the kind of results the public wanted to read, and, more importantly, editors would run.

Another gambit. 'Steve told me to wait if he was a few minutes late.'

'Never told me that,' Cannon replied.

'I dare say you weren't s'posed to meet him at two, were you?' Jack replied, adding a little irritation to his voice. 'Come on, Mark, it's brass monkeys. And the longer I stand here, the more the neighbours' curtains are going to start twitching.'

'How about just sodding off round the block for half an hour?' Cannon suggested, baring yellowing teeth.

But the grinning youngster had no idea who he was dealing with. Jack Latimer – veteran doorstepper – had blagged his way into more homes than the lad had broken into, which, according to Williams, was probably somewhere up near the three-figures mark.

'How about this?' Jack replied, pointing a finger. 'I just sod off for good. Find myself a more reputable supplier. Then ring Steve and tell him thanks to his squirt brother, he's gone and lost himself a guaranteed hundred a week. Ta-ra, Mark.'

'Hang about,' Cannon said to the retreating figure.

Jack turned, checked the elation. This was just a spotty-faced kid, for Christ's sake. It wasn't as if he'd just talked his way past Joan Collins's security team at the Savoy Hotel. Which he'd done only the once – to find a charming woman who insisted the burly bouncers escort him 'gently' away. He got the exclusive about Bungalow Bill, but alas, the price was exacted by the gorillas in suits – two right-handers and a professional size-twelve up the backside. Good days, the stuff of long lunchtimes in the Bell, Fleet Street. Far from a bleak winter's terraced street in an Essex provincial town.

'Have to be careful,' Cannon said, ushering Jack in. 'You looked like filth when I first clocked you.'

'Me?' Jack replied, taking in the darkened living room, pleased to have found a place sparser than his own flat. A gas fire hissed dangerously, a silver-foil takeaway tin half full of old joints on its peeling top, the whole place giving off the vibe of a seedy one-room Babylon – damp, cold, squalid. 'I'm just after some puff, Mark.'

'Yeah, I gathered that.'

Deadlock. Neither said a word, feeling their way round the unease.

Jack broke it, sitting on the battered sofa, trying to look as cool as possible, hoping big brother and long-standing con Steve Cannon didn't choose to return home suddenly. So far it had gone swimmingly, perhaps too well. And at times like these, experience had taught Jack disaster was all too often just an unexpected entrance away.

'Shouldn't you be at school, or something?' he said, adding a conspiratorial wink.

Cannon seemed to relax slightly, edged a little closer, perhaps to befriend the stranger who appeared to have so much influence with his brother. Then again, he'd also spotted his own business opportunity. 'I could sort you some gear,' he said casually. 'I know where he keeps the stuff.'

Jack smiled. 'What, and give you the money for it? Big brother never knows the difference?' He shook his head. 'Quite the entrepreneur, aren't we?'

'Entre-what?'

'Go to school, they'll tell you what it means.'

The boy tried a second time. 'Fifteen a quarter, I'll give it you. Steve knocks it out at twenty-five. Saving you a tenner, ain't I?'

'Just stick the kettle on, son.'

The lad looked hurt, keen to reassert himself, his breaking voice cracking between the innocent child he might once have been, and the inevitable criminal he was to become. 'But I can deal for Steve. He lets me sometimes. I'll tell him you've been, sorted you. He won't mind. Honest.'

'How's your dad?'

Cannon blinked twice. 'What about him?'

'Still banged up?' Another piece of background from Williams the previous afternoon, as the young officer had wearily painted a bleak portrait of the Cannons – one of Chelmsford's most prominent, yet ironically least successful, criminal families.

'Been out about a month.'

'Did two years, didn't he?'

'But they give him four,' Cannon replied, anxious to impress.

'And how's your mum getting on?'

'Know her as well, do you?'

'You're the youngest, are you?'

'Sure you aren't the law?'

'Come on.'

'Asking a lot of questions.'

'Just passing the time, Mark. Trying to be friendly.' Jack could tell the boy liked someone taking an interest. 'How long you been dossing here, then?'

'A while.'

'Mum chuck you out?'

'Sort of.'

'Pisser.'

'It's better here.'

'How come?'

''Cause it is.'

Jack faked a yawn. 'What do you get up to, then? Got to be a bit dull, just hanging around here all day.'

'This and that. Look, are you after some blow, or not? I can nip upstairs and fetch you a quarter of skunk, right now.'

A brief, absurd image of the boy racing down with the hindquarters of a black and white stinking animal flashed into Jack's mind before he placed the street noun. He'd done a piece on skunk earlier in the year – a mixed cannabis derivative, supposed to give a better high than resin. He'd been offered the drug seven times in a single night out in Southend. The *News of the World* ran the story, cutting down his own submitted prose from eight hundred to a mere three hundred words, the space needed, apparently, for another piece exposing the seaside town's other clandestinely booming business, massage parlours.

He shook his head. ''S all right, Mark, I'll wait.'

'Suit your fucking self.'

Jack decided it was time for a little more professional embroidery. 'Steve tells me you hang around the allotments up the Avenues sometimes.'

'So?'

59

'Bit sad, isn't it, kid your age? Got a girlfriend, have you?'

''Course.'

'Bet she loves it up there. What do you do, show her how well your spring onions are coming on?'

'Very funny.'

'Not exactly romantic, is it, the allotments?'

'Depends, doesn't it?' The boy tried his best cryptic smile. 'You tell me.'

And he was off. Jack hoped the microcassette in his inside jacket pocket was still rolling. OK, so the quality of the recording wouldn't exactly be EMI, but at least he hoped to have something muffled for C.F. to transcribe.

'Bunch of crappy old wankers up there. We go and have a laugh.'

'Yeah?' Jack adopted a suitably impressed expression. 'Such as?'

'Fucking about, an' that. Rip up their stuff. Chuck dog shit on their poncey little sheds. Whatever. Old geezers, aren't they? Sad old twats who're too fucking mean to buy their veg frozen like the rest of us. Arseholes.'

'Gets a bit boring, though, doesn't it? All too easy, surely?'

Cannon frowned. 'We're not up there every fucking day. It ain't like we don't do nothing else. Just sometimes. When Picket's about.'

'Picket?'

A malevolent smile crossed the pale, thin face. 'A real old duffer who deserves all he gets. The other day, right,' he explained, 'someone goes and burns his shed down, and he reckons it was us.'

'You and your girl?'

'And me mates, yeah.'

'But it wasn't?'

'No fucking way. He's a wanker, needs sorting out.'

Jack pretended to be deep in thought. He even scratched his cheek for extra effect. 'Can't blame him, though, can you, Mark? After all the grief you've given him.'

'But we never did it.'

'Ah, but how does he know that, eh?'

There was a silence as the boy struggled to grasp the concept. 'But he shouldn't just assume, though . . .'

'You assume he's an old tosser.'

''Cause he is.'

'Because he gets angry when you chuck shit at his shed?'

Cannon grinned. 'Yeah, well, whoever burnt the bastard shed down solved that little problem, didn't they?'

Jack stood, looked at his watch. 'I can't wait around all day, son.' He had enough to be going on with, confirmation Cannon and his gang were hassling the good allotment holders – and, strangely, denial over the arson. Obviously the boy had been back, seen the remains, heard of Picket's allegations, but still chose to deny any part in it. When instinct told Jack that Cannon was the type to confess to any act which might increase his juvenile suburban-outlaw standing. It was something of a quandry, raising the inevitable question – if Cannon didn't, then who *did* burn down the Chairman's pride and joy?

'I'll stick the kettle on if you really want some tea.' It was almost a plea for company, threaded with a looming fear of his brother's reaction to a lost sale.

'That's OK, son.' He stopped by the front door, standing on a pile of unopened circulars. The boy waited silently a few feet away, lost in the gloom of the hallway. He'd made an effort to keep his new friend and Jack had rejected it – for good reason, it was all in the game; he wanted the boy a little more sullen and angry. A sound dose of youthful petulance would be needed to balance out Picket's right-wing rhetoric. A choice quote from the bored young shit-chucker could well be the clincher for the broadsheets.

He made a show of pausing for thought. 'What do you want to do with your life, eh?'

Mark Cannon hesitated, stuck.

'Go to uni?' Jack suggested. 'Job, house, kids?'

Still nothing from the lad, staring back suspiciously.

'Or are you going to be still throwing shit around when you're your brother's age?'

'He don't chuck it, he sells it to dopeheads like you,' Cannon hissed back.

61

Jack smiled. 'Surprise yourself. Go to school. Learn something.'

'Like how to fucking sign on?'

'Beats ripping up cabbages, doesn't it?'

The mean little eyes narrowed in annoyance. 'I said we don't do that all the time.'

'So what else, then?'

'We hang round places. Do stuff. 'Cause everything else in this shitty town is crap and boring. Fucking skating and bowling, swimming and shit.'

'It's a hard life.'

'You taking the piss?'

'Yes, Mark, I am.'

'Who the hell are you, anyway?' Cannon asked, moving out of the darkness. 'You say you know me brother, and that – and I've never heard of you or nothing.'

Jack opened the front door. The fog was lifting slightly. He found himself spiralling out of character, slipping back into Jack Latimer as the late autumn chill surrounded him. 'I know dozens of blokes like your brother, Mark. Losers, all of them. Petty villains one knock away from prison. Stupid little biro tattoos on their arms, all playing at wheeling and dealing.'

'You what?'

'And then there's young lads like you, who reckon the world owes you everything. Who can't stand it when others have got an interest and you haven't. So you screw it all up for them. That's your kick, isn't it?'

He didn't answer, open-mouthed in shock.

'One day,' Jack continued. 'You might grow up. You might have a hobby of your own. A classic car, maybe, lovingly restored and polished. Then I really hope a group of kids just like you starts messing it all up. For a laugh. Because you'll know then, just how Picket feels. And it isn't nice, believe me.'

Then he turned and walked quickly back towards town.

11

Shortly after four the same day, Jack stood before a heavy wooden front door. Quiet suburban contentment surrounded him on all sides. Large, well-maintained 1930s semis ran along both sides of the wide, tree-lined street. Jack wondered if a healthy interest in gardening was a prerequisite to buying a property in Fourth Avenue, such seemed the collective neatness of its front lawns and tidied borders.

The door opened. 'Mr Latimer.'

'Mr Picket.'

'You'd better come in.'

'Thanks.'

Jack followed Picket into the house, wondering how such an apparently spacious hallway could feel quite so claustrophobic. True, the cluttered space was as dimly lit as Mark Cannon's temporary abode, but the overall impression should have been one of airy luxury.

Then it struck him how brown the place was. Brown panelled walls to waist height, brown carpet sitting on dark-brown floorboards, caramel-coloured walls host to indistinct brown-framed landscapes, their once golden ornate frames now dyed dirty mustard by dust and time.

'Lived here long?' he asked the tall figure, dressed in a dark-green tweed jacket, rough trousers, checked shirt and woollen tie. Jack hoped the Chairman wasn't expecting a photograph; he hadn't brought his camera.

'Born here,' Picket replied. 'Front bedroom. Fifth of March, nineteen thirty-eight. Two minutes past midnight.'

Jack paused before asking, 'And is there a Mrs Picket?'

'Dead.' The reply was soft, as if his lips caressed the word.

'I'm sorry . . .'

'Are you a happily married man, Mr Latimer?'

'Divorced. Four years ago. Made the best part of twelve years, though.'

The Chairman smiled. 'Congratulations. Mine lasted less than three. She took off with another man. I fear that the thing with women, Mr Latimer, is that no matter how beguiling they first appear, they're all genetically doomed to wander. It's in their bones.'

'Right,' Jack replied hesitantly, deciding to change the subject. The finality of the remark convinced him Picket had nothing further to say on the matter. 'So you have this place to yourself, then?'

'I can manage, if that's what you're asking. I'm not looking for either lodgers or sympathy, Mr Latimer. I'm retired, manage to make the pension stretch.'

'Retired from what?' Jack pressed, anxious for background to flesh out the tale.

'Civil service pen-pushing,' Picket obliged. 'Took early redundancy at fifty-five. Looked forward to uninterrupted years tending to my allotment duties. Somehow it didn't work out as I'd planned.'

Jack joined Picket in a back room, only marginally lighter than the front of the house. Here the decor was predominantly dark-green. An open fire burnt coal quietly. An Art-Deco clock ticked reassuringly. A soot-darkened set of french windows looked out on to an old-style conservatory. The room smelt of damp, and Jack guessed the doors had long since begun to rot.

Picket sat in a high-backed armchair facing the fire.

Jack sat down in a frail-looking dining chair, realizing how old everything appeared. He reckoned the entire room could be opened to paying members of the public, keen for a glimpse of a bygone age. Jack was no expert, but he guessed most of the fixtures and furnishings were pre-nineteen-sixty, with precious few bought any later. There were books, too, hundreds, lining shelves which ran the room, only interrupted by the moss-tinged french windows.

Yet the more Jack looked, the more he discovered that

for all the room's apparent military order, it was, in fact, semi-organized chaos.

Darkened corners hid more books, piles of what looked like newspapers, shoe-cleaning polish and brushes, all sorts of abandoned tattle. The carpet was thick with soot, and Jack noticed food down the front of Picket's tie. He found himself wondering about other rooms in the house, prepared to wager money they were much the same – well-ordered to a casual observer, but a grubby mess to anyone who looked a little harder, or stopped to run a finger along a greasy, dusty shelf.

And Picket himself, Jack pondered in those first few seconds, was he the same? Outwardly clean-shaven and upright, inwardly chaotic, perhaps even a little unsavoury?

Jack pushed the thought from his head. He had read all the seventies American room-psychology manuals detailing apparent links between an individual's character and the way they chose to furnish their environment, and in his opinion, some of the nastiest characters he'd ever met had lived in conventionally immaculate houses. Never judge a book by its cover, had been the lesson learned – or, in this case, an old man by the dust on his shelves.

He cleared his throat. 'I've just spoken to one of the youths involved, Mr Picket. The leader of the group. The one you say burnt down your shed.'

Picket nodded solemnly, as Jack thought a vicar might. 'And I suppose he denied everything?'

'He did, yes.'

The Chairman thought for a moment. 'So it's a thug's word against mine, presumably?'

'I think,' said Jack cautiously, pulling out a notebook and pen to record proceedings by hand. 'That if he he'd done what you allege, he'd have been the first to admit it, be almost proud of it. But he didn't. He volunteered the whole story without me asking him a single question, and not knowing me from Adam.' Jack decided against using the microcassette, feeling Picket would be less obliged to open up in front of the battery-powered device. As a hunch, it was the right one.

'Then perhaps he doth protest too much,' Picket replied coldly.

Jack flushed slightly, feeling too heavy in his overcoat. The room was still with hot, dead air, as if the fire had been burning for years. 'He was really quite annoyed to be accused of arson.'

'*He's* annoyed?'

'It's just that, I'm not sure I can get away with saying these kids started the fire when there were no witnesses, and the ringleader denies it.'

Picket struggled to contain his anger. 'How do you know it was him, anyway?'

'A good source.'

'Make it sound like something that goes with Duck à l'Orange, Mr Latimer. A policeman, no doubt.'

Jack nodded, eyes caught by a sudden gleam in Picket's immaculately polished shoes, flames mirrored so keenly it was as if his toes were on fire. Jack knew that even if he spent six weeks polishing his one pair of two-year-old brogues, he'd never come up with a shine like that. His eyes remained rooted to the reflected flames. It was unsettling, borderline obsessive, weird, the brightly shining shoes suggesting the tall, thin man opposite might launch into an elaborate tap number at any moment.

Picket's smile matched the flames – small, bright, dying, devoid of warmth. 'Oh, what it is to have contacts in such high places.'

At which point he rose, walked out. Jack waited a moment before following. They stood in a yellow kitchen, another testament to the enduring qualities of domestic products in times past. An Aga dominated the one side, a set of shelves stacked with pickles and pulses, the other. Jack looked in vain for a fridge-freezer.

He watched as Picket poured himself a cup of brown tea stewing in a brown pot beneath a brown tea-cosy. The Chairman disappeared out of the back door for a second, returning with a carton of milk. The contemporary packaging looked almost shameful in the unbranded environment. 'I have a cold-store outside,' Picket explained. 'It'll keep milk from souring for up to two days.'

'I once heard,' said Jack conversationally, 'that if you

leave a pint of milk outside in a thunderstorm, it all turns to cream.'

'About as likely as the fairy story you were told by the young thug,' Picket replied, begrudgingly pouring a second cup. 'Sugar?'

'Two. Thanks.'

Picket handed Jack the lukewarm mug. They resettled in the green back room. 'Tell me, Mr Latimer,' Picket suddenly asked. 'Do you believe in capital punishment?'

Jack was thrown by the unexpected change of subject. 'As a deterrent, or barbaric retribution?'

Picket's eyes remained fixed on the glowing coal. 'As the ultimate act of law enforcement.'

Jack thought for a second in the heavy silence. 'I don't really think it achieves anything. Look at America. Thousands on Death Row, not one of them deterred by the prospect –'

'America,' Picket interrupted. 'Does it all wrong. Lets the condemned wait years before carrying out the sentence. Damn civil rights gets in the way. I hear they're stepping it up now in some Southern states. One a month to clear the blacklog.'

'Backlog, you mean?'

'It's all negroes in there.'

Jack was fast beginning to take a dislike to his latest client. True, there'd been many over the years whose opinions he'd disagreed with, but none who'd aired such outdated ones. It was as if the Chairman's mind was stuck in the same time warp as the house. A part of him could well imagine the thrill Cannon and his little gang might get out of harassing the old bigot.

And he still wasn't sure how much of a valid news item there was in the story. Certainly, there was a glimmer of a clichéd 'old versus the new' article. But Picket's character, central to getting the reader to side with him, turned the potentially downtrodden old gent into a right-wing recluse frothing with little but insult and prejudice at a world which had rapidly evolved and changed outside his four sullen walls. He needed more – an angle to force a news editor's hand.

Picket took a loud slurp of tea, watching his guest, gauging him.

Jack made another discovery. There were no photographs to be seen anywhere. He assumed that this was the living room, and that Picket would have spent most of his time here, so why were there no photographs? Everyone kept a few family photos in their living rooms, didn't they?

'My father took up the call, you know.'

'He was a priest?' Jack replied, pen poised.

'An executioner.'

Jack felt as if he'd just been slapped in the face. 'What a . . . ?'

'Hangman,' Picket supplied. 'Assistant, actually.'

'What, in case the main man got ill, or something?' Jack asked. This was it, the nugget which had so far eluded the story.

'Oh no, he was there, right until the Number One sent the condemned through the trap. He had a hand in most of it, preparing the gallows the night before, walking the fellow on to the trap, strapping arms and ankles, then dealing with the body afterwards, washing, stripping, nailing down the coffin lid. A highly detailed procedure. The training was most intense.'

'Your father did this?' Jack asked, taking frantic short-hand.

'Oh yes,' Picket replied brightly. 'Not that I knew at the time – perfectly unaware. Mother told me shortly after he died.' Picket clicked his tongue loudly. 'A brown envelope would arrive, from the Home Office, requesting his services. He'd leave us for a few days sometime after. Mother always told me it was "business". Which I suppose it was, in a way. Miserable damn pay, though. I think he did it because he wanted to. I think he thought it made a difference.'

Jack said nothing, unwilling to break the spell. Picket was speaking quietly, softly, humanely, even. Gone was the austere retired gent, replaced by an older man in fireside contemplation – the real Picket? Jack mused, guard slipping a fraction? He hoped so; the latest incarnation made a much more sympathetic figure than the first. And the

68

broadsheet editors would love the hangman's-son connection.

Picket continued. 'He died in nineteen-sixty-nine. Mother said she thought it had destroyed him.'

'The job?'

'The abolition. It wasn't his full-time profession, Mr Latimer, more of a crusade. He helped rid the world of its monsters and wrongdoers. He was a devout Christian.' Picket turned to face the eager reporter. 'And what will this century be remembered for, Mr Latimer? When all's said and done, and we limp past this wretched millennium nonsense? How will future historians rate this century?'

'A time of great change?' Jack guessed.

'A time of colossal destruction,' Picket replied mournfully. 'A time when supermarkets, cars, new towns, liberal politics ripped the heart, the communities, out of this nation. A time when family values and Christian morals were bludgeoned by corporate greed, American burger chains, political corruption, and massive economical blunders.'

'It hasn't all been bad news.' Jack tried for optimism. 'Science has pushed back the boundaries of –'

'Science has lined the fat cats' pockets, Mr Latimer. Choice has isolated us all in our rabbit hutches.'

'I'm not sure I follow you.'

'Freedom of choice is a wicked misnomer,' Picket explained. 'Just like the supermarkets, forcing genuine traders out of business, destroying lives, livelihoods. In my day, Mr Latimer, we shopped for each meal, left our homes, mingled, talked, exchanged views, grew as a community. My God, if I struck up a conversation with a stranger in a damn supermarket, they'd think I was a nutcase.'

'Times change,' Jack echoed.

'Back then, every man-Jack had an allotment. We all grew our own fruit and veg. Now, we're either looked upon as a bunch of Luddite freaks, or championed by long-haired hippies as organic freedom fighters. It's got worse, so much worse. These days, what with fridge-freezers and microwaves, the average family can shop for a goddamned fortnight in two hours, cook each meal in under five minutes, before eating it in miserable silence in front of the ruddy television.' Picket carefully put three more lumps of coal on the dying fire.

'Your father,' Jack asked, anxious to steer the Chairman back on to matters more saleable. 'How many executions did he assist at?'

Picket scratched the side of his smooth waxen face, leaving a coal smudge on his cheek. 'I remember my mother telling me what pleased him the most. The draught.'

'Draught?'

'Of the condemned as they fell past him through the trap into the pit below.'

The fire popped suddenly, sending a tiny shower of glowing sparks up into the chimney. Jack felt a tiny shudder course through him.

'He only had seconds to strap the ankles and leap clear of the trap doors, Mr Latimer. The Number One was fitting the white cap and noose as my father buckled the strap below. Once done, he'd fling himself off the trap, the Number One pulled the lever, and virtually the whole floor opened. Next came the last terrified gasp of the condemned, and the draught as they whistled past. Finally the massive crash of the trap doors hitting the walls of the pit. The whole prison would wait for that sound. Justice booming out.'

'Your mother told you all this?'

'Only after he'd passed away. The Home Office forbade him from talking to anyone about his work. People knew, of course. Locals, up and down the street, saw his photograph in the papers, standing outside the prison with other officials after each job. But he never gave away any details. Father was a highly principled man. About thirty, I think.'

'Sorry?'

'Executions he assisted at. You did ask.'

'Right.' The hideous crash of the trap doors was still echoing in Jack's mind. 'And after he died?'

'Hard times, Mr Latimer, very hard. Father's main job as an accounts clerk left a meagre widow's pension.' Picket smiled. 'Curious, isn't it, how death shapes us?'

'Both my parents are still alive,' Jack confessed.

'Spending their time watching television, I'd expect.'

Jack returned the smile, made a mental note to phone them later, but only after *Coronation Street*.

Picket coughed, a deep chesty growl. 'People say I'm a moaning old so-and-so, Mr Latimer. They're probably right. But I have no need of their opinions or the so-called luxuries of their miserable little lives. Until a few months ago, I lived quite happily here, minding my own business, fulfilling my role as Chairman, tending to other allotment holders' needs.'

'Then the kids arrived?'

Picket dismissed the suggestion with a flick of the wrist. 'There's always been kids around. I'm not down on children, Mr Latimer.'

'But these are different, right?'

Picket nodded. 'The police, the papers, the council, they all seem to think it's some kind of joke. But it's not. They've started burning our sheds, now, along with all the rest.'

'Like I told you, the lad I spoke to swears it wasn't him.'

'Then he's a filthy liar to boot.'

Jack shifted slightly in his chair. 'Mr Picket, I was wondering if you wouldn't consider some sort of meeting with these kids?'

Picket frowned. 'Face to face?'

'For the article. A meeting of minds. A chance to learn from one another, adapt, who knows, maybe coexist? A resolution to the problems. It'd make for great copy. With a story like yours, there's an outside chance I could sway a national Sunday broadsheet to take it.'

'Idealistic claptrap.'

'Can I ask why not?'

'Because I'd be made to look a fool.'

'But until you try –'

'No, Mr Latimer. No.'

It was going to be pointless trying to dissuade him. Jack managed to finish the last of his tea, then stood, eagerly anticipating the cooling chill of the outside. 'I'm going to try and put all this together, Mr Picket, formulate the article. Can I mention your father's . . . part-time job?'

'If you must.'

'And I'll need a photograph.'

'Of my father?' Picket looked confused.

'No. Of you, standing where the fire happened. Perhaps a few of the other allotment holders as well.'

'Now?'

Jack shook his head. 'Soon. When I've finished the piece. I know some freelance snappers who'll oblige.'

'You really think you'll interest the national press?' Picket asked hopefully.

'I can't promise anything, really. There's the makings of something here, but there's still a lot more people to talk to.'

Picket rose slowly from his chair, and began showing Jack back to the front door. 'If I could say one thing, it's this,' he said, opening the thick oak door. 'Once we had a Garden of Eden. We turned our back on the Lord. We toiled to make life easier, consumed with our own petty luxuries. The heaven that the inventors promised us, is now a hell of our own making.'

Jack shook Picket's hand, promising to be in touch very soon. Jack began walking back into town, passing the allotments at the end of Picket's road, with a noticeable spring in his step.

The persecuted executioner's son had just given him the quote he wanted.

Inside the house, Picket poured himself a fresh cup of tea, before making his way back upstairs. He settled himself in a small bare room, and began carefully stripping the fading wallpaper. The cold space echoed with his occasional shuffling footsteps.

He paused when he reached the window, wondering what the best way of completing the next stage would be. Yes, he decided, the sill would have to go. Whistling, he went downstairs to find a crowbar.

There was still so much to do – and so little time.

12

For the first few minutes, neither man said a word, simply savouring the food served on a tiny table between them.

Kenny Samson spoke first, a forkful of lamb passanda held loosely in his large fist. 'Hat's off to you, Jack. Tell me, how do you get the sauce to thicken like that? Jenny always seems to make it runny.'

'Cashew nuts and almonds, crushed then added at the last,' Jack replied, opening another bottle of Tiger Beer. For him, authenticity was everything in both the cooking and the consuming, an attitude hungrily shared by his occasional dinner guest.

'Plus, you have to really pulp the onions first,' he said through a mouthful of food. 'Give them ten minutes to brown, take the bitterness out.'

'Right,' said Samson cautiously, unwilling to admit he had trouble cooking anything which didn't comprise beans and sliced bread as fundamental ingredients. He took another mouthful. 'Bloody beautiful. Really sort of . . . herby. Authentic.'

'Fresh coriander,' Jack replied. 'C.F. brings the seeds into the office. We have it growing in a little window box outside. I think the diesel fumes give it a certain extra something, don't you?'

'And how is the lovely C.F.?'

Jack paused. 'Gutted. Her dad's got secondaries.'

'Shit. He's a mate of yours, right?'

Jack nodded, reached for another home-made nan, tore off a chunk and dipped it into the curry. 'A fine man, Kenny. Taught me all about food. Indian feasts, culture, preparation, mythology . . .'

'What? Of a Ruby Murray?'

'It's food with a history, man. Not like the fast-frozen crap that's shovelled into half the nation's mouths each night.' He took a great mouthful, wondering if he was beginning to come across like George Picket on his 'grow your own – down with the supermarkets!' soapbox. Maybe the Chairman was getting to him.

Samson finished his plate, replete. For all the time he'd known Jack, it was as if he'd somehow never really got to *know* him. The quality of the home-made curry was a typical example. Kenny couldn't help but feel both a grudging admiration and a suspicion that Jack's hidden depths ran deep. And maybe those same depths, occasionally revealed, were the very reason that Kenny preferred Jack's company to his fellow officers'. Cooking to them was a woman's pursuit, curries best left to the Pakis.

'Got to hand it to you, Jack. If anyone's cut out for the single life, it's you.'

'Ha ha.'

'I'm serious,' the detective replied, opening another beer and looking round the sparsely furnished, yet tidy, room. 'Can't be a bad way to live. No kids running riot, no wife pulling her hair out with the strain of it all.'

'It's quiet,' Jack conceded.

'How are you and Amy?'

Jack shrugged. 'Alive. She's got a new man in her life.'

'Bound to happen, given time. Maybe you should join one of these singles clubs, grab yourself a granny for a quick game of Zelda back at your place.'

'I'll pass,' Jack said, eyes drifting to the abandoned computer standing on a hastily cleared desk-top in the far corner of the room. Kenny had done his bit, arriving shortly after eight with a dozen bottled beers and a CD of Alex's favourite role-playing game. Whereupon, after taking a swift look at Jack's hastily purchased second-hand out-of-the-local-paper computer, he had calmly informed him that firstly the machine was a 486, and therefore almost certain to crash come the millennium; and secondly, the fifty-quid electronic investment had neither the disk space or the CD-ROM drive to take the game. At which point Jack's plan to familiarize himself with Alex's passion had been abandoned in favour of the food, Kenny assuring him he'd have a word with the stolen goods officer on the quiet, see if he couldn't 'find' a better machine from the Essex Police warehouse. He'd stood and watched as his friend silently stirred the curry, grim-faced.

'Crazy situation, Jack.'

'Sorry?'

'You, getting jealous over Amy's new fella.'

'Am I bollocks.'

'Are.'

'Am not.'

Samson began to giggle, popping a fresh bottle for them both.

Jack sighed, took the plates into the tiny kitchen, ladled out some more food, returned to the table.

'Really excellent rice, too,' Samson enthused, taking a rugby player's forkful.

'Basmati,' Jack replied. 'Ten ounces for twenty of water. Fry an onion in a little ghee, add the cloves, few cumin seeds, half-a-dozen cardamon pods, cover and leave simmering for ten minutes once it's come to the boil. Any longer and it'll stick to the bottom like porridge.'

'Bit like a marriage,' Samson replied, smothering a philosophical belch. 'If it simmers too long, it's ruined.'

Jack rolled his eyes to the ceiling. 'Don't get smart on me, Kenny. Try this one, Kojak. A thousand pounds says you'll never guess the identity of Chelmsford's biggest serial killer,' Jack said suddenly.

Samson stared blankly back.

'George Picket's father,' Jack announced, enjoying the confusion on the detective's face.

'Did you slip something funny into the food, Jack? Only I swear I'm hearing things.'

'S'true. Did over thirty, according to his son. And never served a day's time for it.'

Samson squinted, unsure. He'd been victim to Jack's wind-ups before, yet something in the intensity of the reporter's eyes told him Jack wasn't bluffing – enjoying the game, but telling the truth.

'And the really weird thing,' Jack went on. 'Is that the method of dispatch was always the same. Some reckoned the killings were so efficient, it had to be a two-man team. A fact confirmed to me not only by Picket, but also the Home Office.'

'Tell me this is crap. Please.'

'Stranger still, each victim was found dead in any number of prisons across the length and breadth of the land. The late Richard Picket's reign of terror knew no bounds.'

'You're shitting me?'

Jack shook his head, then hung himself with an invisible rope, tongue lolling unsavourily to one side.

'Jesus!' Samson protested. 'Put it away, Jack. He was a hangman?'

A savoury nod from Jack this time.

'It's unbelievable.'

'But true. I've checked with the Home Office. Richard Picket's name appears on an official list of Assistant Executioners.'

'And it's the same Picket? The shed guy?'

Jack nodded.

'It's er . . . news, right?' Kenny floundered. 'I'm shocked. Amazed. You must be chuffed to buggery with a lead like that.'

'It's interesting background, yeah. But I'm not doing the man's biography, Kenny. OK, so he's a strange bloke living in a weird place on an otherwise normal-looking suburban avenue – but none of that's going to make the front page, is it?'

Samson opened another beer. 'But the thing with the kids at the allotment is?' he guessed.

'Maybe,' Jack replied. 'I went and saw Mark Cannon yesterday.'

'Oh yes?'

'What's going on, Kenny?'

Samson adopted his most innocent face.

Jack ignored it, having known the man too long. 'There's

a thirteen-year-old kid living with a dealer. Drugs on the premises. Shit, the kid even tried to sell me some. Where are the social services in all this? Your juvenile officer knows the score. All right, Cannon may be a young arse-ache, but living there isn't helping him. Jesus, the more I look into this stuff, the bleaker it gets. Seven billion, juvenile crime costs this country. Three per cent of young offenders account for a quarter of all juvenile crimes. I say to myself, "Fuck, this can't be right" – then I see the Mark Cannons of the world and it all falls hideously easily into place.'

Samson frowned, made a show of finishing his mouthful, when Jack knew full well he was merely buying time before replying. 'Sometimes, you just have to leave well alone,' he said eventually. 'The Cannons are a right ugly bunch. But then every town's got one.'

'I heard that about Picket.'

'Him too. But it's the old adage – better the devil you know.' Samson blushed slightly. 'This is off the record, right?'

'Kenny, if I'd wanted to muckrake, I'd have slipped a truth serum in the pickle.'

Samson took another swig. 'Steve Cannon is . . . tolerated.'

'I'm listening.'

'He's what we call a "criminal necessity". He pushes some weed, gets involved in a few ABHs, gets nicked, does some time, gets out, pushes some more weed again. The junkies know where to score their stuff, we know who's supplying it. If we were to bang him up for possession, he'd get maybe three to five, taking in his previous. Which allows any other dealer to walk in on his patch. Result? We get a drugs war on our hands, new dealers pushing all kinds of shit on the town's freaks, and we haven't got the foggiest what's going on.'

'And young Mark?'

'What about him?'

'Ready to start dealing like big brother Steve? A kid of thirteen? You happy with that?'

Samson shrugged. 'Come on, Jack. This is Chelmsford. We get one murder every five years. Crime's limited to a spot of B and E coupled with some predictable drunk and disorderly arrests every Friday night. If we started taking people like the Cannons off the streets, who knows how many boats we're going to rock? It's only pot – not class-A, Jack.'

'Right,' Jack replied, unable to lid the sarcasm. 'And I suppose all the punters who turn up looking for half an ounce of black are MS sufferers taking it as a painkiller?'

'All I'm saying is that sometimes, it isn't politic to upset the applecart, that's all.'

'So who decides, then?'

'What?'

'Who takes the decision to leave Mark Cannon where he is? You, the social services, who?'

'Shit, Jack, it's nothing so formal. It just happens.'

'So you're saying the Cannons run round getting away with it – because the authorities are letting them?'

'Might be one way of looking at it. Hands being fairly well tied by the ass of the law's another. Listen, kids like Mark can be arrested on the Monday, bailed the next day, rearrested for another offence that same day, bailed again on Wednesday. He's too young for detention centres. There's damn-all we can do till the little sod turns fourteen. He's Chelmsford's very own pint-sized Teflon Don. Nothing sticks to him.'

'And the trouble he's been causing up at the allotments? Another blind eye?'

'It's just a shed, Jack. Hardly *Crimewatch* material, is it?'

'George Picket mightn't agree.'

'He doesn't have to police this town, Jack,' Kenny insisted. 'Regardless of what you may think, good policing's got sod-all to do with the rule book. It's about compromise, balance, sensitivity. Jesus, if we nicked every felon for every known offence, the jails would be even more overcrowded, we'd be even more despised, and we'd have a riot on our hands.'

'Where do you draw the line, then?' Jack asked. 'Suppose Mark Cannon and his gang *did* start burning down allotment sheds every Friday night, when do you step in?'

'Hypothetical. Not going to happen, is it?'

'But what if it does?'

Kenny sighed heavily. It had been such a pleasant evening

until now. Jack's persistence was starting to give him heart-burn. 'Don't you think you'd be better off thinking about something else? You and Amy, for instance?'

'Answer the question, Kenny, come on.'

'No.'

'Won't or can't?'

'Neither. I've already told you enough. You're a smart bloke. You figure it out.'

Jack sat quite still, holding the intent stare. With precious few real and reliable friends, it would be crass in the extreme to fall out with Kenny, yet he sensed it could happen if he pushed the detective further. He smiled. 'Just asking,' he said quietly.

They finished their beers, washed up and popped out to Jack's local, Samson paying for a few pints as thanks for the meal. In the ensuing two hours, nothing was mentioned about the Cannon family by either man.

And yet, for all the jocular small talk about football, women, cooking and cacti, Jack couldn't help feeling, Samson was holding something back, worried perhaps that the forth-coming article on Picket would cast the caring, community-minded boys in blue in a somewhat uncaring light.

As he said goodbye at the end of the evening, Jack still felt a strain of tension between them. It bothered him all the way back to the darkened flat.

He was into the office early the following morning, having typed out and faxed twelve treatments of the proposed article as C.F. arrived with two styrofoam cups of coffee at just past nine.

An hour later, the *Observer* had made a preliminary offer, swayed largely by the hangman's-son connection, a feature Jack had deliberately underplayed in the treatment. Which in turn bought him a little more time to research and deliver the full piece. But it was a fair sale for Latimer Associates – eight hundred for a single page in a lifestyle supplement, from a story which had willingly brought itself to his doorstep.

And, quite frankly, with so many supplements to feed and fill each week, the truth was that the editors would take just about anything providing it met with their precious demographic profiles. No searing exposés, no heart-stopping exclusives – just a regular weekly diet of the lives and struggles of ordinary folk in ordinary towns, encompassing supposed issues which affected the rest of their readership. And in that sense, George Picket's battle with young vandals perfectly fitted the unwritten broadsheet brief.

After the sale Jack put down the phone, too long in the game to feel completely elated. He still trusted to his instincts, and couldn't shake the feeling that there was more to the simple tale of an allotment shed going up in flames. Something about Picket bothered him, not just the rhetoric, but the man himself, the house, his father, the sense of menace which prevailed.

Perhaps it was all as the Chairman had described, simply a long summer war of attrition with juvenile vandals. But what if there was more, other hidden motives, a subtext gently smouldering under the ashes? Mark Cannon had denied the charge, Kenny was reluctant to commit himself to anything beyond the standard set of harassed policeman's clichés, and Picket's insistence that he knew the youngsters responsible without any real proof all began to eat their way into Jack's mind.

And the longer he pondered, the more he realized he simply couldn't let it go.

13

The Chelmsford Avenues Allotment Society AGM had been in session for an hour and forty minutes before Audrey Baxter (in her non-elected capacity as secretary and sandwich-maker) read out item seven from the agenda.

'The hooligan problem,' she calmly announced, before inquiring if now was a good time to get the kettle on.

George Picket waved her away to his kitchen, then turned to the only other committee member. 'As you know, Bill, I went and saw a local reporter chap the other morning.'

'Shocking,' William Kent echoed. 'Little sods should be birched.' He was dressed as immaculately as his pension would allow, a jumble-sale jacket engulfing a fraying shirt held together by grey polyester kipper tie. There were crumbs on his lap, liver spots on both hands, and his brown plastic shoes made his feet swell intolerably. He'd done his best to iron his trousers, but the creases were a mess, something Picket hadn't missed earlier.

'Oh dear,' he'd said simply upon Kent's arrival. 'Eyes not so good these days?'

Bill Kent had blushed and smiled apologetically, saying nothing.

Audrey Baxter had arrived shortly after, bearing clingfilmed plates of cheese and tomato sandwiches, and a notebook and pen to record the minutes of the prestigious proceedings. She was, in George's silent opinion, dressed little better than a common street-whore, showing far too much knee upon sitting, and smelling quite dreadfully of cheap perfume. However, as she looked to have made a passable job of the evening's refreshments, he allowed her reluctantly into the house. Besides, the prostitute look could always be filed away to join Audrey's other personas stored in his erotic imagination.

As for Audrey, it was her first ever visit to the Chairman's house. She'd spent a good deal of the afternoon planning just what to wear for the occasion, changing her outfit five times to get it just right. In the end she opted for what she hoped passed as the right balance of feminine grace and secretarial elegance. She had been both shocked and excited when he asked her to minute-take for the evening, trying her best not to look too keen on the prospect of an evening in such close proximity to the great man. Mrs Cardington, elected secretary to the committee, had a bout of flu. Well, Mrs Cardington's loss was Audrey's temporary gain. And after, who knows, perhaps the tall, suave, mysterious Chairman might persuade her to stay for a sherry or two . . .

She returned from the kitchen with three steaming mugs of tea.

Picket cleared his throat importantly. He was having trouble concentrating tonight, his mind wandering to the alterations upstairs. Twice during the day, he'd been caught by painful lapses in concentration, paying the price with a heavily cut thumb and badly bruised elbow. It was harder work than he thought. He needed help, ideally, a trusted ally with extensive DIY knowledge. But who? Kent was no use, didn't appear to have the strength to lift a sledgehammer, let alone use it to demolish a wall in preparation for an adjoining door. No, he needed some uncomplaining muscle, a silent navvy to join him in the business of the glorious work. But who?

His son would have been the obvious option. Father and son together, forging a new relationship from the ruins of the house. But his son was gone, back to wherever. George was on his own once more. Perhaps it was better that way. Who else would understand, share his vision? The Baxter woman? After all, she seemed pathetically struck on him, love-sick, on heat almost. But what use was a woman during men's work? How many cups of tea would she bring him before he found her presence pathetic and disgusting? No – for the moment, he'd forge on alone, quietly dedicating himself to the cause, ignoring the voices endlessly taunting his efforts.

Those fucking voices . . .

Kent was droning on. '. . . really was a first-class move, Mr Chairman.'

Picket fought hard to drag himself back into the banal here and now. 'Seems he's managed to interest a broadsheet newspaper.'

'Good-oh,' Bill Kent added.

'So it won't be long before we receive some contrite apologies from the police, amongst others.'

'About time, too, Mr Chairman,' Audrey said, beaming. 'Those children have been making our lives a misery.'

'Quite.'

'And will we be getting television security cameras?' Kent asked, slurping on his tea.

'All in good time,' Picket confirmed.

'The article's bound to strengthen our cause,' Audrey enthused.

Picket nodded. The phone rang, suddenly shrilling out from the gloomy hallway. 'If you'll excuse me,' he said, leaving the room, making his way to the Bakelite machine, hoping against hope that it wouldn't be his son . . . not now . . . not when things were just starting to resolve themselves in his favour . . .

Because it had been so fortuitous up till now, including the shed fire. And what else was a loving father expected to do, sit by and let his only son drop deeper into the mire, while he did nothing, ignoring the warning signs?

George Picket had done a very bad thing, but only because he hadn't the time to explain. Besides, Mikey never left a contact number, Mikey drifted in and out of his life like the night wind, and those damned, bastard children's voices. Mikey always called George, not the other way around.

So when the time had come for the talking to happen, George had no idea how to find his son. He knew he couldn't wait any longer, knew he had to act for Mikey's sake. Then and there, because regardless of what the boy thought, irrespective of the past, he'd realized just how much he really loved the boy.

Picket's hand hovered over the receiver. Please don't let it be Mikey. Not yet. Not until he'd had a chance to get it all straight in his mind, explain. Because he knew Mikey would be upset, which would make them both mad, and George didn't want that. George wanted them to sit down and talk – honestly, openly. Then maybe work out how they were going to begin again, together, father and son in a far-away place.

He lifted the phone to his ear.

'Dad?' It was Mikey.

'Son?'

'Need to see you, Dad.' The voice was shaky, frightened.

George swallowed hard to beat his drying throat. 'What about, Mikey?'

'I need to come over. Now.'

'Are you in trouble?'

'Can I come tomorrow? It's important.'

'Listen, Mikey, is this about . . . ?' George found every word excrutiating.

'What? Tell me, Dad.'

So he did. Every last detail.

'You stupid old cunt!' the voice on the other end of the line exploded angrily. 'You've done *what*?'

So Picket took his son through the scenario once more, this time stressing how much he cared for the boy, how worried he was, how it wasn't too late to start over. They could put so much behind them.

'I can't believe this!' Mikey was protesting, his voice strangulated by crushing desperation. 'You've killed me, Dad. They're going to fucking kill me, and it's your fault!'

'Mikey, listen to me. Tell them it was an accident. They'll have to believe you. Won't they?'

'Oh, Jesus Christ. Jesus, Jesus Christ.'

'Come home, Mikey,' Picket pleaded. 'We'll leave. They won't find you.'

'Too late, Dad.' The voice was curiously high-pitched. 'They're already here. Now I've got to tell them, haven't I?'

Picket's legs shook uncontrollably. 'Mikey, please listen to me. Please. Let me speak to them. I'll tell them everything . . .'

But the line had gone dead. Picket held the receiver in his hand for a haunting moment, before replacing it gently back into the cradle, wishing for once he owned a digital phone in order to trace the incoming number. For now all he could do was wait in the empty hallway for the ancient silent machine to ring again.

Ten minutes later, the others had gone, meeting curtailed. George Picket returned and sat quietly by the phone.

Waiting.

Hearing nothing but the repeated obscenities of Mikey's young tormentors, tearing into his mind . . .

. . . Louder and louder . . .

14

There were four men in the room, three standing, one tied to a creaking wooden chair. His swollen, bloodied face already bore brutal testimony to the previous hour's faltering interrogation.

The standing men were silent now, the two younger ones panting, sweating despite the cold, drinking neat vodka from a bottle passed between them, waiting for the thicker-set, older man to give the orders. He paced the length of the room in quiet contemplation.

He had something of a problem. He liked the kid, despite what had happened, but the boy had fucked up, big time. Which meant he'd be blamed for the unexpected losses. Others higher up would demand answers, and all he had so far was a ludicrous explanation which defied belief. Yet in a bizarre way he half suspected the kid was telling the truth. He almost wished he'd videoed proceedings so far, evidence for his superiors that he wasn't bullshitting them, merely telling it as the kid had told him. But he hadn't brought a camcorder. The very thought was crass stupidity. What if the filth got a look at it?

So, sighing, he set about the sobbing tied body with renewed vigour. The kid would have to pay, regardless of his feelings for him. If he still walked the streets and word of the balls-up got round to the other outfits, the firm would be a laughing stock for weeks. And he couldn't have that. No way.

The young men looked at him expectantly. He gave a slight nod, watching as the older of the two plugged in an electric sander, then began removing a tattoo from the kid's upper arm.

The gag was slipping, and once or twice, hideous screams slipped from behind the blood-soaked rag. It was quickly retied.

Next, all three men worked at removing fingertips. They tried industrial bolt-cutters, amazed at the strength required to snip through stubborn bone. The thumbs took one man on either limb of the cutters.

More vodka. The older man was pleased to see the kid had passed out with the pain. He was a businessman, not a sadist. Others, lesser hearts than he, would have revived the boy with smelling salts and cold water, prolonging the agony for as long as feasibly possible. He'd heard whispered cases of men taking eight hours to die at the hands of real professionals. Some outfits even had their own 'call signs' for occasions such as these, a severed penis stuffed into its previous owner's mouth, beer bottles forced unceremoniously into bleeding rectums. But such things were for the real sickos. His mob had no need of employing the services of a deranged psycho for the job – they took care of their own dealings, quietly and efficiently.

Next, the teeth had to go. There was a definite order to it all, a ritual he'd observed many times, but never actually commanded before. The point was for the body to be found devoid of all identification, yet in such a state that to those that knew, this was an execution. Somebody had fucked up, then paid the price. There really was no other way.

The wisdom teeth were proving unsettlingly difficult. The older man took the gore-ridden pliers himself, instructing the others to hold the unconscious head still, forcing the jaw open at a near-impossible angle, pressing down on the bloated tongue for easier access. Still the upper wisdoms held fast. Midway through the unorthodox dentistry, he noticed the boy's eyes rolling open in bloodshot fear, boring into his own with utter confusion. The pain must have been intolerable.

There was too much blood pouring from the severed fingers. The men were slipping, cursing the boy, slapping, punching him. The older man gave up on the pliers, cold sweat streaming down his back. Swearing, he returned for a claw-hammer, before bringing it swiftly down on the kid's head, hoping for a death blow.

It took four more strikes before the straining body slumped against the chain. Urine puddled out on to the bloody floor, and a stench of violently expelled human shit caused all those left alive in the room to heave and gag.

Untying the body, they worked again on the teeth, prostrate on the cold concrete floor, swearing, cursing, and the youngest crying. They stopped for a cigarette break. One of them opened the up-and-over garage door a fraction to allow in a cleansing breath of cold night air.

They talked, low, slurred voices, realizing the only option was to remove the head altogether. They couldn't risk dental records tracing the wisdom teeth's owner. It would be sheer folly, especially as they'd done so well with the sander, the fingerprints and all other distinguishing characteristics. Decapitation – no other option. The headless body would still bear the essential hallmarks of gangland retribution. Those that needed to heed the warning would soon connect the kid's sudden disappearance with the headless corpse found floating in the river. And they'd know then, not to fuck up like he did. Other mobs would be content that the matter had been 'dealt with'. Including the paymasters.

It took seven minutes to saw through the cold grey neck. The first few inches were fine, all soft muscle and gristle. The time was spent finding a gap between vertebrae for the slipping hacksaw blade. One held the head, another the torso, while the older man sawed through. Twice, a drop of sweat fell from his forehead into the gaping open wound.

They let the remaining blood pool out on to the concrete, swigging more vodka. The youngest of the party was clearly the worse for wear, unable even to place the severed head and fingers into a canvas bag as the other two struggled to wrap the body in tarpaulin prior to removal to its final resting place. His older colleague did the honours.

After, they bundled the body into the boot of the stolen Ford. The eldest called his superiors on the mobile – the job was done, the kid had screwed up, then paid the price. They'd have to write this one off. The voice at the other end of the line seemed satisfied, told them where to dump the body, then where to collect their payment.

Finally, the Ford Scorpio drove away into the night, taking the decapitated body of Mikey Picket on its last ever ride.

PART 2

SOWING THE SEEDS

———————— ✳ ————————

15

George Owen Picket's first memory of his father was of a skin-covered skeleton waiting to greet him when he returned home from school. It was mid-February, 1946, young George was one month from his eighth birthday, cowering behind his mother at the wasted human being sat in the deep sitting-room armchair.

'George,' she said, shoving him forward. 'This is your father.'

The youngster's legs began to shake inside his short trousers. The skullman was grinning at him, arms outstretched, bony hands beckoning him towards the ghoulish apparition. George had screamed, fled the house, refused to come back inside until later that night, coaxed in by his mother, clinging to her housecoat, frightened eyes frantically searching dark corners for the horror-show purporting to be his father.

Because the fantasy bore no earthly resemblance to the hideous reality. George had a rudimentary understanding of his absent father, his mother had often sat the boy on her knee during the long winter wartime months, showing him grainy black-and-whites taken at their wedding several months before he joined up to fight the Japs in the Far East. She'd show him letters, too, long, handwritten love notes sent from Burma detailing his heroics in battling the yellow peril. Then, in 1944 – nothing. All correspondence ceased, save for a single brown MOD envelope telling mother and child of Richard Picket's last-known battle position. It seemed his unit had been in a skirmish with a Jap patrol, deep in the muggy jungle. None had returned. Although the Ministry acknowledged that the brave British soldiers might well be alive in a Japanese prison camp, they were keen to warn all relatives not to raise their hopes.

George's mother stopped telling the boy about his father. There were no more nights looking at photographs of Dad. It wasn't as if he was potentially dead, rather that he'd never existed in the first place.

George, in his youthful confusion, supplied an elaborate fantasy to unravel the mystery. In it, his father single-handedly stormed a Japanese machine-gun nest, hurling grenade after grenade at the slant-eyes who'd kept his father's unit pinned down. Then fell with a single shot to the heart, the last retort from the dying Japs. Thus his father had 'died' a hero. George kept the explanation from his mother, who daren't even hope that her husband was still alive.

However, as word spread of Richard Picket's return, and family, friends and neighbours descended to their Fourth Avenue home, George was reluctantly forced to face, then accept, the emaciated reality of his father. And as months of home cooking gradually put flesh on the wasted frame, George began to spend more time with him, watching as he silently laboured long afternoons in the nearby allotments, sucking on a cigarette, growing piles of fresh vegetables to supplement the long post-war rationing still in wearisome operation.

And sometimes, during a break in digging, planting and weeding, George would sit by his father and listen as the ex-prisoner of war told him of the horrors inflicted by his captors. British soldiers, suffering horrific cruelties by an ever-inventive race of master-torturers with no respect for international conventions made in oak-panelled rooms thousands of miles away. One died for every sleeper laid in the infamous Burma Railway. Thousands of lives lost during one of the most incredible engineering feats of the century, a jungle cut in two by a starving army, a railroad hewn from blood.

The nightmare images found a keen home in George Picket's eager young mind. Bodies, too weary to work, skin flayed by razor-sharp bamboo, bayonets callously thrust into hideously swollen, undernourished bellies, heads lopped off with just one blow from an officer's gleaming sword. All swirled inside the impressionable boy's head, especially at night, when his father's screams would wake him, then leave him alone in the silent threatening dark.

There were no brothers and sisters for George. By the time he was able to question his only-child status, he was glad of it. The thought of his father sticking his thing in his mother repulsed him. At thirteen, he'd had a brief explorative fling with a local girl, curtailing the affair when she'd revealed the gynaecological separators between the sexes. All those flaps, and the smell . . . Once again, George's volatile imagination came to his prudish rescue. In his fantasies, the female organs were neat, dry, symmetrically functional, a neat hole, not a leaking gash. The sweet girls of his masturbatory fantasies all had large, firm breasts, all kept their knickers on, all smelt cleaner than rosewater.

George saw out his teenage years in ferocious study. He determined that he would pass his Oxbridge entrance exams and read law at either of the two esteemed universities. Cambridge was the intended destination, and he worked long into the night with the sole aim of a place at Trinity College in mind. But one afternoon, George's father changed all that. The house, he explained to his son, needed another wage. University was out of the question. His own job as a clerk, coupled with occasional work for the Home Office, fell short of the required income to sustain the family. George would have to get a job. An apprenticeship seemed the best solution, a junior post at his father's office. Inquiries had been made. The boy was to start the following spring. All George's dreams lay in ruins.

From time to time, during his early twenties, George would have occasion to bump into old school pals, home for the long summer holidays, expanded by university life. Some had cars, exotic girlfriends, and all seemed bored by their former associate. George even had the feeling that they made fun of him, met up with him solely in order to laugh at his expense, the neat haircut, the woollen suit, the provincial boredom of his life. He'd been the most studious of all of them, yet ended up a lowly clerk, living at home, all income sunk into a decrepit house his elderly parents could now ill-afford.

There were rumours too, about his father's 'other work'. Sometimes people would invite him out merely to press him for information he didn't have. His father had told him nothing of his occasional jaunts away, save that it was Home Office business, nothing he need worry about. Once a local girl asked him if his father kept any ropes at home, implying she'd accommodate his baser desires if he could produce one. George stared back in confusion and disgust. When he quizzed his reluctant father about the incident, he was told he'd done the right thing, that he should ignore the ignorant speculation of others.

Which George did – because, above all else, he was a good boy. Neighbours were impressed with the young man's polite bearing, his dedication to both parents, his willingness to please. Outwardly, he seemed settled in his job, well on the way to a rewarding career in the civil service – not like some of the youngsters these days with their coffee-bar beatnik morality, rock-and-roll music, motorbikes and disrespect for the elderly. The Fourth Avenue community liked George Picket. But then . . . they didn't know the *real* George.

His father died in 1969 after a two-year battle with cancer. George duly took his mother to the local undertakers, where together they stood in silent contemplation over the open coffin, George reminded of the skeletal nightmare man who'd first walked into his life twenty-three years previously. It seemed to George that his father had never recovered from his wartime starvation, and that in death, he'd shrunk back to the bony frame the Japanese had made of him.

After the funeral, George set his accountant's mind to matters more practical. With his mother still in almost permanent mourning, the house needed another woman about the place. A woman to cook, clean, and tend to the jobs his mother (now hitting the bottle with increasingly sombre ferocity) was ever more incapable of doing. It seemed the most 'sensible' thing – a solution his father would have endorsed. And without the money to employ a housekeeper, George set out to find himself a wife.

But underneath, he fumed, trapped by yet another moral duty, shouldering the burden of a mother who drank gin in the afternoons, and was mostly drunk by the time he returned home from work. And alone – George had never felt so alone as he watched his mother's previous good character drown under a lake of alcohol and apathy, knowing it was his duty to love her still, provide for her, as the good son must.

Then she told him about his father's 'other' work.

It was a Wednesday evening. Surprisingly, she was stone-cold sober. After he'd finished cooking supper, then washed up, she'd produced a leather-bound folder full of newspaper clippings, some yellowed with age. Here it was, then, a rogues' gallery of those sentenced to die, who'd met their fate at the hands of his father. Every word of the gossipmongers had been true. Dad had been a hangman.

His mother took him through the times, dates, places. Some had been notorious celebrities, others plain murderers mourned by no one. On each occasion, his father had kept a written record of the condemned's last few hours. There were invoices, too, stamped by the Home Office. Twice the money for a double-hanging.

And lastly, was a letter in his father's hand, addressed to *The Times* newspaper, written shortly after the abolition in 1967. George listened intently as his mother read aloud.

'It is of my opinion that Britain has developed and refined the most humane method of execution in the world. Its abolition negates the good work carried out by so many over the years in developing a system of dispatch which affords its clients a great deal more mercy than they inflicted on their innocent victims.

'I have personally undertaken many executions in which the condemned has been pinioned, walked to the trap, strapped, hooded, noosed and hung in well under thirty seconds. Death is instantaneous, resulting from a severed spinal cord within the second and third neck clavicle. If only such efficiency could have been afforded to their victims.

'I consider myself a craftsman, a prematurely retired servant of the Law, made redundant by ignorant liberal-thinking legislators with a callous disregard for society's victims. How many murderers

will shortly consider taking another's life, now that the vengeful shadow of the gallows has been so short-sightedly removed? What is left to deter the most evil minds from their wicked ambitions? How can prison life be compared with the noose in terms of an active deterrent?

'It greatly saddens me to see society overrun by a culture of teenage rebellion and licentiousness. We can never turn back the clock. I fear for my own son that the waters of his future are already muddied by so-called "free thinking".

'I am a man made monster by the Abolition, a curiosity. Almost daily, I am accosted by one fool or another who demands to be told personal details about those I have helped to hang that I will never divulge. I take their secrets to my grave, along with my pride that I served, I made a difference. I was prepared to take lives, even lay down my own when called upon to do so.

'It is the last bizarre irony in the wake of the Abolition, that by banning the noose, we have given society too much rope. Even now, it takes daily steps to hang itself.'

After, George asked his mother why the letter had never been sent.

'He had no need to send it,' she said simply.

'Why not? He believed every word, surely?'

'Certainly. But it was personal, George. Not to be so publicly displayed. Not for something as disposable as a newspaper.'

'But *The Times* is a quality paper,' George argued. 'Plenty of important people read it. He should have sent it if he was so passionate.'

His mother looked him in the eye. 'He was only passionate about one person reading it,' she replied. 'And only then, when the time was right.'

George tasted metal in his mouth. 'Me?'

'You, George.'

16

It wasn't long before George Picket had found himself a match. With his deceased father three months in his grave, and his mother falling an ever more incapable afternoon victim to Gordon's gin, the tall accountant set about the task with as much vigour as his quietly determined temperament would allow, treating the whole exercise with the same skill and precision as he gave to double-entry book-keeping.

And he *would* succeed. His own life's books of frustrated ambition, crushing duty and eventual happiness would balance in the end. He'd make them. And this new woman would help, naturally. How could she possibly refuse? It was a wife's duty, after all. He'd watched his own mother holding her tongue while his father had raged. That was what women did for men – acquiesed, provided, serviced.

He started by drawing up a list of suitable unknowing applicants, dividing them into those with whom he'd had some vague acquaintance, those who lived locally and he'd never found the courage to speak to, and finally those whom he'd taken on shambolic dates in the past. The final column was struck off immediately, George having no desire to marry either of the women who'd humiliated him quite so gleefully. Sluts – the pair of them. Gossiping vultures who'd seemingly left no ears unsullied in their willingness to broadcast their dismal night's fun and games. One had even coined the nickname Georgey-No-Dick specifically for the purpose, a label which was to live in his memory long after it faded in sniggering others.

The vague acquaintances seemed equally flawed, second cousins, friends of friends, and worse, all possessing a modern female arrogance which seemed born out of the times. It was the turn of the decades, the semi-stoned sixties sighing before giving way for the comically decadent seventies. Sometimes, George would wonder why he was so very loath to 'tune in and drop out' with the others, until he realized it was simply beyond him. He had too much respect, for others, and himself. The 'hippy' thing was just a nonsense, a pathetic distraction. He was far too sensible to ever consider buying a kipper tie.

So he set out to wed a girl whose demeanour suited the house she was to be enslaved in. An uncomplaining forties girl, familiar with Mrs Beeton's culinary opus, content with her lot, aware of her duties and her husband's role in choosing them for her.

Which really only left the middle category. Girls who lived locally. Of which there were only two George could recall who might fit the bill. One, Melissa Sharwood, although clearly something of a simpleton, was blessed with elderly parents who had often stopped by while his father was alive and remarked on George's potential as a clean-cut, upstanding husband for their daughter. However, the more he pondered the possible match, the less he doubted Miss Sharwood's domestic abilities. The bodywork might well have been in fine shape, but the brain was quite clearly malfunctioning, a fact made vividly real to George when he called round one day with a sharply pressed woollen suit (another of his father's) and a bunch of flowers, to be told by the slightly blushing girl that she would give them to her teddies upstairs.

So, by a logical process of elimination, George began courting the only other feasible contender, one Jane Watkins, a twenty-one-year-old, sullen-faced, overweight girl from Sixth Avenue, her parents also impressed by the smartly dressed professional man now taking their daughter to local dances, quietly affordable restaurants (where George always felt Jane ate too much) and long walks in order that she might shed a few pounds before the big day.

However, as the registry office wedding grew closer, his mother's drinking habits took on a sinister new energy, commanding the heartbroken widow to taste its delights almost the moment she woke. Which suited Elizabeth Picket fine. Indeed, sometimes she would wonder why she hadn't started drinking long ago – its pleasures were so wonderfully, fuzzily cosy. Then again, dear departed Richard wouldn't have approved. There would have been a scene. Not that she ever dared argue back, that would have been sheer folly. He'd hit her, but only the once, shortly after they'd married, and before the war took him away. Just a few short slaps to let her know who was boss, that he was capable of worse if provoked.

She couldn't even remember what caused the blows, the origin quite insignificant. The stinging pain, sudden shocked fear, was the intent. A punitive lesson; Richard Picket believed in the power of deterrents long before his conscience called him to the gallows.

She'd witnessed the same happening to George, and had had to hold herself back from bursting into the boy's bedroom as Richard took his belt to him soon after arriving back from Burma. It was, after all, for the young lad's good. He was receiving the same as she had, a foretaste for future misdemeanours. Elizabeth could remember the mixed emotions flowing through her rationed body – sorrow that her son had had to learn his lesson; joy that the angry red weals on both buttocks proved her dear husband's strength was fast returning. After all, a man who could so easily cause the flesh to blister and break during such a beating, was surely only weeks away from toiling on the allotment – which meant the Pickets would be eating piles of fresh vegetables that winter.

And with her husband called by the Lord, Elizabeth Picket was as liberated as she was lonely. Free to experiment, free to go out on her own, forge new friendships and alliances. Gin had been the first to make her acquaintance, and regardless of the costs and what Richard would have thought, part of its pleasure was the secret thrill of knowing her behaviour would have been frowned upon.

George, God bless him, had so far refrained from criticism, although it must have been obvious what she was up to. The empty bottles were a steadily growing pointer for a start. But perhaps, she mused, he *had* tried to stop her, only she'd always been too smashed to listen, too hungover in the morning to remember. Although gradually, as the weeks turned to months, Elizabeth took her son's stoic silence as indifference, the alcohol speeding the paranoid mechanisms of her gently eroding brain. She began sobbing too much, hugging him too long when he arrived back from work, or else operating at the opposite emotional seam, haranguing him for no reason, accusing him of terrible things. Unfortunately for George, his silence only made matters worse. But it was a silence born out of duty and ignorance. He wanted to help his mother, yet squashed his feelings, crushed the angst, hoped she'd come out of it in her own time. Meanwhile, he had a wedding to plan, and very little money to do it with.

However, against all the financial odds, three months later, in July 1970, Chelmsford Registry Office recorded the marriage of Jane Sally Watkins to George Owen Picket. The bride looked embarrassing in her dress. Just seven attended the function, both witnesses strangers called by nervous registrars intent on performing the rites as quickly as possible before the groom's mother began singing again.

The honeymooning couple spent an uncomfortable weekend in a bed and breakfast in Clacton before returning home. The problem had come (or hadn't come) with the required act of consummation. Old ghosts had returned to haunt George, taunt him, impairing a performance he'd secretly dreaded for some time. Time, however, was the one thing the new Mrs Picket wasn't prepared to give her reluctant husband. She had an understandable lifetime's virginity to lose, and he was the person to do it. However, after a frustrating hour of listening to George throwing up in the bathroom across the corridor, she finally succumbed to sleep.

Things didn't improve upon their miserable arrival back in Chelmsford. Elizabeth had been uncharacteristically productive, producing a timetabled list of chores and menu suggestions for her new daughter-in-law, coupled with crude written instructions for every piece of domestic equipment in the house. Young Jane was understandably annoyed, declaring that the marriage was null and void until 'George fucks me'.

There was a long and terrible silence.

Later that night, after putting his mother to bed, George somehow managed to sustain an erection long enough to inseminate his sweating wife. He managed partially due to a near photographic memory of the girls he'd often stared at in his secret magazines, coupled with a raw anger driving him viciously on into the layers of pale, white flesh. George didn't make love to Jane that night, neither did he have sex with her, rather he stabbed his wife repeatedly in the vagina, his engorged penis mutating in his mind into one of the bloodied Samurai swords his father had so often described.

His unspoken motive was simply to deny her any pleasure. George would have sex with her as requested, but his angrily boiling vitriol demanded that he make the experience as unpleasant as possible for the other party. It was the only way he could go through with the disturbing ordeal.

However, to George's dismay, Jane mistook the energy of his sexual revulsion as deeply buried passion. She cried out with increasing joy at every vicious thrust, gasped with pleasure when he turned her to take her from behind.

After, he left her sleeping contentedly, wandering hazily downstairs to make a cup of tea. He sat in the silent gloom, shaking, suppressing the waves of shaming nausea which threatened to overwhelm him, ruminating on his father's words. It was a warning, the unsent letter from beyond the grave, an instruction to serve, just as he'd done by stringing up society's monsters, just as George was doing now in the oppressive carnal claustrophobia of the creaking marital bed.

The months passed, Christmas and the New Year flew by in an increasing pile of empty gin bottles and Jane's ever constant sexual demands. For both women seemed quite happy with the arrangement. Elizabeth felt her daughter-in-law's cooking could be improved in places, but by and large she mostly approved of the girl's attitude. Jane herself couldn't have been any more content, quietly thrilled that strange circumstance had plucked her from her parents' house and transplanted her into this lovely detatched home. True, the mother-in-law was a drunken old bitch, but then again, by mid-afternoon she was usually sleeping off the booze, and, barring preparing supper, she was mostly free to idle around the place as she pleased, waiting in quiet anticipation for her stud of a husband to return from the office.

And excepting the expected bedroom gymnastics, George too had cynically resigned himself once more to his role as provider to both wife and mother. There was even a certain satisfaction in the arrangement, a feeling that he'd found a solution which his father would have approved of, taken the burden of looking after the place from his mother. Meals arrived on time, windows were cleaned, surfaces polished. The cosy status quo of the assistant hangman's home had been respectfully maintained by a son whose sacrifice seemingly knew no bounds.

However, beyond the four walls, times were changing. New attitudes, shameful values, swept through the land exactly as his father had predicted. George began to despise the long-haired, sheepskin-wearing hippies fast populating the town. For a part of him still felt enslaved, even envied them their freedom and peace-loving ideology. Most of all, he envied them their dizzy-looking girlfriends, slim, supple, compliant.

Sometimes, he would commit a particular girl's face to memory, mentally masking his wife's grinning jowls as he impaled her – a sexual coping mechanism which just about made the almost nightly bouts of bedtime athletics tolerable.

One night, in May 1971, a tiny, almost imperceptible thing happened which was to change George's life forever. The Durex split. Now, most times this wouldn't have mattered, as both George and Jane individually preferred the act of sodomy to intercourse, but on this fated occasion, George's unfettered sperm were perfectly placed to begin the hazardous journey to Jane's waiting egg.

It was Elizabeth who was first to realize she had a grandchild on the way. The girl's eyes had changed, taken on a light-blue hue in the whites. She was slow to get up of a morning and set the fire, and once or twice she'd heard her snapping at George. She was pregnant. How would this change things?

Elizabeth even broke the news to an astonished George

before his wife could. It was a Sunday, just after lunch. Jane dutifully cleared away as mother and son sat at the table.

'She's with child,' she said simply.

'What?' George had replied.

'George, she's pregnant.'

He turned to his blushing wife. 'Jane? Is this true?'

The expectant girl just nodded.

'Oh dear,' he replied.

Whereupon she ran from the room.

Mikey Joshua Picket was born in January 1972, on the coldest night for thirty-five years. The labour took an agonizing twenty-three hours, with three midwives eventually assisting the bloodied, glistening youngster's arrival. George sat with his mother downstairs, assuring her the baby wouldn't change things, she'd always be looked after and cared for.

Elizabeth was less than convinced. Already her increasingly demanding daughter-in-law was insisting on expensive changes. A room had been turned into the tot's nursery, money lavished on modern devices she never needed when raising her own boy.

'A mobile?' she'd said to George as he and his wife had returned home from a trip to the shops one Saturday. 'What good is one of those?'

'It's for baby to look at while he's in his cot,' Jane had replied, stroking her heavily pregnant belly.

'Another goddamned waste of money, George!' Elizabeth spat back accusingly. 'You'll bend over bloody backwards for her, yet you won't even spare a thought for me.' The morning's gin brought forth heavy salty tears on cue. 'And when the baby's born, I'll be out on the street, won't I? Abandoned like an old rag. Don't think I don't know what the pair of you are up to. Do you hear me?'

But dutiful George was already helping his weeping wife upstairs.

The one benefit of the pregnancy was that George's sexual services were no longer required after the third month. He was intolerably grateful for the unexpected reprieve, and if anything, began paying his heavy wife a little more attention. He marvelled at the way mother nature was physically and mentally reshaping her. Gone was the dim nymphomaniac, replaced by a maturer individual, a mother in the making, planning sensibly for their first child. It might almost be said that George even admired her a little.

They began to talk, communicating as expectant parents, George listening as Jane detailed the various changes needed for the child. The nursery conversion for starters, then the whole house brightened by some much needed redecoration, a car, a twin-tub washing machine, television for educating the child. Jane had it all set down on crudely written lists, which George would proudly tick as each task was completed, each item purchased. It was, in many senses, a new beginning for him, he felt re-roled by a simple sexual accident – a potential father.

Sometimes, however, late at night, he and Jane would discuss his mother's drinking. George would shift uncomfortably, reluctant to side with either woman, disturb the precarious equilibrium of the nervous household. They talked in hushed tones, Jane declaring a child was at risk from his mother, she wasn't prepared to bring their imminent newborn up in such dangerous circumstances. The old woman could easily start a fire, collapse, endanger them all.

George would shrug and try his best to reassure her that it wouldn't be a problem, denying himself the obvious, taking the easier course – avoiding tackling his mother about the issue. At times, he felt like a circus plate-spinner, dashing from one woman to the next, righting each with empty assurances, before racing to the other to do the same.

Because, deep down, he couldn't face dividing his loyalties. His father's instructions to serve constantly came back to haunt him, inhibiting his natural progress, pushing him down.

The name Mikey was Jane's idea. A friend of her sister's had had a stillborn child of the same name the previous year. She liked the name, and managed to convince George it would be both a fitting tribute to the dead little 'un, and a 'with-it' name to boot.

George hated the name, cringed at its every mention, even hoped that perhaps they might have a girl, so that the damned thing would be forgotten. His choice was Joshua. But come the night, George was made proud father to a son. As the midwife handed him the swaddled, screaming bundle, Jane wearily mumbled, 'Say hello to your father, Mikey.' So the name stood.

Elizabeth, unsurprisingly, wasn't so keen. When George took his son downstairs to meet his grandmother, she was quite incapable of getting out of the sitting-room chair. Her long grey hair hung in a lanky mess.

'Mum,' he said excitedly. 'This is Mikey, your grandson.' He held the bawling infant close, bursting with new-found pride.

'Ridiculous name,' she snorted, barely giving the boy a glance. 'Stupid idea, saddling a child with a dead baby's name. Cruel, that is.'

'Mum,' George returned generously. 'I'm sure there were plenty of dead Elizabeths before you were born.'

'You don't care, do you? That bloody woman has turned your head.'

'Mum, don't . . .'

'You're forgetting about family, young man. Your father wouldn't have approved.'

'Mikey *is* family, now.'

'I'm calling him Joshua,' she replied angrily. 'Your name, not hers.'

The child began to cry once more. George shifted awkwardly, unaware what to do, feeling his pride vanish as naive inexperience rushed in to replace it.

'For God's sake, George,' his mother shouted above the din. 'Take it upstairs and stick it on one of her teats. Can't you tell he's hungry?'

'But he is beautiful, isn't he?'

'Yes, George,' his mother sighed. 'He's beautiful.'

'Dad would have loved him, wouldn't he?'

'Of course, George. Now be away upstairs with him.'

'Right,' George replied, struggling with the writhing bundle as he headed back upstairs. A midwife waited for him on the landing, taking the baby from him and offering it to Jane's breast.

He watched from the bedroom doorway as the screaming gave way to contented suckling, realizing with startling clarity that for the first time in his life he loved another human being quite completely.

Utterly.

17

The arrival of young Mikey precipitated many changes in the Picket household, almost as if the tiny, fleshy blob was catalyst to a new order.

Elizabeth began living entirely downstairs, sleeping on a camp bed in the spartan front room, distancing herself through drink and space from the ever-screaming tot. And young Mikey did like to scream, on and on, day and night during the first six months, apart from when his father gathered him into his arms. Amazingly, George just seemed to have the knack, a way with the child, and was as bewildered with his success as everyone else.

Jane began a remarkable transformation. In the first three months after the birth, she lost just under two stone, all quite naturally, young Mikey voraciously suckling off the excess body fat six times a day. Two months later, she was a full three stone lighter than when she married. And when Mikey began taking solid food, Jane resolved to continue the weight loss with strict diet programmes taken from *Women's Realm* magazine.

She began eating little more than salad, urging George to grow a never-ending supply of lettuce and tomatoes on the family allotment. And when demand failed to keep up with supply, Jane began emptying supermarket shelves of all things raw and tasty.

For Elizabeth, this was possibly the last straw. One day, Jane arrived back pushing a pram piled high with peppers. There were so many of the red, green and yellow fruits, that sleeping Mikey was barely visible beneath.

'She's eating foreign food, now,' George's mother warned

him later that night. 'Not right for Joshua, is it, to have a mother poisoning herself like that. I said, it's not right, is it?'

'Please, Mum. I'm very tired.'

'Your father wouldn't have heard of it. Grew everything we ever needed on the allotment.'

From upstairs came the distant wailing of an agitated baby. George rose wearily and made his way slowly upstairs, listening as Jane's temper began to rise. In the bedroom, she handed him the screaming child and left the room, muttering something about 'needing some space'.

George took his bawling son in his arms, pacing the room slowly as the sobs gave way to the contented rhythms of deep sleep. He lay gently on the bed, Mikey on his chest, closing his own eyes and sharing an hour's peace with the thing he loved more than anything else in the world.

From Mikey's earliest days, George had discovered that for some unknown reason, he had a deeply calming influence on the child. It seemed that he had merely to be cuddled into his father's arms and the tears would stop, struggles slowly desisting, replaced by sleep or happy burbling.

As with all conundrums in the new, challenging world of fatherhood, George had no answer for the phenomenon, and indeed, often felt the guilt of its burden, watching as Jane reluctantly gave her child to him, her expression of failure unmissable, creased on her slimmer face. The guilt, too, was just as much a surprise, George finally being forced to admit to himself that his frigid feelings towards his wife were (in the absence of nightly sex) growing by the day.

Once or twice, they'd rowed about his ability with the boy, George declaring that surely it was a good thing that one of them could put an end to the near-continuous cacophony; Jane responding angrily that he just didn't understand 'a fucking thing'. Which led George to suspect that he didn't, feeling compromised, trapped by his gift to his son. Often he would hover close by as Jane tried her best to offer succour, caught between relieving her of the burden, and not wanting to appear to be putting her down. As a result, he succeeded in neither. The frustrations of the predicament grew daily between them.

By Mikey's first birthday, Jane had lost four and a quarter stone in the year. A new woman had emerged from the fat-insulated shell, a slim, beautiful, bored young mother. And with the new look came a new attitude. Jane determined to improve her mind as much as she'd done her body. She embarked on a series of courses at night school in order that she might earn some qualifications leading to a job. Too many of her former friends were now wage-earners with the latest clothes, haircuts and interests. She felt life passing her by. Here she was, twenty-three, married to a lily-livered mummy's boy ten years her senior, and saddled with a child who preferred his company to hers. The house, too, had long since lost its early allure. The place was too old, too cold, and worst of all, home to an embittered gin-drinking old bag who rarely concealed her contempt for anything modern or progessive.

Jane was sick and tired of listening to the old woman harping on about how many murderers her beloved husband had strung up. She found the very idea repulsive, and determined to move to another, more modern, maintenance-free house. Such was Jane's new-found resolve that sometimes she thought that it wouldn't even matter if her older husband couldn't find the strength to cut the apron strings – she wasn't about to deny herself any of the fantastic opportunities awaiting her outside the deathly dull Avenues, Chelmsford.

She began quite modestly with evening classes, and promptly met Ivan, a twice-divorced builder, dope-smoker, and long-haired Jim Morrison lookalike cruising the town's many available options for bored women. Evening classes was one such venue. He'd signed up for the same class in O-level mathematics three times, as it seemed healthily populated with appropriate skirt awaiting his magic touch. For Ivan (real name Ian Pearce) made no secret of the fact that he was as good an oriental masseur as he was a bricklayer.

Sometimes both pursuits had gone magnificently hand in hand. On four occasions he had managed to persuade various women that the true pathway to karmic self-expression lay within extensive tantric massage (always nude) coupled with a new extension. The latter would serve as an essential meditation room, while the former acted in part-payment for the unnecessary alterations. Jane was the fourth to feel his magic touch . . .

It had taken her the best part of three months to convince her sceptical husband of the money-making potential in the project, finally getting a cautious go-ahead when she told him it would be more for Mikey's benefit than anyone's.

'A playroom for him, George,' she summed up late one night as the pair lay in bed. Before deliberately adding, 'Something to show Mikey just how much you love him. Besides, the builder's coming at the weekend to measure up. Chances are we won't be able to afford it, anyway.'

'OK,' George mumbled, turning over to sleep, then dream of a life less complicated.

However, Ian Pearce's victims soon found they could always afford his prices. With a plethora of dodgy friends and acquaintances in the construction business, 'Ivan' cannily priced his work to come just under budget of his clients' expectations, writing off varying degrees of profit as befitted the attractiveness of the individual woman he was trying to bed at the time. And Jane was, by this time, quite a stunner.

Work began in the spring of 1973, though one could hardly say in earnest. For six weeks the Pickets' back garden was home to an enormous pile of builder's sand, twelve cement bags, an assortment of timbers and three hundred house-bricks. George, who had little knowledge of such things, was easily convinced by his happier, vaguely hashish-smelling wife that Ivan was hard at work drawing up plans and submitting them before the town council for approval, and that construction would start any day now.

In order to finance the whole deal, George had found himself a new post, pen-pushing for Chelmsford Borough Council, for a slightly higher wage. And it was here that he managed to have a few words in the right ears to ensure the planning application went smoothly through. George couldn't understand his wife's annoyance when he returned home to tell her the good news – that Ivan could start building right away, and the proposed extension would surely be ready for the summer.

Elizabeth, if she had any idea of what was going on during Ivan's frequent trips to the house when he wasn't building, never let on. Perhaps she wasn't altogether surprised by her daughter-in-law's attachment to the long-haired, self-confessed guru, or maybe she turned a blind eye, in exchange for Jane's silence regarding her constant drinking. For by now, she had reached the stage of sleeping with a bottle of Gordon's and two glasses by the bed – one for her teeth, the other for her morning 'pick-me-up'. On several occasions, she'd woken, bleary-eyed, and poured herself a large shot in the wrong glass.

On May 14th, 1973, George returned home unexpectedly from work to find his mother passed out beside an empty quarter-bottle of gin, a sleeping child in the kitchen playpen, and the muted sounds of energetic copulation drifting down the stairs.

It took a few seconds for the appalling truth to register. In it, he stood quite still, hands tightening round the neck of the soft toy he'd brought back for Mikey, an innocent child oblivious to the deviant carnage all round. George felt tears begin to mist his eyes, all sound seemed to disappear, and for a while he lost focus with the world, stood in pale blankness, a void of his own naive stupidity.

Suddenly, he was a boy again, a frightened child, staring into the pale-yellow eyes of his father, wanting to pee, feeling the first few drops run from under his coarse short trousers, hypnotized by the laughing, wasted figure, its croaking, mocking voice the only sound in the oppressive silence.

'You've really messed up, George,' it said in an appalling whine. 'How easily your head's been turned. You know what they're doing up there, don't you? You can hear it, can't you? I've seen them, George. Watched them in your bed for weeks. Look at you, snivelling like a coward, blubbing like a girl. That's the trouble with the youth of today – no values, George. No backbone. You've lost your values, my boy. You're a bad boy, George. A very bad boy indeed. But you know what to do, don't you, George? Know what you've *got* to do . . .'

The figure faded, and George was back in the brown hallway, everything real, undeniable. Pre-orgasmic wails rushed into his ears, and he found himself looking at the strange furry lump in his hands. Three hours earlier it had been a stuffed toy rabbit, grinning cutely from a shop window as he'd wandered the town during his lunch-hour. Now its head lay torn off and abandoned at his feet.

He picked it up, then left the house as silently as he'd entered, without any of the four occupants ever knowing he'd even been there.

His new bosses at County Hall were only too glad to give him two weeks off following the funeral. Many felt truly sorry for the tall, sombre-faced accountant, following the news that his young wife had died in a tragic accident. Even worse that she left behind a young son, in a house, rumour had it, that was already home to a drunken mother.

However, domestic problems aside, all who mattered at County Hall agreed George Picket was perhaps the most devoted book-keeper on the payroll. They marvelled at his ability to keep going in the face of such an appalling tragedy. Other employees familiar with the grief of losing a loved one couldn't fail to be impressed by the quiet accepting dignity of the man. One or two had even noticed a change in him since the funeral, the vaguest beginnings of a look of relief creeping round the previously harassed face. But if anyone nursed suspicions about the poor woman's death, they kept them well to themselves. For in the mourning husband's eyes was a colder glare than before, challenging, a look which produced goose-bumps if met for too long.

Death and liberation were becoming inextricably linked in George's mind. Killing the slut had been both a challenge and a magnificent activity in itself, providing him with quite the most majesterial feelings of pleasure and contentment. Indeed, compared to the more mundane orgasms which Jane had sought out with the hippy, the adrenaline which had surged round his system as he'd pushed her from the top stair must have taken the best part of a week to subside. And throughout, George's body pounded with liberated vengeful zeal – knowing absolutely that what he was doing was *right*. The woman deserved to die. She was worthless. Couldn't ever be mother to his child. Therefore better dead. He wondered if his father had felt this way as he stooped and strapped condemned ankles on the gallows. The sheer joy of corrective action, solving a problem, preventing others – being a man, liberated by the death of another.

It was time for a new regime in Forth Avenue.

George sat late into the night, making notes. The house wasn't a problem, paid off when his father died. Childcare, however, was. His mother, as Jane had often pointed out, was quite incapable of looking after the infant while he worked. Mikey was an agile toddler now, fast on little feet, with a keen urge to explore every dangerous plug socket, every nook and cranny. She couldn't be expected to care for the boy on a full-time basis. Besides, George rather liked the thought of doing it himself, or at least some of it, three days a week, perhaps. He made a note to ask if he could change his job to part-time.

Which really left only his mother as a problem. Specifically the dent on the family income made by the drink. Needs and priorities dictated that the financial belt had to be significantly tightened. George, empowered by the change in circumstances, decided to tackle his mother first thing the following morning.

'Why?' Elizabeth said, eyes crusted with sleep, as George sat by the creaking campbed. 'I'm sixty-seven, I'm entitled to a drink every now and then.'

George held up the half-empty bottle.

'It helps me sleep,' she said defensively. 'I'm still a woman in mourning for your dear father, George.'

'You're a drunk, Mother.'

'And you're insensitive! Give me that bottle.'

'No.'

She was incredulous. 'No?'

'It's time to stop. We can't afford it.'

'But you've got a good job,' she protested. 'What else do we spend the money on?'

'I'm going to ask for a part-time post.'

She raised herself painfully on to one elbow. 'Part-time?'

'In order that I can spend more time with Mikey.'

She collapsed back down. 'George, for God's sake, listen to me. Joshua needs a woman around him, a mother-figure. Whoever heard of a man bringing up his own child? Your father would have –'

'Dad's dead.'

Elizabeth began to cry. 'The world's going mad. Please, George, I need a drink.'

'You need to dry out.'

Elizabeth paled, chilled by the cold detachment of his reply. She began to whimper, a woman exhausted, drained of life by the simple need for alcohol.

But he was gone, taking the bottle with him.

18

The following few weeks saw George trying hard to adapt to the new routine. County Hall were reluctant to let him take a part-time post, saying they might review the idea sometime in the 'near future'. And George, fast becoming a veteran of council double-speak, knew well what that meant – no, no, never.

However, he decided to lie low for a while, resuming work full-time, and employing the services of Mrs Dougan, a part-time nursery nurse from Third Avenue, to look after Mikey at her house. It wasn't the best of arrangements, far from George's domestic ideal, and, as the weeks passed, increasingly expensive.

All seemed to be nose-diving once more, when Lady Luck, in the form of a Ford Cortina driven by an inebriated youngster, came knocking at George's door, after first colliding with his mother in a pub car park. On a minor point of historical irony, it was noted by the coroner that Elizabeth Picket died due to the near-instant severing of the spinal cord, between the second and third neck vertebrae. If ever there was such a thing as revenge from beyond the grave, then Richard Picket, former assistant hangman, would have been hard pressed to do a better job on his fast-deteriorating former wife.

Thus, in a little over eight weeks, George had lost both the women in his life. Virtually the whole of the neighbourhood descended to offer condolences. However, upon returning home after the cremation of his mother, he said goodbye to the last of the family mourners, sat down with Mikey on his knee, looked into the bright blue trusting eyes and smiled, and smiled . . .

Granted, he hadn't made much of a show about mourning his mother, but the truth was that even in death, the woman still had it in her to rile him. He'd had to pay for the funeral by selling (for a fraction of their value) the car and a substantial number of the white goods Jane had insisted he get for the house. George had discovered that his furtive mother had cashed in her life-insurance policy shortly after his father died. The surrender value was negligible, but it answered one question for him – now he knew where she got the money for the gin from.

County Hall, too, were beginning to cool towards their once impeccably reliable new accountant, now asking for a further two weeks' paid leave following the unorthodox death of his mother.

'Any more impending tragedies I should know about, George?' his boss asked sardonically as he signed the leave papers.

'I hope not.'

'So do I, George. So do I.'

He used the two weeks as fruitfully as possible, dispensing with the services of Mrs Dougan (who, in George's opinion, smoked too much in front of Mikey), and negotiating a part-time post with his old company. They weren't surprised to see him return, having heard through the grapevine of George's ill-fated time since leaving, but carefully explained that the only post on offer was of junior office boy – fourteen hours a week for twenty-one pounds, before tax.

George went home, did his sums, worked out that with the allotment offering the lion's share of fresh fruit and vegetables, and provided he was absolutely frugal with the electric, he might just about have enough to pay the rates and survive.

The realization was as stunning as it was liberating. He could *survive*, without Jane and his mother – just him and Mikey. And perhaps Jane's mother, Mrs Watkins, would come in to look after her only grandchild on the days he worked. Not since Mikey's birth had George felt so ecstatic.

Granted, it would be a drastic scaling down of lifestyles,

but he was prepared to do without, simply to be with his son – the boy to whom he was prepared to wager everything. The young lad who, George felt absolutely certain, with his father's input and devotion, would surely grow to scale all the heights George felt he'd been so cruelly denied. Mikey was George Picket's new beginning – the chance to live out all his frustrated ambitions through the boy.

With the right training, Mikey Picket would take his father's place as an Oxbridge undergraduate. Mikey Picket would be smart, charming and intolerably witty. Mikey Picket would have the pick of any girl, not suffer the sham of his parents' marriage.

But the dream required a supreme commitment. And, George reasoned, the sooner he started, the better. So, at thirty-five, a single parent determined that he would do the best for his boy, he took the humiliating job. Every Monday and Friday he dutifully arrived to take orders from those who, in former times, he'd given them to. Old colleagues shunned him, embarrassed perhaps at befriending 'sad old George', who cycled to work on a battered GPO bike. Other, younger staff saw the opportunity for revenge, taking great delight in sending their former crusty boss out on ridiculous errands, then sniggering behind his back. But George couldn't give a stuff. He was diligent at his work, never once rising to the bait, his mind always focused on the one true objective in his life – Mikey.

Tuesdays, Wednesdays and Thursdays he devoted to the boy. It was a gloriously sunny summer, and together they spent the long hot weeks dividing the time between work, chores, tending the allotment and fun. George found the fun part the hardest, but threw himself into it as best he could, pulling silly faces and participating in endless chase games or reading and rereading Mikey's favourite book before bedtime. Fun as an investment. Fun as an incentive. Anything but spontaneous fun, which in his opinion was rather vulgar and unnecessary.

He also determined to finish the extension Ivan had so dangerously left half built. He got books from the library on the subject, and gradually began to realize that the only real expense would be a glazier to fit the glass on completion. The rest he could damn well do himself, which he did, young Mikey watching as his dad mixed cement, laid bricks and joined roof timbers to the main house.

The glazier's bill of one hundred and eleven pounds was met by selling more from inside, again at a considerable loss, but as George figured, they rarely watched the television, or needed the beds upstairs, or the old wardrobes, for that matter. The extension was going to be bright, airy – the perfect antidote to the dark, empty space it stemmed from. For by now, former Assistant Executioner Richard Picket's old house was home to mostly draughty, unfurnished rooms, all fittings sold to unscrupulous dealers in order that George might buy a new outfit for Mikey, a second-hand tricycle perhaps, and shoes – he was a fast-growing boy.

As a consequence, George got used to going without himself, living in a small portion of the house, determining that when Mikey was of school age, then he'd set about finding more permanent work, doubling, even tripling, their paltry income. Besides, a drastic financial solution was needed if Mikey was going to achieve George's dream and attend a private prep school. Not for George Picket's boy the scum-infested state schools. The very thought brought George out in late-night sweats. Up until now, he'd managed reasonably successfully to screen his fair-haired pride and joy away from other kids, but he knew full well what awaited Mikey if things went wrong.

It was on Mikey's second birthday that Mrs Watkins first delicately broached the subject of her grandson's development with his obviously devoted father. The boy had long since gone to bed, and she'd offered to stay a while and tidy up, hand-wash a few clothes. George had conceded, looking tired and harried. The house was bone-chillingly cold, inadequately heated by just the kitchen range and a small coal fire in the back room.

'He loved his car,' she said, thinking her way slowly round the most diplomatic approach.

'I think so,' George replied, suppressing a yawn.

'I think you've done very well, really.'

'Sorry?'

'You know,' she said, putting another pot to boil on the ancient stove. She couldn't believe how he managed without an immersion heater. But he did, somehow. 'Looking after Mikey like you do.'

'It's any father's duty.'

'And you love him, too.'

'Of course.'

'Only . . .'

'Yes?'

'I was just wondering if you'd noticed anything . . . well . . . odd about his behaviour.'

'Odd?'

She busied herself with a terry-nappy and the mangle. 'Sort of different, I suppose. Different from other boys his age.'

George began to feel a little agitated. It had been a long and tiring day, with hours spent trying to calm Mikey's wild birthday excitement. Several times, he'd had to smack the shrieking child, which seemed only to make matters worse. 'It was his birthday, Norma,' he said. 'He was just excited, that's all. It's different in the summer. He can go outside, run around, let off some steam.'

Norma nodded, then added, 'But . . . I find he's like that most of the time.'

'How do you mean?'

'A little bit . . . wild, I suppose.'

George sighed, desperate for sleep. 'Probably just a phase. Terrible two's. He'll calm down.'

'I've had to clear all my shelves of my valuables. Throws them right across the room, he does.'

'Are you saying he's getting a bit too much for you, Norma?' George asked, dreading the reply. Times were hard enough without having to find a new childminder. Who else did he know that would work for free?

'Heavens, no. I love the cheeky little so-and-so. I just thought that seeing as you don't have that much experience with kids, Mikey being your first and all that, that you ought to know.' She turned from the sink and sat down opposite

121

him. 'I think perhaps you should take him to the doctor, George. Get him looked over. A woman I know from the flats had a similar thing. Young boy playing merry hell, he was, turned out all he had was an ear infection which –'

'There's nothing wrong with Mikey,' George replied tersely. 'He's not going to a doctor just because he got excited on his birthday.'

'But, George, I'm only –'

'No, Norma. It's really none of your business.'

The following April, one Tuesday morning, George opened the door to an officious-looking female visitor.

'Mrs Hadley,' she said quickly, trying to see past him into the gloom beyond. 'I'm from social services.'

'Oh yes?'

'It's about your son.' She consulted a clipboard. 'Mikey. Just routine. Can I come in?'

'I suppose you'd better.'

George led her into the back room, where she sat, frantically scanning the interior. Mikey played in the conservatory, a happy chatter coming from the absorbed child. George closed the glass doors, as if he didn't want the boy to hear. 'What can I do for you, Mrs Hadley?'

She flipped over a page on the clipboard. 'Just need the answers to some questions, if you don't mind, Mr Picket. Shouldn't take long. Now then, how old is Mikey?'

George went through the formality of answering a series of innocent-sounding questions, whilst all the time knowing exactly why the damned woman was there, and furthermore, who the interfering whistle-blower was. Mikey, although he knew very few of the other local children, had been invited to a birthday party of a little girl just a few doors away some three weeks previously. It was his first ever invite, and George had gone to some trouble to make the boy look respectable. He liked the girl's parents, and was happy for Mikey to associate with their kind, as opposed to the scruffier council-house children he saw running the streets at all hours.

At two in the afternoon, George had dropped Mikey off, resplendent in trousers, shirt, maroon tie and tiny waistcoat.

122

He'd found the outfit in a jumble sale, an old page-boy's costume, once used, now sold for two pounds. He told Mikey to behave, exchanged a few pleasantries with the birthday girl's parents, and left to spend a couple of hours further down the road on his beloved allotment.

At four, he collected Mikey. The father opened the door, grim-faced. Mikey was upstairs, cooling off. Apparently he'd got into a dispute with another boy over a toy. The result was a furious fist-fight in miniature, the cute page-boy biting off the end of the other boy's nose. Both boy and nose-endpiece were sent to Casualty. Birthday Girl was in tears, the other children wandered round the blood-flecked living room in a daze as bewildered parents arrived to collect them.

When George left with his still-smiling son, he clearly heard one of the other mothers remark that in her opinion, the boy was 'as strange as his father, as stupid as his mother and as odd as his dead grandparents'.

Upon arriving home, George spent half an hour searching through his father's effects for the belt he had been beaten with as a boy himself. Then he set to Mikey, administering the blows with indecent accuracy, as the youngster struggled violently on his lap.

Discipline was the new road, a strict regime of harsh beating at the slightest midemeanour. George had no alternative – after all, he *loved* the boy. Without the belt, and fear of the belt, the youngster was headed towards the gutter.

George determined that Mikey Picket wouldn't only be the brightest, wittiest, best-looking Oxbridge undergraduate, he'd be the politest, too.

'His speech is a worry,' said Mrs Hadley after spending twenty minutes on her knees playing with the boy.

'He speaks a lot to me,' George replied, wondering when the nosy woman would go. Couldn't she see how the belt had transformed the lad in just a few short weeks? He was certain the parents of Birthday Girl had alerted the social Services, so why didn't the stupid woman ask him the obvious questions? Like how had George managed to bring about such a spectacular change in the boy so suddenly? Although, when he thought about it, the woman was most likely one of those do-gooders who'd ban the cane in the ludicrous name of 'human rights infringements'.

'He's missing a lot of vowel sounds, Mr Picket, and in some instances makes no effort to communicate at all.' She was writing on the clipboard all the time, making tiny marginal notes. She was particularly struck by the boy's dull, cowering blue eyes, as if he was afraid to open his mouth. 'He's big for his age, too.'

'Rugby prop-forward in the making,' George tried, combining the remark with his best smile. 'Come here, Mikey. Come to Daddy.'

Mrs Hadley watched as the boy obediently walked to his father, clinging to his leg, looking at her whilst sucking a thumb. Certainly, it was hard to believe this was the same boy who had allegedly maimed another child. 'And are you managing all right, Mr Picket?'

'Fine, thank you.'

'It can be hard, bringing up a youngster on your own.'

'I like to think of it as rewarding.'

'Do you have any central heating in the house?'

'No.'

'Double-glazing?'

George shook his head. 'We manage.'

'Diet OK?'

'I grow most of what we need. I have an allotment. Then I'll buy a joint or a chicken once a week. He always gets fresh milk.'

'Well,' she conceded. 'He seems healthy enough.'

'Fresh fruit and vegetables,' George replied, warming to the theme. 'So much better for you than all that fancy supermarket stuff.'

'Quite.'

He noticed she was looking at him with the merest hint of a frown. He felt unnerved in the awkward silence that followed, then realized why he was suddenly so unsettled.

He was beginning to sound exactly like his father.

19

George Picket had determined six things – that by the time son Mikey walked through the gates of his private prep school he would know the alphabet, up to his five-times tables, the days of the week, months in the year, be able to write his own name clearly and count to a hundred.

In the event, on the seventh of September, 1976, the nervous youngster tottered through the gates of Mildean Primary (a regular state school) knowing none of them. But not for the want of trying. My, how he and his father had laboured away, trying to hammer home the basics. Night after night, as soon as his dad had washed up, Mikey would be sitting obediently at the table, waiting for the ordeal to begin, heart pounding, knowing before he even started that he'd fail.

The one-times table was occasionally manageable. Parts of the two, sometimes. But anything beyond became a throat-drying nightmare for the boy.

George tried every way he could think of, slaps, shouting, treats, the belt – none of it seemed to work on the boy. With frustrating clarity, George Picket was fast beginning to realize that his precious son Mikey had inherited his mother's brains and his father's looks. To add further insult to injury, the physical resemblance was so startling that strangers would often pause to comment on it.

'Looks just like you,' they'd say, beaming, wondering why the proud father wasn't warming to the compliment. Little did they realize the turmoil in George's mind. How could they? How could they possibly understand his steadily growing disappointment in the boy, at times boiling over into a damaging confusion of love and revulsion.

Somewhat inevitably, Mikey hadn't been accepted for prep school, didn't have what it took mentally, despite George's pleas to the stony-faced staff that he would ready the five-year-old by September. Mildean beckoned, and short of the monies to escape its lure, young Mikey took his chances with the rest of his schoolmates.

At least Mildean meant that George could resume working full time. He took up his old post in his father's former firm, becoming group head to four junior accountants, all of whom had once delighted in giving him the office runaround. And although George wasn't one to describe himself as a vindictive man, he made sure a few old scores were settled with bouts of sudden, unexpected and unpaid overtime given to the demoralized youngsters. It was petty, but satisfying.

As the years passed, and Mikey made the transition from infants to juniors, his limited academic prowess became ever more apparent. On parents' evenings, George would be regaled by sweetly smiling teachers with tales of young Mikey's impeccable manners and politeness, coupled with countless stories of his willingness to help. Then the atmosphere would change, and George would hear of their concerns for his boy – how he still hadn't grasped the basics, and perhaps needed more attention at home.

At which point George's proud jaw would tighten, unwilling to tell them of the hours still spent labouring over reading, writing, tables by rote. His mind still clung desperately to the notion that his son merely needed a little more work, rather than accepting the full-scale mental disaster he actually was. And with the denials came a surfacing raw anger, born from frustrations buried over the years. The fury began a slow transition to eventual eruption.

Simple, George had bloody-mindedly decided, eventually losing faith in the boy. He'd sired a a grinning simpleton.

A defective brain had ruined his dreams of attending the boy's Oxbridge graduation, following his career with a father's glowing pride. Mother nature, in the form of a duff egg expelled for accidental fertilization by his one-time slut-wife had cruelly conspired to thwart his ambition at the last.

Unfortunately, it wasn't only George who had figured out the truth. Mikey's classmates were hot on the case too, teasing and bullying the boy mercilessly. It pained George that his son wasn't ever invited round to other children's houses to play, gutted him when a group cycled past the allotments sniggering while he and Mikey tended the plot together.

Sometimes, it bit so deep, he was scared, frightened at the depth of his rage, terrified what he might do if ever he caught up with them. Because complaining to the school was useless, only made matters worse, highlighted the problem. George was close to utter despair, caught between protecting his flesh and blood, and raging against the injustice of the situation. Why had God seen fit to deliver him a dunce? It seemed the cruellest blow, and the local children delighting in tormenting Mikey only made matters worse.

'Dad,' Mikey had asked one evening, as they cleared away supper together. 'Brian Feeling keeps spitting at me. And the others. Calling me names.'

'Just ignore them, Mikey.'

'It's hard.'

'They're stupid, vindictive children. Not worth the bother.'

Mikey waited several moments before asking, 'What's vindictive mean?'

There was one quartet in particular who seemed to make it their mission to dog the boy. And George hated them for that. He grew tired of Mikey's tales of their abuse, yet felt impotent to protect his son. His dearly beloved son. They may as well have been bullying George himself, and he grew to loathe the very mention of their names – John Shannon, Karen Foster, Simon Ruddell and Brian Feeling. Bloody Brian Feeling, a crop-headed little shit of a human being, who made George's teeth grind at every mention. Poisonous filth with no manners, uneducated layabout parents, and, in Feeling's case, an older brother who called himself a 'punk', had green hair and spat at shop windows in the high street.

At times, especially late at night, George would sit in the back room, remembering his mother's words. Because for all that the drink had addled her brain, she was never so

127

insightful as when she had once said: 'The world's going mad.'

One night he woke up well past midnight to hear a gang of children outside, shouting abuse, laughing, blaspheming. But when he got to the front door and peered outside, there was no one there. If indeed there ever had been. George consoled himself that it was just a vivid dream. However, the voices, the vile taunting, had seemed so *real*. They were outside, but almost as if they were coming from inside too – invading his head, living in his mind.

He returned to bed, too scared to sleep.

Word had also spread through the playground regarding 'Thick Mikey's' grandfather's dubious part-time profession. Coupled with the story of the bitten nose, the decrepit house with no television and the weird dad he lived with, Mikey stood no chance, really.

But he was growing at an alarming rate, filling out faster than his skinnier peers, fed on a solid diet of home-grown fruit and vegetables which put him several inches higher and nearly a stone heavier than the second-biggest boy. And none of it was fat. Mikey Picket hadn't eaten a burger in his life. But he exercised hard, digging, weeding, running errands for his dad. In truth, at nine, he could pass for any well-built teenager.

George began using the belt a little more sparingly, secretly wary of the boy's potential for violence. Once, he'd asked him to help him shift an old, solid bag of concrete. Mikey had simply smiled, picked it up, then asked where it was to go.

And Mikey always smiled – a simple boy who always wanted to please. Perhaps, in these more enlightened times, he would have been singled out as a child with severe learning difficulties, dyslexia, even, then given one-to-one teaching by qualified staff. But in 1978, Mikey's deficiencies went largely unnoticed, smothered by the well-disciplined manners his father had beaten into him, and the boy's natural pleasant demeanour.

Things began to take a more sinister turn as Mikey hit his

teenage years. It was the mid-eighties, and he was attending Royden's Comprehensive, streamed in the lowest class, still eager to please all around him. Indeed, it was this very urge to befriend others through any number of ludicrous tasks which first attracted the attentions of the older boys. Thick Mikey was useful, a big lad with very little upstairs, an essential pawn in any bully's armoury. He began hanging around those that seemed most pleased with his company, carrying out routine beatings on weaker boys as and when they asked. Part of Mikey knew what he was doing was probably wrong, but the pay-off was that, regardless of the detentions, slipperings and lectures from the headmaster, he'd never been more popular. And it was all so easy – simply punch and kick someone, refuse to rat on your friends, take the bollockings (and thanks to Dad, he was near impervious to those) and life was distinctly rosy.

Although on occasion, he would sometimes spend an evening in his father's allotment shed, crying, cutting himself, wishing the pain away, wondering about his mother – but for the most part, he couldn't have been any happier.

Shortly before his fifteenth birthday, Mikey was expelled from Royden's. George was neither surprised nor infuriated by the inevitable action. He'd long since grown tired by the fruitless trips to the school to discuss his son's 'problem'. None of the so-called teachers could handle the boy. George despised them for their unprofessionalism. What the bloody hell were they getting paid all this ruddy money for, if they couldn't handle a fifteen-year-old boy? Mikey wasn't at fault – the system was, completely unable to teach the boy. And it didn't matter to George that his own efforts in home education had fallen on such super-dim stony ground; he wasn't a teacher, was he? These people were. And they'd failed. Other kids were leaving the so-called school with a handful of GCSEs, and his boy had nothing. The school, and the wretched, vicious children there, had doomed his son, condemned him to a wasted life.

Gradually at first, George began to drink, finding as his mother had previously that it helped him find a solution to his angst – a blame-point, something to focus the suppressed rage on. And there was so much rage. Genuine wrath, hot, putrid, constantly simmering, then bubbling over into roaring fits as he'd pace the house, shaking, salivating from the accumulated injustices.

Sacrifice – the one word which had caused him so much pain. At times, he felt like his contorting mind would explode with the sacrifices he'd made on behalf of everyone over the years. He'd read and reread his father's unsent letter to *The Times*, shaking with fury at its instruction to serve dutifully, respectfully. Hot tears of hatred would run down both cheeks as he remembered the holidays he'd never had, the promotion chances he'd passed by, the women and relationships he'd shied from – all so that Mikey would be the man he'd been denied.

And with the pain of his son's failure came the futile attempts to blame the persons responsible. And the more George agonized the dilemma, the more two solutions became ever more apparent. Mikey's descent from polite, well-disciplined toddler into grinning mental thug either down to him (*impossible* – George had done everything for the boy), or another, altogether more dangerous source. A group of evil-doers who had made their ghastly, taunting presence felt ever more luridly over the preceding years.

Four 'children' – John Shannon, Karen Foster, Simon Ruddell, and the devil-boy, Brian Feeling. A quartet of filth who had corrupted his boy.

The revelation had come during a Wednesday evening as George had set the fire. Using a local newspaper to start proceedings, his half-drunk eye had been caught by an all too familiar face beaming innocently out of the faded newsprint. Brian Feeling, now sixteen, grinning as he received a Young Achiever award from the mayor. Apparently the enterprising boy had managed to collect a vast amount of silver foil for a television appeal. He stood next to the smiling mayor, resplendent in King Edward's Grammar School uniform, as though butter wouldn't melt.

That single black and white image felt like a hot needle

working its way into George's brain. Brian Feeling had 'made it', seemed cut out for a full set of A-grade exam results, university place, the damn lot. While his boy was left on the scrapheap, a broken statistic, left behind somewhere in the angelic-looking Feeling's past. Passed over and forgotten. In that one moment of monochromatic revelation George wanted to kill the smart young boy.

Over the next few weeks, George began tracking down the others. Using phone directories and a bogus series of important-sounding lies and excuses, he made inquiries of the parents of John Shannon, Karen Foster and Simon Ruddell. To his utter dismay, all seemed to be doing well, ensconced in better schools than Mikey, mapping out better futures. Yet these were the children who'd destroyed his son's chances. He knew this because he still heard them, late at night, yelling their obscenities.

And it wasn't going away. George was a practical man, a realist, and suspected his mind was perhaps playing tricks on him. But only because *they* had control of it, not as they were now, sixteen, smiling, past crimes forgotten – but then, as miniature thugs, little louts, the ones who'd taken his son's life away.

In the deepest recesses of his mind, when the alcohol kicked in, they resurfaced, four six-year-olds, cruel tormentors to remind him of his failings, their success with Mikey.

Four bastard children – George had found the key to it all. He was in the clear, forgiven by his dutiful conscience. They were the ones who'd corrupted his son, thwarted his efforts to succeed. Not him, or the biologically inferior mother. But these hideously twisted children, now well on their merry way to the kind of life he'd always dreamed of for Mikey. They were responsible.

Their private mental 'visits' became increasingly frequent. But by now George was ready, engaging them head-on with long-drawn-out fantasies wherein he subjected each and every one to a terrible bloody revenge. And he always saved the most protracted death for Feeling. That boy really suffered at his virtuous hands, often for hours, begging for forgiveness that George never provided.

Indeed, such was the intensity and gratification of the murderous nocturnal fantasies, that George began losing interest in Mikey himself. Besides, the boy was hardly ever in the house any more, out with a new circle of thugs and hooligans, eagerly involving himself in their criminal scams and dubious pastimes.

Sometimes, he wouldn't see Mikey for days at a time, coming home from work to discover the boy sitting forlornly on his doorstep, mumbling apologies, eyes wrecked with a life George had no desire to understand. On these occasions he felt more disgust than pity for his son.

The police would call round occasionally and inform him of Mikey's latest law-breaking adventure. Petty stuff mostly, late-night fights, a spot of breaking and entering. If Mikey was at home, he'd cower respectably as the uniformed men took tea with his father. He'd earnestly agree to change his ways, become a good boy. But it wasn't as easy as that. No matter how he tried to please, there were always others who'd ask him to do stuff, people, houses. And they were the ones who *really* liked him, they were the ones who bought him drinks, gave him cigarettes, blow, let him sleep on their sitting-room floors. He couldn't let his friends down, could he?

The house, too, was dark and unwelcoming. Mikey knew other houses now – homes – and they bore little resemblance to his own. When he gathered the courage to ask his father why they didn't own a television, or a new furniture suite, there was always a tremendous row, his father staring back at him with hate-filled eyes, posing unanswerable questions about guilt, sacrifices and responsibilities. Apparently it was all Mikey's fault that they had gone without for so long.

Once, Mikey had even brought a television back to the house, freshly robbed from a big house on First Avenue. He couldn't understand his father's thunderous reaction, the abuse, the fight that followed. That night, Mikey put the television back on the rightful owner's front lawn, then knocked at his pal's place, where they got him drunk and smoked pot, before setting out on another wave of burglaries.

It was the end for Mikey, they all told him so. Time to leave his 'nutter' dad and break out on his own. They'd look after him, show him a good time. They liked him, trusted him, knew he wouldn't grass, just do the business without baulking. They knew some other lads up in Ipswich who could really do with someone like Mikey.

So Mikey went, joined his mates heading north in the stolen transit, leaving no forwarding address or telephone number. He felt sad for much of the journey, his large hands running themselves over and over the cutting scars on his muscular forearms. At one point he began to cry, refusing to be consoled by his friends' insistence that he was doing the right thing getting away from the 'old wanker', his dad.

But on arrival in Ipswich, things brightened for the morose twenty-three-year-old. The new people were pleased to see him, impressed with tales of his prowess. They found him a place to live, began giving him small errands, money, the occasional girl to play with. Memories of what he'd left behind soon faded.

For George, too, life took an unexpected upturn. Early retirement and a substantial redundancy meant he could finally devote his energies to the things he loved – simple pleasures – his allotment, polishing his shoes as he listened to the radio, and (less frequently since Mikey's departure) occasional fantasies involving Brian Feeling's neck and his own hands.

He was, by this time, prominent in the Chelmsford Avenues Allotment Society, working his way steadily up as each member died. He'd still see son Mikey, occasional weekend visits mostly during the summer, but wanted no part of his life. For George Picket, this time of his life was *his* time. Mikey was obviously able to stand on his own two feet. He'd tried his damnedest with the boy – and failed. And whenever he felt bitter about the past, he corrected it, mentally summoning Feeling's gang for another drawn-out slaughter session.

Besides, Mikey's insistence that he didn't have a phone to call his dad from, or a permanent address at which to visit, send or receive post, made sustaining whatever tangible thread of a relationship they once might have had nigh on impossible. But the boy always seemed happy, well-dressed, polite as ever. Maybe, George sometimes reasoned, maybe he hadn't done such a bad job on his son after all.

In 1995, he was made Chairman of the Chelmsford Avenues Allotment Society, a position he'd always struggled to achieve, dreamed about for so long.

At long last life had apparently served him up the just rewards for a past spent in moral servitude, hatred and frustration. He *was* somebody now.

At fifty-seven, he'd finally arrived.

PART 3

REAPING THE HARVEST

20

OF CABBAGES AND KIDS
HANGMAN'S SON AT WAR WITH JUNIOR VANDALS

By any normal standards, it was just another fire, another call for nine Essex firemen, this time to a blazing shed on a Chelmsford allotment late one October evening.

Within minutes the blaze was out, leaving local resident George Picket's wooden pride and joy in ruins. And perhaps it's easy to be too dismissive of such an occurrence. Suburban vandalism, it happens, even in the nicest of towns.

But it wasn't that way for George Picket, Chairman of the Chelmsford Avenues Allotment Society. The burning of his shed was something more sinister, the latest escalation in a summer-long 'war' with Chelmsford's dispossessed youth. A 'war' in which he feels he's been fighting a lost cause on behalf of his fellow allotment holders, dismissed by both police and the local media as little more than a serial complainer.

The tall, gaunt-looking sixty-one-year-old speaks bitterly of the experience. 'All I was doing was alerting police to a very specific group of individuals who were making our lives a misery. Their animal behaviour was largely conducted on the allotments, with increasingly bestial severity. Friends of mine who have an allotment were shocked and sickened by what they witnessed. But no one listened. And we knew it was going to get worse. We felt invaded, terrorized.'

There was burning intensity to his words, a man mourning not only the loss of his shed, but also precious moral standards in a town he's lived in all his life. However, the 'army' which has made such an unwelcome stranglehold on the quiet earth-turners of Chelmsford's Avenue Allotments are five children, the eldest just thirteen.

Alleged offences George detailed included drinking alcohol, underage sex (used condoms have been found in other allotment holders' sheds), vandalism to lovingly tended vegetable patches, and smoking. Indeed, it was the last nocturnal activity which George believes started the blaze.

'They come on their cycles after dark, mostly, break into a shed. Then their fun begins. During the day, they'll come and taunt us from the pathway, all sorts of disgusting filth. When they know damn well they should be in school. What's happened to the truancy officers? Why are so-called children being treated with goddamned kid gloves? No one cares. No one bothers any more. We're just a bunch of silly old fools with a hobby – fair game for these vandals. The Lord only knows how many times I've asked for a security camera up here. But the answer's always no.'

Senior police officers at Chelmsford's busy New Street Station confirm George as a 'regular' at the front desk.

'Our hands are tied,' one told me confidentially. 'Unless we spend a fortune on an undercover operation disguising our officers as broccoli sprigs, there's very little we can do. Any offence involving underage kids is difficult to prove unless there's concrete evidence. At which point any number of social workers and soft legislation intervenes.'

But there's a twist to George Picket's current dilemma. A man who sees himself as a lone crusader against falling moral standards, George is also known locally as 'the hangman's son'. It's a reputation over which he has no control. His father assisted at over thirty executions, helping swing many of Britain's most notorious criminals in an age when George is convinced people had more respect for law and order, the rope, and, more importantly, each other.

'My father served his country as a prisoner in a Jap camp, and also in his office as executioner,' George tells me in his spartan living room. 'I was born in this house, lived all my life here. Mother always said the abolition of the death penalty

138

broke my father, hastened him into an early grave. That he died with all his beliefs shattered by liberal free thinking. One minute he was legally required to help kill a man, next a bunch of politicians bowed to ignorant, ill-informed public pressure and declared his work outdated and cruel. Which is rubbish. There's never been a more humane of method of execution than hanging. And as a deterrent, the record speaks for itself. Since 1967, there's been over thirty murders committed by criminals released from prison who would have been swung by the likes of my father.'

George intends to buy himself a new shed, refusing to be hounded from Chairman's office by his juvenile tormentors. He has his own theory regarding the increasing problem of persistent juvenile offenders, and the law's inadequacy to deal with them.

'Human beings,' he told me. 'Need love, warmth, food and discipline. Otherwise, what are we? Animals. I used to beat my boy, and I'm not ashamed. He's not the brightest of lads, but he's grown up to make me proud. You're not born with respect. And I didn't flinch once when I had to wallop some into him. Just as my father never shrank from his duties. There's not a shred of discipline or respect left in this country, and it's people like me who pay the price.'

For the Chelmsford Avenues Allotment Society, the battle rages on, a suburban war of the old and the new. Tiny, seemingly trivial skirmishes to outsiders, but a final defence of a lifetime's values to the besieged weeders in this typically quiet Essex town.

'They won't beat us,' George proudly announces. 'And when they come back next time, we'll be ready. We've had enough. It's time to fight back.'

Dave Higgs's tired eyes filled with tears as he read. He wanted to read the article again, but the black print had simply misted into a dark incoherent mess.

He didn't *want* to believe a word of it, but it had to be true, didn't it? Even the photo of the belligerent old fool stood defiantly in the ashes of his once-proud shed bore a startling resemblance to the young man who had so dreamily shared his bed. There was no doubting it was Mikey's dad.

Higgs wiped his wet cheeks and glanced furtively around the stinking room. Of the five other beds, only two were occupied with contented snorers. Filthy men, street types, riddled with sores and body odour. Midnight ranters and vomiters, whose crazed eruptions kept him from sleeping.

How Higgs appreciated the cruel irony. As a lone forty-seven-year-old, spending the night at a men's hostel had often been a favourite fantasy, ranking alongside taking a group of young, athletic college students on an exotic field trip, or soaping up with a muddied rugby team after a gruelling match. But inevitably, the fetid reality fell far short of his perfumed imaginings. There were no half-dressed hunks in the hostel, no rugged young men willing to climb into his bed for some deliciously abandoned rough trade. Just casualties, dirty, unkempt losers with wild yellow eyes shot by a life he hoped he'd never know.

But the hostel was where Higgs was forced to make his anonymous bed now, the only place he felt *they* wouldn't come looking for him. The last place, surely, they expected to find a gorgeous, preening queen used to champagne cocktails, designer labels, the sunbed, sauna, and the contented warmth of Mikey's smooth skin next to his.

He found himself dragged back to the whispered violence of his former lover's death, and fresh tears began spilling from his weary eyes.

The bloody article! It wasn't as if he was a regular Sunday broadsheet reader. No – he stumbled upon this one, half-read and abandoned by a dour Scottish cigarette-smoking volunteer making tea and toast for the other nightly residents. But who could have guessed at the awful surprise to be found on page eleven? A grisly clue as to Mikey's disappearance.

Higgs's mind spun back to that night, when Mikey had taken the coded call telling them to have the stuff ready for collection. The stuff they'd entrusted to him – Higgs – which he'd stupidly handed to dear Mikey in fear. The police were closing in, operations had to be suspended, gear hidden. Which Mikey had dutifully, cheerfully done for him – in entirely the wrong place.

There was a knock at the door. Chucking out time. The

two sleeping men moaned and cursed, well-used to the drill. Higgs began packing his rucksack for another day in hiding, another twelve hours seeking out the calm of a back-street pub, far away from his pursuers.

Because these guys were killers. Former colleagues, associates, lovers, some of them – but murderers also. They'd done for Mikey, he'd been told. Word had already spread through the network, a horrible tale of incompetence and punishment, crime and criminal retribution.

Higgs had few enough people left who he could trust, but he'd phoned one, asked about Mikey, his voice straining with fear and concern.

'They've done him,' he was told. 'Now they're after you. Just get the fuck out. Split.'

'Oh Christ. I'm so scared.'

'You should be. They took his fucking head off, the lot. Didn't believe the poor sod. Reckoned you must have done a runner with the gear. After all, two large ones of Charlie is one fuck of an investment to lose.'

'But I haven't got any of it, I swear.'

'That's what Mikey kept saying. Right to the end. Whether they believed him, I don't know. After all, he weren't no brains of Britain, was he?'

At which point, Higgs hung up the pay phone, went to the bus station and caught the first coach to Colchester. And from there, to the hostel where he'd been ever since.

As he left the room, he took the paper with him, feeling that in some way that perhaps its new revelation could serve a fresh purpose. He needed money to put as much distance as possible between himself and the others – fast. Like yesterday. In leaving the flat in such a gut-sickening hurry, all he'd taken was underwear in a rucksack. His wallet was still there, but returning would be suicidal. Higgs was down to his last three twenties, secreted in separate pockets lest the hostel zombies decided to roll him in the night.

He walked Colchester's frosted streets for twenty minutes before finding a café for breakfast. He ordered a tepid coffee and smoked a cigarette, finally gaining the courage to read the article again.

The shed – that was where the answers lay.

Higgs remembered long slow summer evenings with Mikey, as the huge grinning boy had spoken with deep affection about a youth spent toiling with his father on the family allotment. He wanted his own one day. And Higgs had smiled and held him closer, caressed the short blonde hair on the everwilling head that would shortly be torn from its shoulders.

Over his second coffee, Higgs resolved what to do. For his sake, and dear Mikey's, the world would be told the truth about the Chelmsford Avenues Allotment fire. There was a vital thread missing to the story – and if all went well, it was a thread which could possibly save his life.

21

Sunday, November 21st

'I know why you're doing this,' Anwar Patel said slowly, handing the newspaper back. 'You're telling me my daughter Veema's going to be all right, yes?'

Jack blushed, took back the paper, avoided the intent glare from the dying man propped up in the single bed. From downstairs came the muted sounds of children playing, occasional happy exclamations finding their way upstairs into the gloom, intermingling with a delicious aroma of ginger and fried garlic.

'Well, aren't you?' Anwar pressed. 'Jack Latimer's still selling stories, so my daughter still has a job?'

Jack sighed. 'Guilty.'

'What happened? Veema told me you finished this article two weeks ago?'

'Delays, complications,' Jack shrugged. 'It was due out last Sunday, but they pulled it for another Millennium Dome story.'

'Ah. The famous Dome. One trip I'll be glad I won't have to take any more. Death provides its own relief, if you know where to look for it.'

Jack said nothing, finding no such relief in his friend's terminal condition.

Anwar smiled, then whispered, 'Know what the strangest thing about dying is, Jack?'

'Anwar, you're not . . .'

'People like you,' Anwar continued. 'Carrying on as if nothing's happening, refusing to believe.' He smiled, then waved a finger playfully. 'When I'm gone, it'll be too late. That's when you'll all wish you'd told me the things you really wanted to.' He paused for a moment, as if finding the words. 'Tell me you love me, or that you're sorry to see me go. Something – anything, just make it real.'

Outside, a heavy lorry trundled by. Jack wondered how Alex was doing downstairs, aware that visiting a dying friend was hardly the way Amy would describe a Sunday morning's 'quality time'. But Anwar's dying wisdom had the inescapable ring of truth about it. Jack had felt compelled to show his old friend the article for precisely the reason Anwar had so easily identified. He did want him to know Latimer Associates had struck temporary gold with the Picket story, that post-Nottingham credibility had been restored with national broadsheet coverage – and that as a central employee, C.F.'s short-term future was assured.

'Crazy thing is, Anwar,' he explained. 'It's been staring me in the face for years. All this time, I've been searching for the big exclusive, when all I had to do was find a few nuggets like Picket. Real lives, suburban dramas. The bloody broadsheets are so desperate to fill their half-dozen supplements, they'll take anything provided it's within their political remit. I don't know, maybe I was trying too hard for professional credibility all this time.'

'And banality sells, right?' Anwar smiled. 'Don't lose your edge, Jack. You're too good. It'll bore you to pieces.'

Jack shrugged and smirked. 'Maybe. Then again, why the hell shouldn't I opt for some easy money? My bet is there's more where this came from. Especially in a town like ours. When punters discover I've put a case like Picket's in the nationals, who knows? – maybe they'll be queuing up to tell me the full tittle-tattle of their lives.'

'You reckon?'

'I'm trying to convince the guys at the *Observer* to go with a weekly column, a sort of "Life in Chelmsford" deal.'

'Then I'm bloody glad I shan't be around long enough to read them,' Anwar replied, coughing painfully. 'Then again, how about this for one of your suburban dramas? Daft little Paki dies upstairs while rest of family is cooking coriander rice downstairs.'

'Anwar, please. Everyone's really very concerned.'

'Pah! Even Mala acts like all I have is flu. The whole house is full of her damned bloody family, twenty-four hours a day, consoling her. It's worse at night. She cries when she thinks everyone else is sleeping.' He sighed, then chuckled. 'Thirty-four years of marriage, and it comes to me dying in one room while she weeps downstairs.'

Jack found himself scratching at his wrist, nodding, avoiding eye contact. 'It's difficult,' he mumbled. 'Shit, even I don't know what to say, so God only knows how *she* feels.'

There was an awkward silence, during which Jack's mind raced to engage in a suitable conversational topic which wouldn't appear crass or phoney. Nothing came.

'Veema tells me you're still acting the arsehole over your lovely wife,' Anwar said eventually.

Jack shrugged. 'Ex-wife. It's a complicated situation.'

'Complicated further by the fact that you're harbouring thoughts about a reconciliation.'

'C.F. told you that?'

'She's a woman.' Anwar tapped the side of his bald head. 'They read us all like bloody books, Jack.'

Jack smiled for the first time.

Anwar's eyes twinkled. 'And Alex, how is he coping with his parents' stupidity?'

Jack flinched, somehow made even more uncomfortable with the direct questioning. Despite the twenty-year age gap, theirs had always been a relationship based on the equality of shared struggles, good food, family, and occasional nights spent earnestly discussing and laughing at nothing in particular. Seriousness had never been on the agenda, smothered by fun.

Even after their redundancies, Anwar had refused to let the seeping depression in, taking time to call in on his young friend, encourage his freelancing, rebuild the shattered Jack Latimer confidence. And God knows, Jack really needed the man's humour and wisdom in the early days of Latimer Associates. He'd gone from a potentially stable and exciting news career to scraping around for a living above a kebab shop in his home town. Pride stood like a giant impassable monolith, blocking his efforts to kick-start the opportunity he'd been given – that Amy had funded for him. She'd rescued him, 'solved his agony', helped find the premises, set him up in business, just like one of her confused telephonic clients. The darker, petulant side to him felt processed, patronized, emasculated.

But for Anwar, and the shrewd inclusion of his own daughter as PA, Latimer Associates would have gone belly-up in the first few months. Jack had a hell of a lot to thank his friend for, but somehow he feared that acknowledging it would confirm the cancerous screaming inevitability before them. As if by putting off the thanks, he could somehow delay the final ghastly moment. Which perhaps he dreaded just as much as Anwar.

The bedroom door opened, and Alex walked in. 'Hello, Anwar.'

Anwar's eyes brightened. 'Alex! Such a big boy now.'

The thirteen-year-old sat on the single bed, carefully scrutinizing its weary occupant, flipping back a shock of dark hair. 'Can I ask you something?' he said softly.

'Ten pounds says I already know the question,' Anwar replied. 'What's it like to die?'

Alex blushed, then nodded.

'Bloody painful,' Anwar said, holding up a hand to silence the outraged father. 'Boring, too. Boring as bloody arseholes.'

Alex smothered a laugh. 'I just can't imagine it, really.'

'That's enough,' Jack warned, acutely embarrassed and shocked. Maybe it had been a bad idea to bring Alex over, but then he'd never anticipated the boy taking such an interest.

'Shut up, Jack,' Anwar fired back brightly. 'At last, someone who acknowledges what's happening. What do you want to know, Alex?'

He thought for a moment. 'Is it scary?'

'Not really.'

'Are you sad?'

'Not for me.'

'Angry, then?'

'A little.'

'Who at?'

146

Anwar shot a look at Jack. 'Those who are in denial. It's very disrespectful. Such a waste of my precious time. It's like I'm already dead. Yet here I am.'

'Do you believe in God?'

'Come on, Alex,' Jack tried, deeply uncomfortable. What had got into the boy? He'd never had a conversation like it with him in his life. Yet now, the blush had given way to a look of real interest, absorbed almost in the spectacle before him. It was simply too morbid. 'Perhaps it's time we were going, eh?'

'*A* god,' Anwar replied, eyes locked with Alex's.

'Think you'll go to heaven?'

'I've no idea. Got to be better than this place, though, hasn't it?'

'S'pose you don't, though? Suppose it all just fades to nothing, forever?'

'Then I'll be none the wiser, will I?'

Jack watched, excluded, in grim fascination as man and boy spoke in animated frankness for the next few minutes, exchanging views about love, sex and death, in what he thought bordered on almost comic disregard for Anwar's desperate circumstance. And yet the longer he listened, the more he realized the conversation was necessary for both of them, a painful series of honest truths given by a dying teacher to an intrigued student.

At the end, Alex shook Anwar's hand, thanked him for his time, wished him well, then left the room to play on the computer with Anwar's nephews downstairs.

'I'm sorry about that,' Jack apologized. 'He's a little lacking on the diplomacy front these days.'

Anwar met him with a fierce glare. 'He's an exceptional young man, Jack. He craves knowledge, that's all.'

'He can also be a pain in the arse at times.'

'Just like all of us, Jack. Especially you.'

'Me?'

'A word of advice, old friend,' Anwar yawned. 'Don't entertain him, love him. Love him enough to nourish him, then let him go.'

'Sure.'

'Now you're patronizing me.'

147

Jack flinched. 'Jesus, no way. It's just that I can't work out if you're being serious.'

Anwar winked and blew him a kiss. 'Neither can I.'

Jack made a bad pretence of becoming suddenly absorbed by a noise downstairs. He hadn't felt this awkward since his days of doorstepping recently bereaved parents in the hope of an exclusive line on their child's death. But even those occasions had been morally tempered by a pay-cheque, his professional career. This was different, and despite Anwar's joke that he might feature in one of Jack's columns, both knew it to be hopeless. It seemed to Jack a cruel irony that the death of a passive smoker in a little Essex town was a lot less newsworthy than a vociferous old man and his shed just a few streets away.

'Well,' he said slowly. 'I shan't keep you, Anwar. Lots to do, I expect.'

'Oh, heaps. Aerobic step workout this afternoon.'

'So, I'll erm . . . go now . . . if that's . . .'

'Just bugger off,' Anwar smiled. 'Don't come back.'

'No. No.' Jack stumbled. 'I'll look in next week.'

'No,' Anwar insisted. 'It all gets too messy from here. Go now, and remember me as I am. Goodbye, Jack. And thank you for bringing the article. Same old Jack Latimer. Bloody awful grammar, but I appreciated the sentiment.'

Jack shook the thin brown hand for the final time and wondered why no tears came.

'Save them for the funeral,' Anwar replied, turning to face the wall.

Jack stood in confused silence, listening to his old friend's breathing gradually give way to shallow sleep. ''Bye, then,' he whispered. 'Good luck.'

Then he turned and left the room.

Jack took his hand off the wheel and lit up his third cigarette in less than fifteen minutes. Alex sat in the passenger seat beside him, saying nothing.

'Fancy a McDonald's for lunch?'

The adolescent silence was deafening. Undeterred, Jack took another drag.

'Pub lunch, maybe? Full English Sunday roast somewhere.' Anything, Jack reasoned, to take his mind off Anwar, the creaking bed and the godforsaken room. 'Only I haven't got much back at the flat to eat.'

'Fine.'

'Be nice to eat out, eh?'

'Just wish you wouldn't smoke, Dad, that's all.'

Jack stubbed out the cigarette, and cranked down his window. 'Sorry.'

'It's like what Mum says, you're too arrogant to believe anything bad's going to happen to you.'

Jack turned left, smothered a grin. 'Your mother ever say anything nice about me?'

'Sometimes.'

Half a mile later, Jack could stand the silence no longer. 'Listen, Alex,' he began, mindful of the conversation he'd just witnessed in the darkened bedroom. 'If there's anything you ever want, or need to ask me, well . . . you only have to ask, if you know what I mean?'

Alex opted for the standard 'fine' reply, knowing he never would. How could he? There was so much he wanted to know, craved, but where to start? How do you 'talk' to a father who's the local bloody Indiana Jones/James Bond rolled into one? What's the opening gambit when you simply want to be heard, not given gung-ho bullying solutions you're too afraid to instigate. Because he'd tried all that before, in the times before his dad had walked out, and been told to fight back, seize the world by the balls, stand up for your beliefs. Then been treated to an hour's retelling of Jack's involvement at Fortress Wapping, standing defiantly before police riot shields, he and Anwar, colleagues in a struggle, going down defiantly, together.

But Alex also knew the flipside, the consequences his father didn't detail. The depression after redundancy, sudden mood swings, fights and arguments with Mum, her finding solace in the arms of another, the end to the once happy family, the beginnings of life alone, a latchkey boy, nannies, the whole frightening deal.

Because when his father had stood up to the world, Alex

felt he'd paid the price for the folly. Big Jack Latimer lived to lunch off the story, Alex picked up the broken pieces of his ambition. Running away, compliance was the key to life. For every hero who stood tall on the parapets of injustice, there were innocent family victims who suffered for their adventuring.

There was simply no way he could ever talk to his father as he'd talked with Anwar. Because he'd resolved that he could never *be* his father. The gulf of their separate lives was too wide, too unscaleable by mere words.

They ate a miserable lunch of tepid sliced beef and over-priced frozen vegetables at a country pub packed with happy Sunday ramblers.

'Doing anything for the millennium?'

'Mum's having a party with a bunch of her feminist friends.'

'Right.' Jack chewed on gristle. 'Talking of friends, have you met her new one yet?'

He was answered by a blank stare.

'Man, apparently. Went out with him a few weeks back.'

'Don't think so.'

'Sure,' Jack said, wondering if the boy was genuinely ignorant, or incredibly diplomatic. Then admonishing himself for his cowardice, blaming the investigative journalist in him for trying to wheedle the facts out of another party, when in truth, the only way to solve the mystery of his wife's new 'friend' was to ask the woman herself. What kept him from doing it? The more he pondered the situation, the less he liked the possible answers.

'Listen,' he announced, changing tack. 'I've got a surprise waiting back at the flat. Let's finish up and get back, eh?'

'Fine.'

Forty minutes later, twenty of which was spent fumbling with instruction manuals and electric leads, Jack proudly called Alex into his living room.

'Da-na!' he exclaimed, pointing to the knocked-off computer Kenny Samson had brought him late one night. 'Any idea how we switch one of these bastard things on?'

'How about the big button with "power" written above it?'

'I can see you're going to come in handy, Alex,' Jack said, pinging the machine, then watching the screen flash all colours before an incomprehensible menu of instructions awaited a further response. Jack ushered his son to a chair before the screen.

Alex cast an expert eye over the humming hardware. 'This for your work, then?'

'Maybe, amongst other things,' Jack replied, enjoying the look of quiet determination on his son's face. 'Hear you can play games on these things.'

'Slowly,' came the quiet reply. 'This processor's too slow for the modern stuff.'

'Could it deal with this?' Jack asked, placing the PC version of Zelda and the Ocarina of Time next to the keyboard.

Jack thought he knew his son well enough not to expect a bout of sudden hugs and kisses, but he was quite unprepared for the reaction that followed. Alex simply stared at the cover on the box, frozen.

'Thought maybe we could have a go together. You teaching your old man a thing or two. Brighten up the long winter weekends.'

'Together,' Alex echoed softly. How could his father have done this? How could he have been so insensitive? Didn't he know, didn't he understand Zelda was *his* world, his escape? And now he was going to launch gung-bloody-ho into his private sanctuary, tell Alex how it should be done, beat him to the treasure, solve the cryptic puzzles faster, trounce his ambitions again and again.

'You and I,' Jack declared. 'United against the warlocks and beasties. It's going to be a blast, Alex. I should've done this ages ago.'

Alex let out a short breath, trying to stem the tears which threatened to run down his smooth face. It was over, his dreams of commanding the brightly coloured virtual world lay in ruins. With his father barging in, he'd only ever be an ineffectual prince to Jack Latimer's king. 'I don't feel very well,' he managed.

'Maybe you're sitting too near the screen. Perhaps we need one of those visor things.'

'Can we turn it off? Please.' He felt dizzy, invaded, defeated, angry.

Jack stared into the paling face, then obliged. 'You OK, Alex?'

He only managed the beginning of 'fine' before throwing up on the carpet.

Fifteen minutes later Jack left Alex tucked under a blanket watching the second half of the Roma game on Channel Four while he set off for Tesco's in search of Lucozade.

It was the shock, he told himself, coupled with the un-appetizing lunch, which had brought about the sickening end to the fun. They'd finally found something they could communicate through, learn from, forge a new relationship with. Hardly surprising the poor kid was overcome. Sick with the imminent pleasure of it all, Jack surmised, feeling pretty damn good himself.

The weary girl at the checkout couldn't understand why the man clutching four bottles of Lucozade and a jumbo bag of assorted crisps had such a broad, silent grin on his face.

But it was infectious, and she smiled back.

Alex sat in the empty flat, mind and stomach churning.

There was no way to avoid it, sooner or later he'd have to sit down at that damned computer with his father and allow him into his own private world – have his most intimate space invaded. His tummy began to rumble ominously again at the thought of it. Nothing would ever be the same again once Dad had jumped in. Everything would be played by his rules, his schemes. Alex's tactics would be passed over, advice ignored. The only person who'd get a kick out of it was his dad.

There were two solutions. Find a new game, make it his own, relinquish Zelda to a doomed father/son bonding scenario, and keep the whole thing secret.

Or the second solution – the more dangerous of the two, more exciting, perhaps, yet fraught with risk, a chance for some real adventure. And ironically, his father was just as instrumental in this second solution. Or rather his work was – the morning's article about the adolescent fire-raisers in particular. The children mentioned, the 'dispossessed', they were already operating in their own private world, modern-day games-players bucking the system, ignoring its petty rules, simply having fun adventuring in the here and now.

Computer game-play was a matter of role-playing choice. You could choose your character, 'be' anyone but yourself within the confines of the machine. He wasn't Alex Latimer, cringing nerd, but another being entirely, brave, clever, inspiring.

But perhaps there was a chance to 'play' Zelda for real. In the unsettling outside world. With a live cast. Alex, being someone else, with different powers, reinventing a new persona, crushing the old one, learning from the original game, but playing in a space where his father would never find him, where the bullies wouldn't catch him, schoolteachers wouldn't hassle him, his mother wouldn't lecture him. His own sanctuary, back again, but more exciting, so much more exciting than the computer game.

And it would begin right now, right here, in the flat, with the search for the first clue, an address book of his father's, the primary quest in a brand-new game.

By the time Jack returned, he found Alex quite recovered, sitting by the terminal, waiting to start leading him through the early stages of the Zelda's quest.

There was no way he would have noticed the scrap of paper Alex had copied from his address book earlier, because the young boy had hidden it in his inside coat pocket. When he returned home that night there was a new name pressed against his quickly beating heart.

Mark Cannon.

22

A familiar figure was waiting for Jack outside the Duke Street premises of the Latimer Associates media empire early on the following morning. George Picket stood huddled from the biting wind in the kekab shop doorway, dressed in a thick brown coat, hat and gloves.

The sight of the Chairman unsettled Jack. What if the old boy had come to complain of his treatment in the *Observer*? After all, Picket was known as a serial complainer, and from the look of him, the last thing on his mind was thanks or congratulations. Jack thought he looked furtive, distracted almost, as if searching for the perfectly phrased damning criticism of his treatment at Jack's hands.

He took out a key and unlocked the kebab shop door. 'Beautiful morning, George,' he said brightly. 'Crisp and clear.'

'Cold,' came the familiar barely whispered reply.

Jack showed Picket through the shop towards the narrow stairs leading to his office. 'You been waiting long?'

'Long enough.'

He opened the office door, ushering the subdued man inside. 'Sorry,' he explained. 'Can't offer you a coffee until the Greeks get their act together downstairs.'

Picket said nothing, sitting at C.F.'s empty desk, looking through the grimy windows at the near-deserted bus station opposite.

'Going to pull that place down, George,' Jack announced, still wondering what had brought Picket back. 'Whole of this area's going to be done up. Shops, cafés and businesses under the railway arches. Major millennium face-lift to this end of town. Still, there's a part of me that's going to be sorry not to see . . .'

'I want you to find my son.'

Jack paused, looked for the first time into Picket's bloodshot eyes, read the fear and concern on the older man's face. 'Your son?'

Picket nodded.

Jack raised both hands, inviting further conversation.

'I think . . .' Picket slowly obliged, then pulled back, looking away out into the street again. 'I don't know what to think.'

Jack hedged a bet. 'He's missing, is he?'

'He could be.'

It was strangely unnerving to witness the normally upright confident Chairman reduced to such verbal rambling. Jack noticed three deep cuts on Picket's hands. 'Have you had some kind of accident, George?'

'Me? No.'

'Only your hands . . .'

'DIY,' Picket quickly explained, covering the fresh angry weals. 'I'm planning a little conversion for the house. Mind's not been fully on the job. Got careless with a chisel late one night. Stupid, really.'

'Because you've been worried about your son?'

Another nod from Picket.

'Have you called the police?'

The beginnings of anger sparked from the Chairman's eyes. 'And tell them what, exactly?'

'Well, that he's missing, maybe?'

Picket cleared his throat. 'Mr Latimer, you are very aware of their regard for me. To that end, I have no intention of involving the damned police in any of my business.'

'Even so,' Jack pressed. 'A missing persons inquiry is probably treated with, how shall I put this, a little more seriousness than the kids on your allotment. Did you see the article, by the way? I thought it looked splendid, a good position, and the photo's really –'

'It's my son I'm here about.'

'Sure.' Jack lit up.

'Can you find him for me?'

'I don't know, I . . .'

'I'll pay, of course. I have money. Not a lot, but something for your time.'

Jack exhaled, aware there was an imminent danger of being bamboozled into something he had no real intention or experience of doing. 'George, listen to me, please. I'm a journalist. Some people would disagree, but that's what I call myself. If you won't involve the police then what you need is some sort of private investigator. They're set up for this kind of thing. I don't do missing persons. Believe me, I'd like to help, but . . .'

'If you can't sell the story, you won't take the job, right, Mr Latimer?' Picket replied sourly.

Jack shrugged. 'I'm just not set up for this kind of work, George.'

Picket's cold eyes narrowed slightly. 'Yet, if I told you he had a sworn statement from Lyndon Johnson saying he personally pulled the trigger on President Kennedy, I dare say you'd find him fast enough.'

Jack exhaled.

'The point about people like you, Mr Latimer, is that when people like me serve you no more purpose, you move on to the next meal-ticket. You're all damned vultures, picking at our pain for profits.' He stood painfully. 'I can't afford a private investigator. I stupidly thought you might do me a favour, considering it was my story which has most probably paid the rent on this office for the next six weeks. Good day to you, Mr Latimer. I shall leave you to flap away in search of more fresh local carrion.'

Jack pressed his face into both hands and sighed. Twice. Then asked the fuming man to sit down – three times – wondering how he'd been so easily emotionally bullied into doing so. But maybe, a part of Picket's colourful rhetoric had hit home. Perhaps the almost comic combination of clichéd analogy and Picket's haunted face had touched that place where even Jack himself was reluctant to venture too often – his conscience. Here was a father, worried sick about his son, who, for one reason or another, felt driven

156

to ask for a comparative stranger's help rather than the authorities'.

The father in Jack felt a sudden sympathy for Picket – the reporter in him felt the Chairman was hiding something. Either way, he was intrigued enough to give the guy another fifteen minutes.

'Tell me about your son,' he said eventually. 'I can't promise anything, but I'll try. Fair enough?'

23

Alex Latimer had been standing nervously on the opposite side of the narrow terraced street for a little over half an hour, watching others arrive. He'd counted four in all, two boys on bikes, one surprisingly young; and two girls arriving together, giggling, a cute-looking blonde and her taller, dark-haired companion. Each time he'd observed the front door opened by a gaunt-looking ginger-haired boy – presumably Mark Cannon, the Carrot-top referred to in his father's notebook.

Without knowing, his mind had been following a similar thread to his father's when first visiting the temporary home of Mark Cannon – finding an angle, rehearsing his role. And he knew it would have to be watertight. From what he'd seen, Cannon and company were near enough his own age, and therefore uncannily well equipped to spot a bullshitter.

But his training with Zelda had prepared him well. He had weapons and spells, concealed in the rucksack which now held his school uniform. Tools to help him prise his way in to their unknowing confidence.

He'd spent the previous evening in a state of nervous panic, planning, packing the rucksack with casual clothes (nothing with a label, nothing too expensive), money to buy cigarettes and a copy of the *Observer* article – the clincher, he hoped.

During breakfast his mother had carried on her early-morning routine oblivious to Alex's trembling ambitions. He felt guilty to be deceiving her, truanting as he would be, but the promise of what might await him quickly soothed his conscience. Besides, surely every schoolkid had bunked off in their time? This was simply his time, that's all.

To complete the deception, Alex even waved happily to his mother as she dropped him at the school gates, explaining he needed the rucksack for a 'personal development project'. Which was no word of a lie. Crazier still, his mother had added that she was very pleased with the school's mature approach to the humanities curriculum.

A minute later, Alex was doubling back against the flow of uniformed flotsam, back out through the gates towards town. Thrilling from the cocktail of fear and excitement, he changed in the gents in Central Park as planned, had a pee, then called in at a suitably disreputable newsagent's to buy cigarettes, before setting off for Moulsham Street, and the many tributaries of Victorian terraced streets surrounding it.

And now, at nearly eleven a.m., this was it – a chance to make some new friends, be someone more exotic, taste some real adventure. He swallowed hard, wishing he was bigger, taller, thicker set. But he had intellect, a quick mind. His mother had repeatedly told him how well he would do for himself, having 'her brains' not the lumpen porridge which passed for his father's.

He walked slowly up the tiny rubbish-strewn overgrown front garden, little glances right and left, feeling exposed in a no-man's-land of alluring danger. Both legs felt cold and suddenly empty, yet somehow moved him on.

No turning back.

He tried the bell, heard nothing, realized it was probably broken, then flapped the rusting iron letterbox, heart beating heavily.

Muted noises from beyond the door died. Indistinct voices hushed one another. To his right, a dirty net curtain in the front window twitched. He daren't look, just tried the letterbox again.

The door opened. Carrot-top's pale face squinted out at him. 'Yeah?'

'I've got something you might be interested in.'

'Sod off.' There was laughter further back inside the hallway. Alex could make out the others coming to inspect the visitor.

'It won't take a minute,' he said, locking eyes with the grinning ginger-haired boy before him.

'What are you, then? One of them bible-bashers. Them . . . erm . . . ?'

'Jover's Witnesses,' a voice prompted from the gloom. 'Wankers.'

'No, Mark,' Alex replied, enjoying the sudden confusion on Carrot-top's face at the mention of his name. 'But I do want to show you something, all the same.'

Cannon eyed him suspiciously. 'Well, if it's "all the fucking same" to you, I'd rather you pissed off.'

'I want your autographs.'

'You what?'

'Let me in, I'll tell you. You're famous.'

'Yeah, and you're looking for a smack in the mouth.'

Alex shrugged. 'Fair enough.' Then made to turn away, amazed at how calm he felt. The boy looked frightening, true, like some sort of hideous computer sprite, but close up, he was just a kid like him. It was like outwitting an ape – simple if you kept out of range and played the right hand. Boldness rushed over him. He felt two inches taller already. 'Pity, really. You'll never know how you made it into a national newspaper, then, will you?'

'Guess we won't.'

''Bye, then.'

'Ta-ra, cunt.'

Then another face appeared over Cannon's shoulder, the dark-haired girl, chewing gum, inquisitive. 'What newspaper?'

At which point Alex reached into the rucksack and pulled out the rolled-up copy of the relevant *Observer* supplement and turned to the page adorned by Picket's black-and-white *in situ* allotment photo.

The girl's eyes lit up. 'Jesus! That's . . . it's him,' she said, pointing excitedly. 'Whatshisname from up the allotments! What's he doing in the paper?'

Alex quickly pulled the paper away before Cannon could tear it from him. 'Not just him,' he said. 'You lot as well.'

'S'have a look.' Cannon held out a hand.

160

'Inside,' Alex replied, meeting the pale-blue eyes and holding the stare, telling himself that the goose-bumps were down to the cold rather than Cannon's intimidation.

A minute later Alex found himself in the acrid front room, surrounded by all five children. He produced the paper, giving it to Cannon, whose eyes never left his, passing it on to the dark-haired girl. She in turn passed it to the pretty blonde, who quickly found the page and read aloud.

Alex watched as she flawlessly read the piece, wondering at her connection with the others. She certainly seemed brighter, better-dressed, although curiously submissive. Cannon made her read the extract three times, and certain passages over and over, which she did without complaint or question. The older of the other two boys sat by her side, rolling a joint with practised ease, while the younger lad jumped on the battered sofa. Alex put him at well under ten.

All the while, he made quick mental notes of the pecking order before him. Cannon was obviously self-appointed leader, with Dark-hair as his girlfriend most probably ranking equal to Dope-smoker. The young gymnast looked most likely for next in line, with detatched Blondie bringing up the rear.

'Shit,' Cannon exclaimed after the third reading. 'We're famous! Damon, we're in the fucking paper!'

The boy lazily lit up, exhaled, made a motion of passing the joint to Blondie. Alex noticed how she glanced over to him, blushed slightly, then refused. 'Don't mention us by name, though, does it?' he said lazily. 'Could be anyone, really.'

'But it was you, wasn't it?' Alex asked. 'You're the people responsible for hassling Picket.'

'What's it to you, anyway?' Cannon replied, drawing on the joint.

The tiny boy began an impromptu chorus of, 'Picket's a wanker, Picket's a shit. Picket's an arsehole, a stupid old git!'

'Shut it, Giblet,' Cannon ordered. 'He had it coming to him. Went off gassing to the Old Bill about how we was fucking with him. Shouldn't have run his mouth off. Cost him dear.'

'But we didn't,' came a sullen voice from the other side of the room.

Silence descended. All eyes turned to Blondie.

'We didn't burn down his shed.'

'Shut it, Eve,' Cannon warned. 'You weren't even there, pissing off home, back to Mummy and Daddy 'cause they don't like you stopping out late.'

Alex watched the girl give way, feeling her inadequacy.

The boy called Damon spoke up, his voice hoarse and drifting. 'Who would've guessed his old man was a hangman? That's fucking evil, that is.'

'Just like Picket, though, ain't it?' Cannon replied, sitting down next to Dark-hair. 'Like father, like son. Both of 'em's obviously not right in the head. Picket's shot with bad genes an' that. Mental case.' He suddenly turned towards Alex. 'Who the *fuck* are you, anyway?'

'Like I said, an autograph hunter.'

'Yeah, and I'm fucking Napoleon.'

Damon sniggered. Dark-hair stared. Blondie stared. Giblet stopped bouncing.

Alex spoke directly at Cannon. 'My name's Alex. I read about you guys, decided what you'd done to the old bloke was OK. Radical, anarchic. Arson's a real statement.'

'Listen to the fucking dictionary, everyone,' Cannon sneered.

'How did you find us?' the girl called Eve asked softly.

'I told you to shut it!' Cannon barked, before taking a step closer to Alex. 'Thought occurs to me, Posh-boy. How the fuck did you find us?'

'Weren't no mention of names or addresses in the paper,' Dark-hair pressed.

'Luck, I guess,' Alex shrugged, hoping he wasn't about to be pummelled, yet also savouring the taste of fear in his mouth, thinking fast to outrun the adrenaline. He was loath to reveal the connection to his father as he had no idea what reaction it would provoke. Besides, thinking his way out of the dilemma was more of a rush, more dangerous. He felt high, alive. Real-gaming was a bigger thrill than he'd ever imagined. 'I asked around.'

'Where?' Cannon barked.

'Up at the allotments.'

'When?'

'Earlier this morning. Before I came here. Some old woman was weeding or something. She said you had bikes, so reckoned you came from down this way. More than a short stroll, anyway.'

Cannon considered the logic. Nodded slowly. 'Maybe.'

Sweat was breaking from Alex's brow, but he saw a light at the end of the tunnel. 'When she told me about an older boy and a younger one being part of the gang, I had more of an idea about you. Coming over here, I spotted Damon and Giblet. Just followed them, really. Went with a hunch. Then knocked on the door.'

'His name's Tony Minks,' Cannon replied, nodding at the younger boy. 'Damon's brother, and a right little sod to boot.'

The girl called Eve lifted her head. 'But you knew Mark's name,' she said. 'That wasn't in the paper, was it?'

'Asked at a neighbour's house a few doors down,' Alex replied, smiling. 'No mystery, honest.'

'Just luck, then,' she replied, offering the tiniest of smiles by way of return.

'Absolutely.' His skin prickled under her bashful gaze.

Cannon had grown bored, had begun playfully wrestling with the excitable Tony Minks.

'I was thinking,' Alex asked. 'Maybe I could hang out with you guys for a while.'

'Hang out?' Cannon replied, sitting on the wriggling youngster's chest.

'I've got money.'

'How much?'

'Enough.' He reached into the rucksack, pulled out three packs of cigarettes, tossed them on to the threadbare carpet. 'My family's not short. There's more where this came from.'

There was a long silence as Cannon looked Alex over, then eventually pocketed two of the cigarette packets. He turned to the others. 'Well, as some old wanker once said,' he slowly explained. 'Never look a horse-gift in the mouth.'

'Or something like that,' Alex added quietly.

163

Cannon unwrapped the pack and lit up. 'Come on then, posh-boy Alex, or whatever your fucking name is, let's go and spend some of your money, eh? I think we might be real grateful you found us today. Real grateful.'

24

'Kenny?'

'Jack? How's life in cyberspace, then?'

'Confusing as hell. But thanks for the machine.'

'Worked, then, did it?'

'Eventually. Alex managed to run the game. Though I'm not sure how much of an ally I'm going to be. He's light years ahead.'

'Well, I'm glad it's working out. Seen any more of Amy?'

Jack sighed into the phone, looked at the over-large succulent on the windowsill. 'Clint's telling me to sit tight, bide my time.'

'You and your bloody cactus,' Samson replied, clutching the receiver between his shoulder and wide neck as he grappled with a disorderly pile of paperwork. 'It'll be Christmas in a few weeks. Have a go with Amy. You never know, maybe this year we'll invite the pair of you over for a few sherries round the family hearth.'

'If we can exist in same room without killing each other,' Jack replied. 'Besides, I think she's still seeing this new guy.'

'Never know till you've tried.'

Jack heard the faint note of amusement in the detective's voice, and suddenly felt as if he was the only one who wasn't in on the joke – whatever that was. It wasn't unusual for Amy to stop by at Kenny's; she was still friends with his wife, and maybe she'd brought her latest paramour with her. The mental image brought a frown to his forehead. He changed the subject. 'Picket was back earlier this morning . . .'

'Jack, I'm really busy.'

'. . . wants me to find his son. He reckons he's somewhere in Ipswich.'

'Get the phone book and look him up under "Son of Weird Weeder".'

'Little cruel, Kenny. Did you read the article, by the way?'

'What article?'

'Never mind. There's a problem with the phone book.'

'Try directory inquiries.'

'Picket didn't have a number for him. Or an address.'

'Guess that's you knackered, then, isn't it?'

'But it doesn't sound right, does it?'

'Sounds fine to me. Just remember, if your dad was like Picket, chances are you wouldn't want the old man to know where you were living, either. Kid's probably desperate to hide away from him. Leave the poor sod alone.'

'I don't know that I can. Picket was a wreck. He hadn't read the article, either.'

'People do do other things on a Sunday besides trawling through the papers in the hope of stumbling across a Jack Latimer exclusive, pal.'

'Yeah, but not when they're the subject matter, Kenny. Honestly, you should've seen him. He's really very worried. Says the boy's the vulnerable type, easily led astray. A bit simple, almost. Reckons he may have become involved with some dubious types.'

Another reluctant sigh from DS Samson. 'And your hack's nose has smelt a rat, right?'

'Maybe.'

Samson sighed audibly over the phone. 'All right, Send Picket down to us, I'll have a word with Miss-Pers in Ipswich. Beyond that, there's not a lot –'

'You don't understand, Kenny. The last people Picket wants to see is the police.'

'Then there's sod-all I can do. I can't open an investigation without a legitimate complaint. Sorry.'

'But can you just phone Ipswich CID, get an address for a Mikey Picket, phone number, details, that sort of thing?'

'Give it a rest, Jack. Like I say, the kid's most probably

buggered off for a fortnight in the Algarve or something. You know what Picket's like, if he can't find a crisis to fill his life, chances are he'll invent one. Only now he's got you running round for him, finding his son.'

'Because I said I would.'

'Your problem, then, friend. Sorry, can't help.'

'Please,' Jack begged. 'Just a phone call. It won't take you five minutes.'

'You know it doesn't work like that. I can't just ring up on some half-arsed pretext. It's wasting police time.'

Jack bulldozed the objection. 'Listen, there's more . . .'

'Here we go.'

'Picket said that when he last spoke to the boy, he was crying, telling him how he was afraid, that others were coming for him. He made me swear not to tell you lot about it, which set me thinking that maybe there was more to it than he knew.'

'Or was prepared to tell you.'

'Exactly.'

'And there was no forwarding address, no phone number?'

'None. His son would call him every once in a while, tell him he was OK. Sometimes come back to Chelmsford for the odd weekend. He claims to have seen the boy just a few weeks ago.'

'And he never gave his dad a contact number?'

'Seems that way.'

'How long has he been living in Ipswich?'

'About four years.'

'And Picket reckons the lad's some kind of simpleton? Living seventy miles away with no known address? What about emergencies?'

'I asked him. He said whenever he saw or spoke to Mikey, that he seemed well, in good health, dressed smartly, doing OK. He said his dad shouldn't worry about him, he had a good bunch of friends who were looking after him.'

'Looking after him?'

'Between you and me, I got the impression Picket was quite happy with the arrangement, sort of out-of-sight, out-of-mind thing. Almost as if he preferred not to know what

167

Mikey was up to. I don't know, maybe he didn't think it would sit too happily with the Chairman's image.'

'Until he got the last call, the one saying there were people after him?'

'Exactly,' Jack replied. 'Please, Kenny. I'm asking you a big favour. Could you just make one or two discreet inquiries about the kid? I don't know, I just get a funny feeling about it all.'

'I'll try, OK?'

'Top man, Kenny. I owe you, really.'

'Yeah, big time.'

In order to celebrate Latimer Associates' sale of the Picket story, Jack took C.F. for a slap-up ham omelette and chips in the local for lunch. Strangely, it had been a highly productive morning, with four other potential work-related calls as well as George Picket's early-morning inquiry regarding his son. Strictly local stuff, most of it staggeringly duff, but when the final call came, Jack suddenly began to see a looming opportunity for both C.F. and the business. Instead of offering a polite, 'No, thank you', and heading off for juicier journalistic fare, he listened to the woman's story quite intently, mentally planning as she spoke.

The caller was a woman, mid-thirties, from Great Baddow on the east side of the town. She was involved in a neighbourly fencing dispute with 'that lot from next door'. Apparently her rabbit had found a way through to their garden, and promptly chewed through the front tyres on one of 'that lot's' brand-new twenty-one-speed mountain bike. Recriminations were bitter and ongoing, and as Jack was beginning to realize, might eventually prove to be a plausible follow-up to the Picket-allotment feature, a second instalment of a suburban soap opera he just might persuade the *Observer* editor to butt into.

'But it's just a little local news item,' C.F. had said, as Jack pencilled in an appointment to see the irate wandering-rabbit owner. 'Hardly national headline stuff.'

'Who's to say?' Jack replied. 'Bits of inconsequential crap like this are precisely what the broadsheets are soaking up.

It all depends on how we present the thing. The Latimer Associates angle.'

'So?'

Jack paced the office, doing his best OTT impression of a media tycoon. 'We'll make this rubber-eating rodent squabble a millennial symbol of suburban chaos, C.F. – a society desecrated by years of Thatcherite propery ownership which tore communities apart, leaving us a legacy of suspicious people living separate lives, unequipped to resolve even the most trivial problems without resorting to threats of violence. We'll head it up – "Love Thy Neighbour – Not in Chelmsford".'

'I'm not even sure a rabbit is a rodent.'

'Well, find out.'

'Me?' she replied, eyes widening.

'Sure. You can handle this one.'

C.F. brightened a little. 'I go and play at being a reporter?'

'Well, it's about time, isn't it?'

She hesitated. 'I suppose so.'

Jack handed her the paper with the relevant name and address. 'Give it a go. It's yours. Woman's called Mrs Tapper. She's expecting you at around three this afternoon.'

'Thanks.'

'A pleasure.'

'And Jack? Thanks for coming to see Dad yesterday.'

He felt himself blush a little. 'Well, I wanted to see him, anyway. You know, catch up and everything.'

'He appreciated it.'

'How's your mum?'

'Coping.'

'And you?'

'The same.'

'Good.' There was a long silence, during which Jack hoped that the phone would ring, someone would knock at the door, a bomb explode at the peeling bus station opposite. Anything to allow him to relax and uncurl his sweating toes a fraction.

In the end, she broke the deadlock, walking over to him and hugging him. 'Thanks, Uncle Jack. You care, don't you, despite all the preferring cacti to real people crap?'

'I try,' he replied hoarsely, then blushed again. 'Right . . . well. That's that, then.'

She smiled at his awkwardness, watching as he quickly regained his normal casual composure.

'Now then,' he announced. 'Part of being a junior reporter, C.F., involves a long and rigorous training into the specialist art of the long lunch. How about I treat you to lesson one right now?'

25

It was turning into a grim afternoon for DS Kenny Samson.

'Let's cut straight to the chase, Kenny,' DI Block barked angrily. 'I've just had a phone call from Ipswich CID about a body found in bags in a council dustbin and your name's been mentioned in connection.'

Kenny shifted uncomfortably. It was the word 'Ipswich' which struck home. The Picket connection – had to be. The discreet phone call he'd made on Jack's behalf. 'Er . . .' he mumbled, eyes rooted to the date on the desk-top flip-clock. Wednesday, December the 8th – 2.43 p.m. It was raining outside. Perhaps the very last place on earth he wanted to be was in this grey, sterile office, taking a rollocking from the abrasive Block. He was new to the post, a replacement for the smaller, and hugely more popular, DI Archie Crowe, now retired. As such, the external appointment had done little to quell bad feelings for the new guv'nor, but to be fair, Block hadn't exactly gone to great lengths to endear himself to the disgruntled squad, either.

'I want some answers, Kenny,' Block added, playing with a pencil in the chair opposite. 'Seems you made a call to them last Monday, asking after the whereabouts of one Mikey Picket.'

'I did, yeah.'

The superior, bearded man leaned forward. 'And now,' he said coldly. 'It seems they've found the former Mr Picket.'

Samson scratched at his neck. 'Oh, Jesus.'

'No. A Mikey Picket,' Block replied. 'So what's the story, Detective?'

'Well, it was just a hunch, really. A daft thing.'

'Not looking so daft to the boys up at Ipswich. Not with a body in a dustbin.'

'Sure,' Kenny answered, subdued.

'Right,' Block said slowly, eyeing Samson all the while. 'So what was this "daft thing"? Crystal ball, was it? *Sun* horoscope? Only what I want to know is, how else can I put your psychic talents to good use on this squad, eh?'

'It was a sort of tip-off, Guv.'

'Sort of?'

Hating every second, Samson reluctantly explained the favour he'd done for Jack.

After, Block sat thinking for a second, replacing the pen in exact alignment with the rest of his desk. 'Let me get this straight,' he said eventually. 'This reporter friend of yours just happens to call up, ask you to make one or two discreet inquiries outside normal police channels, and low and behold, we stumble upon a chopped-up corpse ten days later?'

'More or less, Guv, yes. I mean, he'd done this article on the boy's father, George Picket . . .'

Block's eyes glimmered in distant recognition. 'I know that name.'

'He's a bit of a pain, to be honest, Guv . . .'

'How do I know that name?' Block pressed.

Samson swallowed hard. 'He makes a bit of a nuisance of himself on the front desk, Guv. Always on about a group of kids vandalizing the allotments. Well, as you'll appreciate, there's not a lot they can do . . .'

Block cut in. 'And there was some kind of article about this? In the local paper?'

'The . . . er . . . *Observer*, Guv.'

'What, the *Observer*?'

'Yes, Guv,' was the quiet reply.

'Have you read it, man?'

'Er . . . no, sir.'

Block threw up both hands. 'I can't believe it. What in God's name's happening round here?'

'To be fair, Guv, it was more a Uniform matter. They were the ones who were dealing with the old boy. Ask Sergeant Stirchley on the desk . . .'

'I will, believe me.'

'They were all fed up of him coming in to complain about this, that and the other. Next I really knew about it, Jack Latimer from up the road tells me he's thinking of running a piece about Picket and the allotments. I never, ever in my wildest nightmares believed he'd sell such a trivial story to the national press.'

'And likewise you never thought to tell anyone else on the squad about this "favour" you subsequently did the journalist.'

'I didn't think anything of it, really. He said Picket had been back, was worried about his son. Could I help?'

Block's fat lips curled into a narrow smile. 'Well, now it's come back to haunt you a little, Detective Sergeant, hasn't it?'

'Like I say, I had no idea . . .'

Block stood. 'Bypassing normal procedural channels is a risky business at the best of times. Doing "favours" for reporters without consulting our own press liaison officer is another.' He turned to face the still-blushing detective. 'It can have a nasty habit of blowing up in your face. Very nasty indeed.'

'Yes, Guv. Sorry, Guv,' Samson quickly replied, wishing he had the puffed-up man in front of him on the rugby field. He'd have been willing to sacrifice the rest of the season for one chance to fell Block in a slush of cold mud and torn sinews.

'Ipswich are spitting blood about this. The narcotics boys in particular.'

'Drugs?'

'Seems they've planted some undercover men to clean up the coke trade. One of them got a tip-off that this Mikey Picket character had been murdered.' Another thin smile from Block. '"Whacked", I believe is their amusing little term for it.'

'Picket was in a drugs gang?'

Block nodded, a tiny motion, more of a twitch than an affirmation. 'According to the undercover boys, Picket messed up rather badly. His own people killed him.'

Samson's head began to swim. How in God's name had

one phone call got him involved in all of this shit? Gangland executions, cocaine smugglers, undercover operations? 'And this is the same Mikey Picket, is it?' he weakly asked. 'I mean, there could be some mis – '

'The source is good,' Block cut in. 'But we still need an ID. They're sending down the head later this afternoon.'

'Sorry, Guv?'

'Packed in ice, straight to the mortuary at headquarters.'

'The head?'

'And as you're obviously so interested in the case, I thought you could take this George Picket to identify it. See if he picks it out as his son's.'

'Right,' Samson quietly replied, dreading the prospect.

'And Kenny?'

'Yes, Guv?'

'For God's sake don't go shooting your mouth off to reporters about this one, will you? Ipswich have asked for a D-notice on it. The whole damn thing. Not a word of it to appear in print. Understand?'

Samson frowned, aware he could well be sliding into something dark and deep. 'Could I ask why?'

'They've got too many operatives in the field. Ipswich feel the less fuss that's made over the boy's death, the more relaxed the villains'll be, the more likely they'll keep operations as normal.'

'So,' Samson asked, slowly, 'there won't be a murder inquiry?'

Block nodded. 'Not a press conference, not a house-to-house, not a routine line-up, not even a fifteen-minute *Crimewatch* appeal. As far as the rest of the world is concerned, Mikey Picket never existed.'

'I doubt his father'll see it that way,' Samson protested.

'I'm only telling you what they told me, Kenny,' Block insisted, softening a little. 'Look, it isn't the way we do business, but then again, we don't have half a dozen feuding coke gangs on the patch, and a dozen undercover officers trying to bring them in.'

'And all we have to do is get this frozen head identified?'

Block nodded.

'Does it have to be the father?'

'Ipswich have already checked. No siblings, no mother. Father's the nearest living relative.'

'The poor sod.'

'It's the legal requirement, Kenny. Body can't be released and cremated without it.'

'There must be someone else besides his dad, surely?'

Block shook his head.

'And just what do I tell him, if it turns out to be his son?' Kenny asked, feeling annoyed. '"Sorry, Mr Picket, the police aren't bothering with finding the killer. You go home and tend your allotment"?'

'Don't be facetious, Detective, you're on thin enough ice as it is.' Block consulted his notebook, looking for the relevant key phrase taken from the phone call. 'You tell him the truth,' he said.

'Which is?'

'That police in Ipswich have suspicions who the killers are, but due to the unlawful activities in which Mikey Picket was conducting himself when killed, investigating officers are concentrating their efforts into a highly sensitive covert operation to bring both the killers *and* a large number of their accomplices to justice at the same time.'

'I'm sure he'll be comforted by that,' Samson muttered to himself.

Block continued. 'Mr Picket will of course be visited by various investigating officers, including yourself, during the next few weeks, but until such a time, it is of the utmost importance that no one else hears about any aspect of his son's premature death. And that means not going shooting his mouth off to local reporters, Detective.'

'Right,' Samson confirmed, thoughts cemented to an old man peering at a head in a box.

'I mean it,' Block insisted. 'Ipswich have been working on this thing for months. Officers lives are at stake. If these villains feel anything's going down that involves us – they'll either shut up shop and quit, or come down hard on the grasses. Either way, the operation's terminated.'

Samson stood. 'Just doesn't seem right, somehow.'

'They're dealing with scum, Kenny. We don't have that problem in Chelmsford. Ipswich do. Remember what they did to Mikey Picket, one of their own. Just for screwing up.'

'And what did he do wrong, exactly?'

'No one knows. But it doesn't alter the fact that we'd be well out of our depth with this lot. So for Christ's sake, keep the father's mouth shut tight until after Ipswich have brought these villains in. OK?'

'Tell me, Guv,' Samson asked as politely as possible. 'What would have happened if this Mikey Picket character had come from a so-called normal home? You know, mum, dad, brothers and sisters. Would all of them have had to keep their mouths shut as well?'

Block raised an eyebrow. 'In such circumstances,' he said slowly. 'I would have thought it was unlikely that he would have got involved with a bunch of drug barons in the first place.'

Samson didn't know how to respond, unsure if the puritanical boss was being straight, or winding him up. His idea of a joke, maybe, a very weak one. Yet something in Block's blazing blue eyes told Samson his guv'nor didn't make those kind of cracks – he'd believed what he'd said.

'Keep me up to speed with this,' Block added. 'I'll be making a full report to the super, including your involvement with this local reporter, so no more "favours", eh?'

'Sure.'

'And an apology wouldn't go amiss.'

'Sorry, Guv.'

'Accepted.'

Samson left the office feeling like an errant schoolboy shamed by the headmaster. The feelings of embarrassment and anger stuck in his throat all the way back to his office.

26

Contrary to what he'd nervously expected, Alex was beginning to find the truanting much simpler. Unexpected breaks presented themselves in the unlikely form of sloppy school gatekeeping and general teacher lethargy, allowing him easier access to his strange new game and its exotic cast beyond.

True, he'd received a standard lecture from the ineffectual head, during which he'd made all the right conciliatory noises – then walked straight back on to the streets on his supposed way back to class. It really was that easy. Playing Zelda for real was even more exciting than on the computer. Indeed, his enthusiasm for computer-gaming had waned considerably, now seeming lame by comparison. There were real risks outside, real possibilities. Over a few short weeks he'd managed to more or less reinvent himself, place himself within a new hierarchy, and all it had taken was the guts to make that first step, plus the odd tenner to keep his new friends in cigarettes and more besides.

'It's like this, Posh,' Damon Minks had explained one afternoon as they sat in the dank front room, listening to the muted sounds of Mark Cannon's dope-infused lovemaking with Dark-hair upstairs. 'School's only got the power over you when you're on their premises. If you just fuck off out of it, they're rubbing their bloody hands with joy, 'cause you're another one they don't have to worry about.'

'I wish I'd known this years ago,' Alex replied.

'Sometimes they get a bit of shit from the parents, an' that, but mostly no one cares. See, legally, they're covered. You go and get run over by a bus, and as long as it ain't in the school playground, they couldn't give a toss. Besides, most of 'em are only too glad to see the backs of us. Less for them to worry about, ain't it? Giblet! Turn that bloody thing down. Fucking machine's ruining my trip!'

Tony Minks turned to his older brother, swore, then carried on shooting electronic aliens from the shoplifted game exactly as before.

Alex wondered if Eve would show. In truth, he was disappointed not to see her. She was, as the others referred to her, a 'part-timer', occasionally knocking on the front door as and when she could walk from school, arriving looking furtive, perhaps giving the odd smile to Alex as he played it cool. She was, he suspected, from a similar background to him, although he still hadn't had the nerve to inquire too closely. Eve was tolerated, it appeared, because Dark-hair's mother and hers were buddies, the former cleaning the latter's brand-new, four-bed, detatched, mock-Tudor home. And because Dark-hair slept with Cannon, the ginger-haired youngster reluctantly allowed the 'stuck-up weird cow' to join their gang.

It took Alex four days of hanging around with his new-found friends before he felt safe to engage Dark-hair on a one-to-one. It was a Friday afternoon, and the pair of them stood outside McDonald's in the rain-sodden pedestrian high street waiting for Cannon, Damon and Giblet to return with a few shoplifted goods, victorious like a primitive hunting party. Alex hadn't been allowed to join the operation, as Cannon considered him to be 'too fucking wet', and thus an unwelcome liability.

Which pleased Alex no end. Truanting he was growing accustomed to, shoplifting was another matter, another level of the game he wasn't trained for. He offered Dark-hair a cigarette.

'Ta,' she replied, lighting up. Alex noticed smudged foundation on the over-made-up face. 'Mark reckons you're a right oddball.'

'And what do you think?'

'Dunno. You talk funny, but you got a few bob for fags and that.' She looked at him, flashing dark-green eyes behind thick mascara. 'When you ain't got no more money, he says he'll do you.'

'Charmed.'

She giggled. 'Talk shit, you do.'

He felt brave, chanced his arm with some bravado. 'But at least I don't smoke it.'

'Meaning what?'

'Can I ask you a question? How old are you?'

'Age ain't got nothing to do with it. S'my life. I'll do what the fuck I like.'

'I don't even know your name.'

She looked a little hurt. 'Hasn't Mark told you?' She took another drag, this time exhaling high into the air through pursed lips. 'You'll laugh.'

She muttered something under her breath.

Alex waited.

'Tracey,' she repeated.

'Am I laughing?'

'Probably are, inside. Joke name, isn't it, Tracey? Essex tart's name.'

'I don't think so.'

She turned to him, the first time he had seen her so intent. 'S'not about me, though, is it? It's all them others. It's what *they* think that counts. They hear Tracey, and . . . that's all they hear, isn't it?'

'Is that why you bunk off?' he asked. 'You get bullied about your name?'

'Nah. School's boring. S'more of a laugh out here.'

Alex went with the impulse. 'I think Tracey's a lovely name.'

She looked at him quizzically, frowning slightly. 'You can't have me or nothing, Alex. I'm with Mark.'

He cursed himself for blushing.

There was a commotion further down the high street. The three conquering heroes were running full-pelt out of the Meadows indoor shopping centre, then off in separate directions. Cannon's laugh ricocheted off nearby shops and offices.

'Shit!' Tracey swore, stubbing out her cigarette. 'Stupid pricks've been spotted.'

Sure enough, a burly looking uniformed security guard ran

179

out seconds later, looking all around for the fast-disappearing boys.

'What happens now?' Alex asked.

'We leave it ten minutes, then head back to Mark's place.' She took his arm, and steered him away from the panting guard. 'Just act natural, so he doesn't connect us with the others,' she whispered.

Which Alex had little difficulty in doing, caught in the thrill of the game. It felt good to be walking away slowly with a girl on his arm; he felt taller somehow, more confident.

In thirteen years, Alex Latimer had never felt so calm and accepted as he did making his way back to the shoplifter's den with a girl called Tracey by his side.

27

DS Samson led the ashen-faced man into the glaringly lit room, feeling Picket hesitate slightly at the sight of all the gleaming stainless steel.

After years on the force, the impact of the mortuary at police headquarters still had the power to jolt him. The overpowering combination of formaldehyde and cheap air-freshener would cling to him for days, a nauseating combination which refused to be showered clean.

'Do you want a seat, George?' he inquired softly, taking Picket's raised hand as a refusal.

Samson briefly acknowledged the others in the room, nodding slightly at the attending pathologist, and two narcotics officers from Ipswich CID standing quietly behind a steel-topped table covered by a small white sheet – in any other situation merely an institutional tablecloth. Except it wasn't only covering the table. A large, football-sized lump lay underneath, staining the bright-white cloth with seeping yellow patches.

After a suitably respectful pause, one of the other officers broke the uncomfortable silence. 'Mr Picket,' he said softly. 'Do you know why DS Samson has brought you here?'

'My son,' Picket replied softly. 'You think you've found my son.'

The officer nodded. 'I'm DI Stretch, and this is DS Manning, from Ipswich CID. Dr Michaels from HQ is the one in the apron.'

'I wish I could say I was glad to meet you,' Picket replied tersely. 'Where's Mikey? My Mikey?'

DI Stretch cleared his throat. 'Mr Picket . . . erm, there's no other way to put this, I'm afraid, but the body we suspect might be Mikey's . . . wasn't intact when it was found.'

Picket turned to Samson, confused. 'Not intact?'

DS Samson scratched his forehead and took a sudden unnecessary interest in the dark-grey floor.

'It had been,' Stretch continued, voice almost at a whisper. 'Dismembered.'

Picket paused, nodded, looked at the cloth-covered lump. 'And this is all you have?'

DS Manning nodded. 'It's all we need for you to perform a positive ID. The rest is . . .' He tailed off, regretting his attempt at tact.

'The rest is what?' Picket asked.

Samson took Picket's arm, moved him a little closer to the table. 'George,' he soothed. 'Let's just take a look, shall we? Hopefully, it isn't Mikey. Hopefully, it's someone else. But we need to find out, don't we? Just to be sure, eh?'

Picket straightened, stood tall, well-practised in holding everything in while doing his duty.

Dr Michaels slowly lifted the stained veil, revealing the ash-grey dampen head. Samson took just the briefest of looks, wondering whose job it had been to give the ruined thing an immaculate centre-parting. The mouth refused to close, revealing smashed teeth and deeply cut gums.

George Picket remained silent, poised over the head, swaying slightly.

Swallowing back the acrid taste of vomit in his mouth, Samson placed an arm round his shoulder.

'George,' he asked solemnly. 'Is this . . . ?'

Picket's sudden howl of anguish was heard by nearly a quarter of the building.

Twenty long minutes later, Samson sat with Picket, Stretch and Manning in an upstairs office. The numb Chairman nursing a cracked mug of tea, stared blankly into the middle distance.

DS Manning sat pen poised over an open notebook and a green wallet-file on a nearby desk. The mourning father sat between the two other officers.

'George,' Samson said quietly. 'DI Stretch needs to ask you some questions. Is that OK? Do you feel up to it?'

'Where's the rest of my son?' Picket slowly replied, voice a catatonic whisper.

'Mr Picket,' Stretch explained. 'Mikey's death forms part of an ongoing inquiry into the importation, sale and distribution of class-A drugs in the Ipswich area.'

Picket's red eyes met Samson's. 'What's he talking about?'

'Please, George. Just listen.'

'I want my boy back. Now. All of him.'

'I know, George.'

Stretch stood in an effort to distance himself. 'The nature of this inquiry is both long-term and highly confidential.'

Picket turned to all three. 'What the hell's this got to do with my son?'

'We have reason to believe Mikey was caught up with some pretty unsavoury types, Mr Picket.' Stretch paused, timing his next question. 'Do you know anything about that?'

Picket shook his head, shoulders beginning to twitch and shake with the effort of maintaining whatever dignity remained. 'I just want Mikey back. All of him. I couldn't give a stuff about "confidential inquiries". I just want my son.'

'Appreciate that, Mr Picket. And as soon as is feasible, we'll be arranging for transport . . .'

'When?'

Stretch sat back down, opened the green wallet, placed a series of black-and-white mug-shots on the table. 'Do you recognize any of these men?'

Picket glanced at them briefly, then shook his head.

'Are you sure?'

'Look, what is this?'

Manning pointed at the photo on the extreme right, a classically good-looking middle-aged man, the only one of the photographic line-up that smiled confidently back at the police camera. 'You might know this guy, Mr Picket. Your son shared a flat with him.'

Picket stared without looking.

Stretch took up the story. 'His name's Dave Higgs. This was taken a few years ago, but his appearance hasn't changed

183

a great deal. His brother, Martin Higgs, is a well-known drug-pusher in the Ipswich area.'

Samson watched the bewilderment spread slowly over Picket's face. He wondered if now wasn't the time to suggest the man had had enough shocks for one day, and needed a lift back home to be left in peace. However, as a detective, he also knew full well the value of questioning Picket now, and not at a later date. In a few days' time, the memory could well be traumatized by the horrific ID. So he simply had to watch, hating every second, his own mind still paused in a bad video freeze-frame of Mikey Picket's sagging, severed head.

'Mr Picket,' Stretch persisted gently. 'Mikey lived with a man intimately connected to the drugs trade. For some years. Our own undercover informants tell us Mikey was sometimes used by these people as muscle. Can you understand that?'

It was too much, a revelation too far. Picket buried his face in both hands and began to weep. Samson put an arm round him. There was nothing to do but wait. Stretch sucked on his bottom lip, while Manning doodled in the corner of his notebook.

Five minutes later, the Chairman had managed to compose himself, taking deep breaths and sips of sweet tea as instructed. 'I suppose I just didn't want to know,' he said eventually. 'Mikey lived his own very private life, and I respected that. He seemed to be making his own way in the world, doing well for himself. I –'

'Mr Picket,' Stretch interjected. 'Every one of our undercover boys who knew Mikey knew him to be a fine young man . . .'

'Always willing to please. Always smiling . . .'

'But from the information we've gathered, Mikey was killed as an example to others.'

Picket stiffened.

'Seems he'd done something to incur the wrath of the other gang members. Sort of executed, really.

George Picket vomited lukewarm tea on to Samson's shoes.

'It's like this,' Stretch explained a short time later. 'Gangland's a strange place. Archaic. These villains spend their lives breaking our rules, but living fanatically by their own. And it's not only the Irish who deliver punishment beatings. It's all about face, credibility. The whisper was that Mikey had done something to incriminate the gang.'

'I just can't believe a word of it,' Picket replied quietly. 'Not my Mikey. No. Never.'

Stretch nodded sympathetically. 'The problem with gangs and credibility is that it has to be maintained, Mr Picket. Whatever the cost. They have to be seen as ruthless, or else other outfits will cash in on their action.'

Picket nodded in vague understanding. 'So he was murdered by his friends?'

'A couple of months ago, one of our sources heard about a big shipment of cocaine coming in. Word was Martin Higgs would take delivery, cut it, wrap it, pass it to the pushers. We got ready to arrest Higgs and his boys in the act, in possession. In the end, the raid found nothing. However, Higgs must have been wondering about the tip-off. We think maybe someone told him your boy Mikey was our source.'

'Mikey? An informer?' Picket replied coldly.

Stretch shook his head. 'It was one of ours.'

'So he died for nothing?' Picket spat angrily, hands beginning to shake as he twisted the cotton hanky over and over. 'Because some ghastly drug-dealing piece of filth thought he was one of your so-called grasses? Is that what you're telling me?'

'It's a possibility, Mr Picket. Yes.'

'And they murdered him for that? A suspicion?'

Stretch coloured slightly. 'From what we know about Mikey,' he added falteringly, 'your son would have been easy to . . . blame for something like that. Perhaps he was easily led.'

'And damn easily killed,' Picket replied. 'Why the hell didn't you do something about it? Where were your bloody undercover men when my son was being murdered, eh? Where the hell were they? Answer me, goddamn you! Why did you let him die!'

Stretch looked away. 'I'm sorry, Mr Picket. Very sorry. Truly.'

185

Picket sniffed loudly. 'Such an easy thing to say. But you'll catch these animals, won't you? You know their names, your precious informers or damned undercover agents must know who's responsible for my Mikey. You will catch them, won't you?'

'I'm afraid . . . it's not that simple.'

'What?'

'As I said, Mikey's death comes in the middle of a confidential ongoing oper –'

'Yes. Yes. Yes,' Picket interrupted angrily, flapping his hands. 'I heard all that claptrap earlier.'

'I'm asking you to be patient, Mr Picket. If we move in on those we suspect of killing your son, chances are the whole gang will clam up, go to ground, cease operations, leave them free to start up elsewhere. Please, I'm asking you to give us time. We're planning on catching the whole gang, not just the one or two minions who murdered Mikey.'

Picket looked aghast. 'And in the meantime, I do what? Bury what remains of my boy in a shoebox and wait for you to swoop?'

Stretch's silence said it all.

'And all the while Mikey's killers are free, breathing the air he should've –'

'Mr Picket,' Manning cut in. 'All we're asking for is a few weeks, three months at the outside. We've got a lot invested in this operation. We have to move very cautiously.'

Picket turned on the younger officer, face puce with rage. 'And I had one hell of a lot invested in my son, you shit-heap!'

'Yes, sir. Of course, sir.'

'We're asking that you don't talk to anybody else regarding this matter,' Stretch continued. 'Any loose talk could have unknown repercussions elsewhere. Please, believe me, we want to catch the men that did this to your son. But we have to do it our way. I can't stress this enough.'

Picket rose, walked towards the door, even managed something of a smile, a thin ironic grin exorcized of all kindness. 'It's like he never existed, isn't it? My son – my Mikey.'

Samson rose too, opening the door for the coldly staring

man. 'If you wait for me in reception, George, I'll drive you back home.'

'All he wanted to do was please.'

'I know, George.'

'And he's dead. Just like that.

'I'm very sorry, George.'

'Is that all you lot ever say?'

Samson cleared his throat, watching as the remaining two CID men packed away their things. 'We might have a problem with George,' he said uneasily.

'How so?' Stretch asked, pulling on a light-grey overcoat.

'Thing is, he's something of a local celebrity at present.'

'Go on.'

'There was this article about him in the *Observer* a few weeks back,' Samson explained, watching the two men exchange glances. 'Some kids were hassling him on his allotment. He thought we weren't paying it enough attention. One night they torched the old guy's shed.'

'And this made the *Observer*?' Stretch asked, puzzled.

'Point is, he's rather sensitive to what he sees as police inactivity.'

Manning sighed. 'And doubtless he's got some poxy little reporter friend to go running to, right?'

Samson nodded.

'Well, you just make sure he doesn't,' Stretch instructed. 'One word from him could compromise months of under-cover work. This whole bloody business is one fucking big headache I could well do without. Tell Picket nicely to can his opinions. The last thing I need is a double-page spread in the bloody Sundays alleging negligence over a severed head.'

'I'll try, but –'

'But what, Sergeant?'

'It's just that I know the reporter and –'

'Fine,' Stretch snapped. 'Tell him we're slapping D-notices on the lot. In fact, give me his number, I'll ring the *Observer* myself.'

'He's . . . er . . . a local man. Freelance.'

'You deal with it, then.'

'I'll do my best.'

'Your best?' Manning asked from behind his guv'nor's shoulder.

Samson swallowed hard. 'Well, I think he may know about Mikey's disappearance already.'

'Fuck's sake!'

'He contacted me just after the article came out, wanting to trace the lad. Picket had been to see him voicing concerns. Apparently, he was still reluctant to contact Uniform at New Street, following the shed-fire thing.'

Stretch frowned as he took it all in. 'And don't tell me, you're the guy who rang up our nick asking about Mikey, right?'

''Fraid so,' Samson replied, colouring slightly. 'The reporter asked if I could help. I just did it as a favour.'

'And do you realize how stupid that was?'

Samson cleared his throat, trying to suppress an urge to smack Manning straight in his arrogant little mouth. 'Not at the time, no,' he replied quietly. 'It all seemed quite innocent.'

'Let me tell you about "innocent",' Stretch patronized. 'If our Uniform boys had taken your phone call seriously, they could've instigated an inquiry which would've jeopardized the whole operation.'

'Right.'

'Do you know why, Sergeant?'

The room was shrinking all around. Samson simply wanted to get out, breathe some of the fresh air denied Mikey Picket.

'Because,' Stretch continued menacingly. 'If word had spread to the mob that Uniform were looking for Mikey Picket, they would most likely have done a runner. Every bastard one of them.'

'Leaving us nothing,' Manning added.

'And a shit-lot of explaining to do to our super,' Stretch concluded. 'Get it?'

'Sure. I apologize.'

'Just tie Picket down. Tie down the reporter. Tie everything fucking down until after we've run this mob in. That's when we'll start asking about who whacked Mikey, OK? And not a bloody moment before.'

Samson turned and left the room, unsure what was worst – seeing the severed head, or taking the bollocking from Stretch and his leering sidekick. Either way it had turned into another in a long line of shit days, which wasn't over yet. He still had to take George Picket home.

And something secretly bothered him with the old gardener's reaction to the news that his dear son was caught up with heavy villains. He'd watched carefully as the Chairman had acted in total shock to the revelation.

But according to what Jack had told him, Picket had gone to see the reporter because of a phone call Mikey had made telling him that people were after him.

Leaving the uneasy suspicion that perhaps Picket already knew a good deal more about his son's mysterious life than he was prepared to let on.

Begging the question – Why was he so reluctant to say anything about it?

28

Jack, Amy and Alex Latimer sat on hastily convened, creaking, wooden school chairs in the headmaster's office. The room reeked of institutional polish, yet still smelt stale, like a second-hand bookshop fallen on hard times.

Jack found himself playing with his hands, hating school processes, the isolating resonance of the room. He'd spent too long in headmasters' offices as a kid to feel even vaguely comfortable there as an adult. He shot a weak smile at Amy, who returned it before quickly looking away.

Mr Rogers cleared his throat and took charge. Outside, a group of freezing boys practised football-dribbling skills on a hard asphalt playground, drilled by a tracksuited PT instructor with a shrill whistle and a less-than-amusing line in personal insults.

'Firstly,' Rogers began awkwardly. 'I'd like to thank you all for attending this meeting.'

'Pleasure,' Jack returned unconvincingly, turning to his son, noticing how the boy looked away, couldn't or wouldn't meet his eye. He wanted so much to be able to put his arm reassuringly round Alex's shoulders, deal with the issue somewhere else, just the three of them, a thousand mental miles from the official pomp. But they'd been summoned, forced to attend by an impersonal letter left blank for the relevant pupil's name. Then crudely handwritten, the blue biro'd 'ALEX LATIMER' jarring with the word-processed script. Similarly, they too were being 'processed', dealt with according to the educational trust's bum-numbing procedures, as if they were all to blame for the problem.

The head nodded. Smiled, though it was difficult to gauge

if he was enjoying his after-hours work, or merely following the corporate script such gatherings demanded.

'It's come to our attention,' he began. 'That young Alex here is perhaps unhappy with the school, and we all hope that this meeting might find a way of resolving this matter to everyone's satisfaction.'

'By doing what, exactly?' Amy asked pointedly. 'Chaining him to the desk?'

'Perhaps,' he replied, turning to a young blonde on his left. 'I'd better introduce you to Amanda Forrest, who not only teaches geography, but has also been instrumental in setting up many of the school's links with external resources.'

Miss Forrest cleared her throat. 'Let's begin by getting Alex's viewpoint. Alex, with eleven recorded absences in the last three weeks, this is your chance to tell all of us why you're doing this.'

Alex said nothing, chewing at his bottom lip as if preventing a bout of nervous laughter.

'Well, Alex?' his mother prompted.

'Just am, I suppose.'

At which point Jack was a split second from walking his son from the room, taking him back to his place, seating the boy down in front of the computer before embarking on another bout of Zelda. Father and son together, he reasoned, connecting, making up for lost time, struggling for the intimacy Anwar had so effortlessly achieved. What purpose was this farce going to achieve? And, more to the point, why did he feel the beginnings of a massive guilt-trip? Fear of being pointed out as the father who fled the nest, instigator of his son's current truanting? Jack chewed down hard on his tongue, the short silence feeling like a lifetime.

'Is it because you're bullied here?' Mrs Forrest asked.

'No.'

'You're a bright boy. Articulate. There must be a reason.'

'Why?' Alex challenged. 'Why does there have to be a "reason" for everything? You wouldn't get it, anyway.'

'Alex,' Jack said, transported back, seeing himself leaving the house, shutting the front door, walking quickly down the path, away from his receding son's wails. 'We simply want to help. You know truanting's no good. Not in the long run.'

Silence from the boy.

'We're all worried about you,' Jack pressed.

Alex frowned, felt the dead weight of the room's expectations, the gulf between his life and theirs. What was the point even in trying to make them understand, the joy he felt every time he walked back out through the gates? He muttered something inaudible at his feet.

'Didn't catch it, Alex.'

He looked up, sighed, then quietly addressed them all. 'You're only worried for you. School because I'm not conforming; Mum because if this gets out it'll taint the image of the perfect Agony Aunt; and you, Dad – because . . .'

'Because of what?' Jack asked.

The thirteen-year-old eyes begged for understanding. 'Because you're always too caught up in your own stuff, Dad. You just want me to be a good little boy. No waves, no ripples, nothing for you to worry about.'

'Perhaps,' Amanda Forrest interjected. 'You don't feel listened to, Alex. You don't feel your problems are understood. Growing up is often a very painful and confusing time for . . .'

'I'm fine.'

Jack nodded slowly. 'Maybe it would help if you told us what *we* could do, eh?'

'Perhaps there's an after-school activity which would interest you?' Amanda Forrest encouraged, making notes. 'The computer club, for instance. I know you like gaming . . .'

'I said I'm fine,' Alex insisted.

'But your behaviour isn't,' the head added. 'Truanting won't be tolerated. Not in this school.'

Jack trawled through his own truanting youth to glorious, hazy days spent by the river with his pals, drinking cider and laughing hysterically at their audacity. Real days. An escape, a chance to exist outside the system, ride the waves of teenage rebellion, gain notoriety, a reputation, girlfriends. And maybe this was simply Alex's turn. Like father, like son.

Yet he also suspected this was different. Because as far as he knew, Alex didn't have a gang of pals to share the experience with. Alex was, and always had been, something of a loner. So what in God's name was he getting up to on his days off? And with whom?

Too many questions, but maybe, given a little more time together on the computer, the game might inadvertently throw up some answers, small talk in between bouts, genuine therapy gradually born from something trusting; in his flat, safe, maybe even with Amy, away from the stifling school office.

'You can always talk to me, Alex,' Jack tried, without realizing he'd reached out and held Amy's hand. 'And your mum. Hell, we're there for you, you know that. Whenever you want.'

Alex looked at the four faces. 'Like I said. You just don't get it, do you?' he said eventually.

'At which point,' Jack said angrily. 'He just clammed up. Didn't get another word out of him. Jesus, I felt so . . . fucking useless.'

He stood, wandered into the tiny kitchen, opened two bottles of beer, brought them both back into the living room, handing one to Kenny Samson, before taking a large swig from the other.

'He'll learn to love you,' the yawning detective replied. 'In the end. Take my youngest boy. Seven, now. I can't wait to see him when the shift finishes, read him a story, just snuggle up to his warmth. Then he'll tell me how much he hates me. Guts me every time. Until he suddenly hugs me out of the blue. But that's kids. The best bloody millstones.'

Jack sat. 'Listen, and I'm only saying this because I'm pissed . . .'

'You don't have to, really,' Samson replied uneasily, trying to recall the local cab company phone numbers.

'I've got a wife who I don't know if I love or I hate, a son who I just can't get through to, a friend who's dying and I'm living here, in this poxy dump, trying to kid myself that everything's fine, a million other men would've done the same when they walked out. Me, Jack Latimer, the big hero. Ruthless exposer for the common good. Can't sort shit from sugar any more.' He paused, took another long pull at the bottle. 'I'm waffling, aren't I?'

Samson maintained a respectful silence. A dog began barking somewhere close by, silenced by an angry owner.

'I mean,' Jack persisted, the alcohol warming him to the melancholic theme. 'How in God's name do you get through to a kid like Alex? I know he hasn't had an easy ride, but he can't stand being analysed, either. Gets enough of that from his mother, poor kid. Shit, I remember when I first met her. Just another junior PA scratching a living on Fleet Street. Stunner. Obviously going places. Spent forty minutes listening to all my woes, then ten minutes putting them right. Woman's a goddamned genius.' He rubbed the bridge of his nose. 'But I was drawn back, perhaps more in awe than in love. And that's not a good beginning, is it, Kenny?'

'Absolutely not.' Samson's mind was elsewhere. 748451 – Whizzcabs, chances are he'd be out of Jack's meandering downer and tucked up in bed inside forty-five minutes.

'But we got by, Amy and I,' Jack was saying. 'So fucking what if we weren't at it like rabbits every night, what couple is?' He finished the beer. 'Know what I think?'

'I have this horrible feeling you're about to tell me.'

'I think . . . I think Alex is just like me, Kenny. Another running man. First sign of a crisis and he's off, whether it's the damned computer or truanting, he's gone. And . . . I guess that's me, too. Fought for principle at Wapping and lost – never got over it, perhaps. Kind of difficult to be the matinée-idol dad when your son knows you're a quitter.'

Through the blurred confusion, another face entered Jack's spiralling mind. Another father missing his son. George Picket, who'd asked for help, swallowed his obvious pride and trusted Jack to find his own flesh and blood.

Jack managed an ironic smile. 'Jesus, Kenny, I bet the Chairman wouldn't have been so keen to ask me if he knew my track record. Hardly impressive, is it? Man comes to me wanting to trace his son, and, to be honest, I can't seem to find my own these days. I better go and talk to the guy. What with one thing and another, he just slipped my mind.' He began pulling on his overcoat.

'What now?' Samson asked a little nervously. 'It's nearly half-nine.'

'No time like the present, Kenny,' Jack winked. 'Old editor taught me that. You fancy coming along?'

Samson shifted uncomfortably. 'No.'

'Shame. His house is a cross between Amityville and the Ovaltinies.'

'I'll give it a miss, thank you,' Samson quietly replied, already familiar with the gloomy Fourth Avenue home after dropping Picket back there following the hideous head identification up at HQ. 'Maybe you should too, eh? At least till the morning.'

Jack thought about it. 'If I didn't know you better, Kenny Samson, I'd think you didn't want me to go up there.'

'I don't. It's too late, and you're pissed.'

'No other reason?'

''Course not.'

Jack shrugged. 'Share a cab, then? We'll flag one down at the top of the road.'

'I guess,' Samson sighed, rising slowly to his feet. Somehow, he couldn't crush the feeling that Latimer was about to open a very rotten can of worms indeed.

And, as he'd been warned, if they slithered out in his direction, Detective Sergeant Kenny Samson might be starting the new millennium in a bloody uniform again.

He silently prayed Picket would do as asked – and keep his mouth shut about the death of his son.

29

It was nearly ten when Jack stepped unsteadily from the cab and turned to face Picket's house. A single light in an upstairs bedroom was the only clue to any occupancy. It was a bitter night, his breath icing the moment it left his beer-dried throat.

Steeling himself, he walked slowly up the short curving gravel path to the sturdy front door, past a large iron skip half full of discarded timbers, splintered window frames and rotting floorboards, evidence to the renovations Picket had mentioned. Jack wondered how the Chairman could ever call the place 'home', it seemed so austere, gothic, out of place with its more modern neighbours. Yet here was the place of his birth, the same house he'd lived in all his life, trapped, perhaps, within its dark bricks and sash windows.

He pushed the doorbell four times before it opened. Picket stood tall in the gloomy hallway, dressed in a paint-splattered overall, flecks of dust and plaster in what remained of his hair.

'Just thought I'd drop by,' Jack tried. 'Sorry it's so late. Not disturbing you, am I?'

'You're here, aren't you?' Picket replied. 'So of course you are.'

'Hard at work on the DIY?'

'A fair assumption.'

'I'd kill for a cup of tea, George.'

'Best come in, then.'

He followed the amateur builder past another heap of wood and plasterboard into the ancient kitchen. A precautionary stick of double-strength chewing gum was going some way to reducing the beer-breath; and simply entering the house seemed to have sobered him in just the one step. He began to wonder if Samson wasn't right – maybe it was a damned stupid idea to see the man so late. 'I've tried ringing you, George, several times.'

'Phone's disconnected,' Picket replied icily. 'Cut off. They say my system needs replacing, modernizing. For a sizeable fee, of course.'

'Bunch of crooks,' Jack replied, uncomfortable with the small talk, deciding to plunge right in. 'Any news on Mikey? I tried a few leads but –'

'He's dead,' Picket interrupted curtly.

It was a hammer blow. Picket stirred two stewed teas, sipped at his, leaving the other on the side for his guest. 'Chances are he was already dead when I came to see you.'

'Jesus, George, I –'

'And they don't want me talking to you, either,' Picket calmly added, moving back out into the hallway.

Jack followed, shocked, confused. 'Who doesn't want you talking to me?'

'The police. Said I'd be jeopardizing a long-standing investigation.'

'The police are involved?' The penny dropped – Kenny's reluctance to come visiting.

Picket began climbing the stairs. 'I think it's procedure in a murder case, Mr Latimer.'

'Murder?' Jack exclaimed, spilling his tea on the threadbare stair carpet.

'They call it murder. I call it an execution.'

'Mr Picket. George, I . . . Mikey's dead? Murdered? I just can't –'

'Hush!' Picket suddenly ordered, silencing Jack's verbal confusion with a raised hand. 'Did you hear that?'

'What?' Jack replied, searching the gaunt haunted face for clues. He heard nothing – but it was obvious the Chairman did.

'There! Listen. Another one. Laughing. Did you hear it? Did you?'

Jack gave a mute apologetic shrug. 'Got dicky ears, George,' he quickly invented, mind racing. Murdered? He said his son was murdered? 'Doctor says I should have them syringed, but . . .'

'Little sods.'

A short silence. 'Er . . . who, George?'

Picket slowly clicked his tongue against the roof of his mouth. 'Kids, Mr Latimer. Damn kids.' He stood stock still, as though lost in thought. Seconds later he returned. 'Come, see what I'm up to.'

Shocked, bewildered, Jack mounted the last few stairs, following Picket as he cautiously entered what would have been the large front bedroom.

'Careful as you go,' Picket warned nonchalantly. 'Place is a death trap.'

Jack entered the bare room. 'Wow,' he said, whistling in admiration. 'You've been busy, George.'

'Had to. Mind's not right when it's not occupied. Wanders all over the shop. Same when my mother died. Hell of a year. Most would've cracked up, Mr Latimer. Not me. Set to finishing the conservatory, and I'd never laid a brick in my life. Read books about it, you see? It's all there, if you look hard enough – all the knowledge in the world. Half the problem today – no one bothers looking. Too damn lazy, the lot of them.'

Jack took two careful paces back towards the stripped wall, distancing himself from the substantial hole which had once been floor. He craned his head a little, peering over into an equally bare room below. 'There's no floor, George.'

'Joists were rotten. Timbers were too old, eaten by wood-worm. Damn liability, really. Lucky the bed didn't fall right through during the night. Hell of a thing that would've been, eh? Waking up covered in dust in another room entirely.' He began to laugh. Then stopped suddenly.

'Is this safe?' Jack, who'd never felt comfortable with any height which could be measured in feet rather than inches, asked. 'I mean, is anyone helping you with this? It looks heavy, dangerous work.'

'I manage,' Picket replied, voice echoing off the bare walls. 'It's an old house, simply constructed. Just a matter of taking out sections of the old joists, fitting some new ones to length, then covering with plasterboard. Besides, it's not as if I've got anything else to do. Thought I'd convert this lot into student bedsits. Then move, retire on the proceeds. Maybe down south, the coast.'

'But you've lived here all your life, George.'

'Good a reason as any not to die here, then.'

'Your boy, Mikey . . . ?'

'What of it?'

'Do they know who did it, who . . . ?'

'Killed him?'

Jack nodded.

Picket ushered the relieved reporter from the room back downstairs. 'I had to identify his body. No, correction, Mr Latimer. His head. They put his head on a table, and I had to say, "yes, that's my son".'

Jack stared back, incredulous. From anyone else, the story would have been laughable; crude imaginings from a deranged mind, yet somehow instinct told him Picket had been there, seen it, was telling it all as it had happened.

Picket took him into the dowdy living room, lit by a single bulb and a dying fire. Jack sat next to the glowing embers. Picket sat silently in his armchair.

'I just can't tell you how sorry I am, George. It's truly terrible news. Awful.'

Picket nodded, staring intently at the barely smoking fire. 'They took it away, afterwards, repacked it in ice, or something. Stuck it in a freezer, can you believe that? God only knows when I'll even be allowed to see the rest of him. Or bury him. I've been on to them. Pure farce. Me standing in a stinking phone box talking to uniformed wets about when I could possibly have the rest of my son's body back.'

Jack cleared his throat, unable to uncrease the frown which he'd worn for the previous five minutes. On the one hand he really felt for the guy, genuinely believed the incredible story. Yet on the other, a gradual professional opportunity loomed. The bizarre tale of the frozen head had all the hallmarks of a potential reporter's payday.

Picket smiled coldly. 'They say it's a suspicious death, Mr

Latimer. I'll have to bide my time. Coroners need to give their verdict. So Mikey stays where he is, bits of him apparently scattered all over the place.' He turned to Jack. 'Do you have children?'

'One, a son,' Jack replied, feeling a sudden desire to hug Alex close the next time he saw the boy. Very close. 'George, can I ask you why the police didn't want me involved?'

It took the Chairman several moments for the question to register, several more for an answer to be readied. Even in the half-light of the rekindled fire, Jack noticed the deep-sunken bloodshot eyes rimmed with wrinkled bags. He looked half-dead. More than half, Jack decided, closer to three-quarters.

'Something about a drugs gang in Ipswich,' Picket mumbled. 'Apparently Mikey may have known someone on the fringes of it. The police think Mikey was blamed for informing, so he was killed as an example to others.'

Jack wished he'd brought his microcassette, wondered how easy it would be to pop back round first thing in the morning for a more in-depth interview. 'And the police told you all this?'

Picket nodded. 'Had to, really, didn't they? Needed me to identify the . . . Knew I'd ask questions, so they told me.'

'But you aren't allowed to talk to the press?' Jack asked. 'Not even their press officer?'

'It's all hush-hush stuff,' Picket replied, voice beginning to crack. 'Apparently, they want to trap the whole gang. Point is, they can't be bothered to arrest my boy's killers. Probably don't think he was ever really that important, do they? After all, he ended up just a head, didn't he? Just a head in a freezer somewhere.'

'I'm just . . . stunned, George,' Jack said, wishing he still had Kenny waiting in the cab outside. There were so many questions. 'You're sure about that? They're not going to investigate Mikey's murder?'

'Thing I can't stop thinking about,' Picket said sadly. 'Is was he alive or dead when they . . . ?' He stared deep into the tiny, bright-yellow flames. 'Strange thing, time,' he said, frowning slightly. 'A few years back I held that tiny body in my arms and swore to love it, protect it, comfort it until my dying day. And it just slept, oblivious. Most beautiful thing in the world, a sleeping child on your chest. The warm weight of it – pure trust, that is, Mr Latimer.'

Jack endured the respectful silence for as long as possible. He was worried about the man, and the longer he looked, the less like Picket he appeared, at least the tall, confident George Picket who had first called in at Latimer Associates with a story about a shed fire and a police force who wouldn't listen. A story Jack had gone on to sell for close to a grand. Indeed, if Jack owed anyone anything, then George Picket, father in mourning, was surely high up on the list.

'Is there anyone who can stay with you, George? Relatives, friends, that kind of thing?'

'I'm fine.'

'My boy says that when I know he's not.'

'I prefer my own company. Plenty to do.'

'Might help,' Jack persisted. 'To have someone around. An extra hand with the DIY, perhaps?'

The Chairman suddenly turned to him, Jack noticing for the first time how dilated the ravaged pupils were. 'Listen. They're back! You *must* hear them now.'

Jack really tried, straining to catch something, anything – nothing. 'George, I really think . . .'

'Feeling and his rabble!' Picket's voice had risen an octave. 'Hounding me.'

'Feeling?'

'Brian Feeling. Hateful little sod. He's there now, outside.'

Jack rose, completely confused. 'I'll go and have a look, George . . .'

'No good! Tried it many times, Mr Latimer. They're too clever for that. Hiding, they'll be. Be damn glad to see the last of them, I will.'

'When you retire?' Jack fudged, fighting for time, struggling to bring the Chairman back on to a saner thread. If what he said about his son was true, it was little wonder he was mixed up. And as far as Jack could tell, there were no children's voices outside, nothing. 'To the coast?'

Picket nodded, calmer now, quick shallow breaths gradually slowing.

'You'll miss the allotment, though, I bet.'

'It's time to accept the losses, move on,' Picket replied, Chairman once more. 'I'll take Mikey with me, scatter his ashes on the beach. He always loved the beach.'

'Nice one, George.'

'And now,' said Picket, standing. 'I have a six-foot-square hole in my bedroom floor which needs attending to, so if you don't mind . . .'

'I could help,' Jack offered, without knowing why. He was crap at DIY, had a history of dangerous shelving units and black, hammered thumbnails.

Picket smiled. 'I saw you up there just now, cowering by the wall. You'd be a hindrance, man, and you know it.'

'Just thought I'd offer.'

'Charmed.'

'George, about Mikey's . . .'

Picket began walking from the room, across the hallway back to the front door. 'I shouldn't have even told you this much.'

'But you did,' Jack replied, slowly following until he drew level. 'The police won't investigate because it might interfere with some sort of drugs operation?'

Picket cautiously opened the front door, Jack watching as the Chairman's eyes narrowed, searching the quiet avenue. 'Like I told you, Mr Latimer. Feeling and his gang have disappeared. But they'll be back. Always are.'

Jack waited a moment before asking, 'Did you have any idea just what Mikey might have been getting involved with in Ipswich?'

'None whatsoever.'

He pulled his coat up against the cold, timed the question. 'Do you want me to look into all this, George?'

'Hardly your style, is it, Mr Latimer?'

'Sorry?'

'You couldn't find Mikey when you thought he was alive, could you?'

'No,' Jack quietly replied.

'So how in God's name do you intend to find his killers? Good night, Mr Latimer.'

30

At five past nine the following day, Jack made the call.
'Kenny?'
'Jack.'
'It's about Picket.'
The call DS Samson had dreaded. 'No, it's not.'
'Come again?'
'I mean,' Samson replied. 'It's a total no-go, Jack. *Nada*, sweet FA. I hear the name Picket once more, and I hang up.'
'Can I at least ask why?'
'As a reporter?'
'As a friend. Come on, Kenny.'
Samson sighed. 'Off the record, Jack, I'm that deep in the shit with the whole Picket deal that I'm going to have bends for a month coming out of it. Listen, I'm staring at seven unsolved burglaries, and the guv'nor wants results. I don't have time for this.'
Jack pressed on. 'Last night, Kenny . . .'
'Don't, Jack. Please.'
'He told me his son was dead. Murdered. Gave me some horror story about having to identify his son's head up at HQ, and the subsequent police reluctance to –'
'I'm going to hang up, Jack.'
'So it's true, is it?'
'No comment.'
'Kenny,' Jack begged. 'Please. I owe it to the old boy. He's shattered, going a bit barmy, if you ask me.'
'Just leave it, Jack. Really, I'm serious.'
'He said Mikey was killed because he was a suspected grass. It's becoming impossible to resist, Kenny.'

Samson took a deep breath. 'Listen, I've already had a slap for calling Ipswich on your bloody behalf looking for the kid. One more fuck-up and I'll be back in uniform. Just leave it.'

'And if I can't?'

'Ipswich are slamming D-notices on it. Whatever you write won't be printed, anyway. Not a damned editor in the land will touch it.'

Jack pressed on, unperturbed. 'Which means there's under-cover involved, right?'

''Bye-bye, Jack . . .'

'Picket says he's being denied the body.'

'It's an exceptional circumstance.'

'And?'

'That's it. End of the story that never was.'

But Jack was still at the beginning. 'Except that there's a head up at HQ belonging to a corpse that was most likely murdered by a drugs baron as a warning to other villains. An execution, Picket called it, and local CID refusing to investigate.'

'Merely cooperating with another force. Different thing entirely.'

Jack paused, marshalling his thoughts. 'OK, if it's a D-notice, then it doesn't make any difference if you tell me, does it? I'm hardly Mr Big of the *Daily Tabloid* lately, am I?'

Samson gave a short, sarcastic laugh. 'So what's your angle, then?'

'Concern – for Picket.'

'Bollocks.'

'True,' Jack insisted. 'I spent most of last night awake wondering – hoping – the whole story was a delusion. Only now I get the distinct impression it was all true. In which case . . .'

'You leave well alone, Jack.'

'So it's true, the head thing? The drugs investigation? You don't have to say anything, Kenny, I'll take a three-second silence as confirmation.'

Three seconds later, Samson said, 'Look, Jack, these coke-heads are nutters. A law unto themselves. They do shit, and sometimes it's just best left where it is.'

'So a villain bumps off another villain, the police heave a big sigh of relief that they don't have to get involved?'

Samson lowered his voice. 'These boys police themselves, Jack. I can't say any more than that. I don't *know* any more. Ipswich have put some men on the ground, if word gets round that there's an investigation into Mikey Picket's death, then the villains'll know something's wrong.'

'We're talking about a dead kid. A simpleton, by all accounts.'

'Hired muscle, Jack. Chances are your innocent local lad was also dishing the knuckle to order, too. Now, please, leave it alone.'

'Just like the police in Ipswich are doing, right?'

'They have their reasons.'

'Try telling that to George.'

'I think they already have,' Samson replied.

There was a moment's silence as DS Samson mulled over the pros and cons of an idea which had been slowly fermenting since his time with Picket up at HQ. In particular, the toe-curling few minutes spent alone with DI Stretch and the objectionable DS Manning, grinning sidekick whose face he'd felt such an overwhelming need to rearrange. But perhaps there was another way to get even, restore some credibility to his own guv'nor. Besides, he also knew Jack well enough to know the gung-ho reporter was no less likely to pass this story up than he was a free Chicken Vindaloo in the Rose of India. 'Jack?'

'Yeah?'

'When Picket came to see you about his missing boy, you said he seemed really upset.'

'S'right. The kid had phoned a few days earlier, said something about people being after him.'

'Which is why Picket came to you.'

'Point being?'

'He took it very seriously, didn't he?'

'Go on.'

Samson obliged. 'It could have been anything, couldn't it? The kid screwing around, or drunk, or out of his head on smack, or any number of things. But Picket knew, didn't he? He knew his son was in real danger from just the one phone call. How? How in God's name, how could he be so sure?'

'Unless he already had an inside line on young Mikey's lifestyle, right?' Jack replied, making notes. 'You're making my brain tick too fast, Kenny.'

Samson took a deep breath – plunged in. 'I'll level with you, Jack. It's an Ipswich case. I've already had my bollocks chewed over it. But put it this way' – he lowered his voice once more – 'if there is more to this than meets the eye, and if there's the vaguest chance I can get one over on those narco boys, then right now, my career badly needs to be in on it.'

'You want a favour from me?'

'Makes a change, doesn't it?'

'And I get the story?'

'We'll see. Maybe after the big bust has gone down, D-notices'll be lifted. Can't say any fairer than that.'

'Big maybe, Kenny.'

'Best I can do. But if you want it, you're on your own. I can't tell you any more. And if it gets heavy, I'm sticking to the fact that I warned you off, all the way. I mean that, Jack. It's your ball if you want to run with it.'

'I was always crap at ball games.'

'Never too late too learn.'

'But you never said that, right?'

'Not a fucking word of it,' Samson replied, before putting down the phone.

206

31

Young Tony Minks was hard at work in the corner of the cold living room, noisily saving the universe. It was, to all intents and purposes, the only animation in the lifeless environment, the seven-year-old's hands a blur as he twisted and thrust the hand-console towards the television screen.

Alex watched, coolly detatched, feeling his own adrenaline rise. It was a gradual, controlled process, outwardly invisible. But inside, he was beginning to seethe, adolescent anger rising with each mind-numbingly boring moment. Were these really the same people he'd actively sought out after reading about their exploits in his father's *Observer* article? The same listless bunch he'd first truanted for, seduced by the thrill of running with the gang, being a part of something so much more real and vital than school, home, the computer? Yet several weeks later, what did he have to show for the gamble? Days spent doing virtually nothing, because the others had decided it was 'too cold'. Pathetic. He knew it, Zelda would have known it, and perhaps, he tried hard to convince himself, now was the time to face it.

His mouth dried a little. He faked a yawn, turning his attention to the others – Tony's brother Damon lying on the floor, smashed, eyes shut, smiling; Mark Cannon and Tracey indulging in some lethargic heavy petting on the worn sofa opposite; Eve Adams reading from a recently shoplifted teen magazine, occasionally looking his way and blushing slightly. The article, as far as he could make out, was something to do with orgasms.

'Ever wondered what Picket's doing these days?' he began croakily, watching as Cannon's thin white hand made its way inside his underage lover's sweatshirt.

The ginger-haired youth broke away from the embrace. 'Fuck knows.'

'Maybe we should go up there, take a look?' Alex suggested.

A sneer appeared on Cannon's acne-flecked face. 'And maybe we shouldn't,' he said, attempting a lame imitation of Alex's voice. 'Maybe we'd rather stay here, instead of freezing our arses off hassling some old wanker.'

'I wonder if he's got a new shed up yet?' said Alex quietly.

Cannon turned to the excited games-playing child. 'Giblet! Will you turn that fucking thing off! Doing my head in!'

Tony Minks begrudgingly complied, sulking in front of the blank screen.

Cannon addressed Alex again. 'What are you saying, Posh-boy?'

Alex smiled. 'Suppose I'm just a bit bored, really.'

'So sorry,' Cannon replied sarcastically, kicking out at the prone figure at his feet. 'Hear that, Damon? Seems that Posh is bored. How about we organize a little afternoon cabaret for the chap? Something to take his mind off spending so much time slumming it with the proles.'

'OK,' Damon Minks replied hazily. 'Your brother got any more blow?'

'You're already too fucking loaded!' Cannon exploded angrily.

'Ah, come on, Mark,' Damon said. 'Skin up and loosen up, for Christ's sake.'

A kick flew into Damon's ribs, causing a pained gasp followed by an extensive coughing fit.

Tracey sniggered. Alex tried to watch the action impassively, ignore the fear beginning to knot his stomach. He'd be no match for Cannon in a fight, no match for any of them, girls included. 'Guess I shouldn't have said anything,' he conceded. 'Maybe I'll just be getting off now.'

Cannon smiled. 'Think you're better than us, don't you, eh?'

'No. It's just that . . .'

'What is it, Posh?' he asked, voice rising. 'You think we're going to weep buckets when you walk out of the fucking door? All we ever wanted was your money, for fuck's sake. You ain't never been one of us, no matter how much you try.'

'What's "us", then, Mark?' Alex fired back, amazed at his audacity. 'A bunch of sad little no-hopers trying to convince the world they're the voice of teenage rebellion?'

Cannon closed in fast, breath spilling over Alex's fear-filled face. 'No one's rebelling, you twat! We're living.' He pointed to Eve Adams, watching the escalating argument from behind the safety of the magazine. 'You're another one like her. Spending some time with the peasants, before pissing off back home to mummy in your fancy great houses. It's all a game, isn't it? A cheap thrill to hang out with the commoners for a while. Well, good fucking riddance, Posh. Piss off now, before I smack your smug little face out the front door!'

Alex glanced across at Eve, saw a kindness in her eyes, a brief connection that thrilled him, somehow gave him strength to go on. 'I just had an idea,' he stammered, voice cracking. 'Maybe we could all do something.'

'Such as?'

'I . . .'

'Well? Come on!'

'I don't know,' Alex said quietly, hating himself. 'Just something. Anything other than simply sitting around.'

'And suppose we don't want to?' Tracey challenged. 'S'pose we just want to do our own thing?'

'Whatever,' he weakly replied.

'Shit idea,' Cannon added with triumphant finality.

The room fell silent once more, while Alex still stood, floundering in a suffocating cocktail of anger and frustration, aware all eyes were looking, waiting for his next move. 'I'm going out,' he said eventually.

'Ta-ra, Posh,' Cannon replied cheerfully.

Alex turned and began walking towards the door.

'Wait a minute,' came a voice from behind him. 'Let me get my coat.'

A moment later, Alex and Eve walked away from the

decrepit terrace, the only sound distant traffic, their footsteps and a receding chorus of abuse and wolf whistles from those left behind.

32

Audrey Baxter had spent the last few weeks wrestling with her conscience. In some ways, she rather wished she'd never attended the Allotment Society meeting at the Chairman's house, hadn't been so easily flattered into minute-taking and tea-making. Not that she was the type to shrink from either the honour or the responsibility, no – it was simply that there were things that had been said which she'd really rather not have heard. Or, more to the point, *over*heard.

After, she'd been to see Bill Kent, the only other attending committee member on the night of the fateful AGM. Audrey felt a little ashamed to involve the sweet old man in any duplicity, but what else was she to do? Her mind swam each night, leaving her tossing and turning, unable to sleep. She simply had to know if Mr Kent had heard the same as she had. He was, after all, less able to eavesdrop than she, sitting in the back lounge as she had busied herself washing faded crockery while the Chairman answered the phone.

That phone call.

Why, Audrey asked herself a hundred times over, why hadn't she simply closed her ears, carried on at the sink, ignored the bizarre conversation? But no comfortable answers came – just an inner feeling that part of her was almost too desperate to know more about George, absorb some of his secretive background by fair means or foul. And this, she shamefully acknowledged, was foul. Eavesdropping, there was no other word for it, and regardless of the motive, the romantic intentions which may or may not have silenced her hands at the sink to catch more of the distant conversation, it was still deceitful.

Which she then compounded by visiting William Kent on the invented pretext of showing him the first draft of the minutes of the evening. He showed her into his well-ordered bungalow just a few doors up, but a long way in style, from the Chairman's house.

They chatted over tea, making small talk, the old man giving the handwritten notes a polite read-through.

'Seems fine to me,' he smiled, handing them back. 'Not that I know about these things. But I dare say George is a stickler for them. You'd be better asking him.'

'I will,' she said. 'I just wanted another's opinion, really. Just in case I missed anything vital.'

'Oh, I doubt that, Miss Baxter,' he replied, eyes twinkling. 'Very thorough, you strike me. Very thorough indeed.'

She blushed.

'Besides,' he went on. 'Wasn't as if we got that far down the agenda, really.'

'No.'

'Phone-call business seemed to upset him.'

'Yes.'

'Kids, I expect. Another one of their pranks. Nothing better to do than play tricks on the one man who's got the guts to call in the press and stand up to them. Shell-shocked, he was, when he got off the phone.'

'He didn't mention what had been said to you?' Audrey asked. 'Only I was in the kitchen at the time.'

'Never said a word,' Kent replied. 'But from the look in his eyes, I knew he was best left alone. He gets like that sometimes. All that living on his own, doesn't do a man any good. I sometimes think to myself maybe he needs a woman around. Some men do, no matter how much they might try and deny it.'

She blushed slightly, wondering if the kindly old man was attempting to act as matchmaker. 'And what does he say, Bill?'

He began to chuckle. 'I think George prefers to sow his seed on the allotment, Audrey.'

She called again, a week later, feeling wretched from lack of sleep, nights spent trying to summon the courage to phone the Chairman, then feeling an aching despair when told by the electronic voice that 'the number you require is no longer available'.

Had he moved, gone on holiday? Or worse still . . . ?

Three times, she'd nearly knocked on Picket's door, negotiating her way past the builder's skip, hearing the distant banging inside. But was it George, hard at work, or a local man, called in to work on the house while the Chairman secreted himself elsewhere? On each occasion she'd turned and walked away, unable to face the emotional gamble ringing the front doorbell would have been. Why didn't *he* make the first move? Or was it simply that she'd misread the signals, that his interest in her was purely platonic? Then again, there were the looks he gave her as she'd sometimes catch his gaze settling on her knee a fraction longer than a friend's would. Surely that betrayed an interest?

One Thursday night she decided the whole thing had become little more than a ridiculous obsession. She'd made the man a post-menopausal teenage crush. Vowing to herself that there was a whole town full of readily available gentlemen other than the dapper, elusive George Picket, she put on her best frock, drank three large gins, then went and sat for two hours in the Compasses on Broomfield Road, waiting to be swept off her feet.

As an act of mental exorcism, it proved more of a humiliation than a success. One old boy stinking of whisky asked her for a light, followed an hour later by a concerned neighbour asking her if she was 'all right'. She returned home half-drunk and weeping with frustration. It was useless, the Chairman had unknowingly wormed his way too deep into her affections. It was him, or nobody.

The second time she called round at Bill Kent's, there was no offer of tea, just a shocked old man with large watery eyes. He'd been to see Picket that very morning. The news was as extraordinary as it was appalling. Apparently his son Mikey was dead, and the Chairman just wanted to be left alone for while. Kent went as far as to say Picket had almost been quite rude to him, but he forgave him the outburst due to the tragic circumstances.

Audrey sat, gathered herself, fighting against the urge to rush straight round to Picket's house to offer both shoulders to cry on. Shock and sadness threatened to overwhelm her. On the one hand, she felt desperately sorry for George, whereas on the other, she guiltily acknowledged the creeping resentment she felt over his son's death. For if anything, his loss would surely build another barrier between the two of them.

'He'll come round, in time,' Kent said slowly. 'Terrible shock for him. For all of us. Mikey was such a nice young boy. Affable. A credit to his father.'

'How did he . . . I mean, what happened?'

Kent shook his head. 'Lord only knows. He's not talking, and it seemed rude to ask. Disrespectful.'

'I wonder if I should go and see him?'

'I'd leave it a while, Audrey.'

'Poor George. And so close to Christmas. It must be awful for him.'

'He'll cope. He always does. Throws himself into another project to take his mind off it.'

'The building work?' Audrey said. 'I've seen the skip.'

'Just like before, I'm afraid.'

'Before?'

'Lost his wife and mother in the same year, poor chap. Quite tested his mettle. George buried himself in finishing the conservatory at the back of the house. Made a damn good job of it, too. He'll pull through, don't you worry.'

But Audrey couldn't stop herself. Later that night, as she sat drinking coffee at two in the morning, all she heard was her mind replaying an earlier conversation – one that now, more than ever, she wished she'd never heard.

214

33

Jack extinguished the half-smoked cigarette, vowing that the fast-approaching millennium was the perfect time to chuck the weed in for good. Not that he considered the five, or maybe max ten-a-day habit to be life-threatening, it was simply that he didn't enjoy it any more. Anwar's grey, ruined face quietly grinned at him every time he lit up. New millennium, new start, he'd resolved. Time for the inhalers and nicotine-flavoured gum – a godawful prospect, by a smoker's standards.

The knock on the office door came at close to eleven. C.F. quietly opened it and ushered in a small, middle-aged, unkempt-looking man with short, wiry, blond hair.

Jack tried his best to offer a warm 'welcome to Latimer Associates' smile, but in truth, he could well have done without the interruption. He was waiting for another tip-off. The Nottingham Semtex tale had risen from its media grave of frustrating obscurity and provided Jack with the first concrete lead he'd had in close on six weeks. Word was that a bunch of heavies in Southend were considering using the almond-smelling putty for a possible bank job in the near future. Millennium Eve to be criminally precise. An ATM in the town centre, although, as Jack suspected, the blast might well be mistaken for pyrotechnic jollity, but chances were the thronging crowds would have emptied the things hours before the crims tried to. But that was the way it went with these people, Jack had often observed. The greatest plots derailed by inept planning, bungled forethought.

Then there were the residual guilt feelings he still har-boured over the Picket business, now relegated to the mental back-burner. The unspoken promise he'd half made to look into the Chairman's son's death. How in God's name was he going to do that? Just where would he start? Kenny wasn't going to be of any use, but seemed to be clandestinely sanctioning Jack's involvement. The whole situation had become as lifeless and impossible as the staring severed head which had begun to haunt his nightmares, mutating from an imagined Mikey Picket to Kenny Samson, George Picket, Jack, and once – when he woke screaming and covered in cold sweat – his own son, Alex.

So Jack had let it slide, despising himself on the one hand, devoting his energies to pursuing new stories on the other.

The stranger stood nervously by the door, C.F. closing it behind him. 'Mr Jack Latimer?' he asked, peering nervously beyond Jack, out into the bus station below.

'Please, take a seat.'

Jack watched as he did so, refusing to be parted from an expensive-looking rucksack. He had a depressing air of failure about him, as if he'd once enjoyed better times, and somehow life had conspired against him, robbed him of his former well-heeled existence. His complexion was flawless, hands soft, tipped with thin fingers white from the cold. As he spoke, Jack noticed a gold tooth dimly glinting on a yellowed upper set of teeth. Former Lloyd's name fallen on hard times? Jack wondered, offering another smile in an attempt to relax the man.

The visitor leant forward, whispering confidentially. 'Would it be possible to talk to you alone?'

'Alone?'

He motioned to C.F. discreetly. 'Without . . . ?'

'Er . . .' Jack shot an apologetic look at his solemn secretary. 'Any chance you could give us some space, C.F.? That lead about the hyperdermics found in the kiddies' playpark maybe needs looking into, yeah? Try the Drugwatch lot, see if you can squeeze a quote out of them.'

She nodded, put on her coat, left without another word.

The stranger waited several moments, listening as her steps receded down the stairs. 'It's about Mikey,' he suddenly blurted out.

Jack stiffened at the name. 'Mikey Picket? Who are you?'

'Higgs,' the stranger replied a little breathlessly. 'Dave Higgs. Mikey was my lover.'

With C.F. gone, it was up to Jack to fetch the coffees. Moments later, he returned with two scalding styrofoam cups filled with a passable imitation of Gold Blend.

'One advantage of working in this pigsty,' he said, placing both cups on his desk. 'Is the on-site caterers downstairs.'

Higgs said nothing, slurping from the cup, cradling it in both hands, gaining succour from the warmth.

'You said you were lovers?' Jack began, taking out his microcassette. 'You do know he's dead, don't you?'

'Well, if I didn't, thanks for breaking it so gently,' came the clipped reply. Another slurp of coffee. 'It's two grand for my side of things. Cash upfront.'

'Whoa', slow down, friend,' Jack said, mind racing. 'This is a tinpot operation. These coffees are on a tab so long it'd run from here to Colchester. I'm not in the buying-stories game.'

'Don't insult me!' Higgs unexpectedly shot back. 'I know how this shit works. You pay me the money, and you get a story to sell for twice as much. And I know full well others will pay the asking price if you don't. Your decision. Your call.'

Jack took a long, hard look at Higgs. 'How did you find me?'

Higgs settled. 'From the article about Mikey's dad. It all tied in. Fitted like some sort of ghastly jigsaw. I rang the paper, asked to speak to you. They gave me this address. That was close on a month ago, now. Since then, I've been mulling it over, trying to decide.' He closed both eyes. 'No choice, really, had to come.'

'Because you need the money, right?' Jack guessed.

Another nod.

Jack sipped his own coffee, feeling the tension tightening the back of his neck. Was he about to be conned, ripped off by a chancer? Or was the man the real deal, the fear genuine, an amazing chance to walk a little deeper into the murky waters of Mikey Picket's life? He thought hard for a moment before trusting to instinct. Something about the man's eyes convinced him, always darting – hunted.

'There's no way I can lay my hands on two grand, Mr Higgs,' he hedged. 'But please, tell me what you know, I'll see what I can do.'

'I need the money today. It can't wait any longer.'

Jack did some double-quick mental arithmetic. Maybe if he cut back on the Christmas presents . . . but two thousand? Ludicrous. However, one thing was certain, Higgs's nervous presence confirmed a theory Jack had nursed for some time – there was a good deal more to an apparently trivial act of juvenile arson than first met the eye. And Jack *was* intrigued to know Higgs's side of things.

'Fifteen hundred, then,' Higgs announced. 'The absolute minimum, Mr Latimer.'

'You're that desperate?'

'You have no idea.'

'You want to tell me why?'

'You going to pay for it?'

'A grand. Tops.'

Higgs sighed, nodded.

Jack turned on the microcassette.

Higgs cleared his throat, composed himself. 'First time I saw Mikey, my heart did a flip. Really, the guy was gorgeous, drop-dead stuff. Not classical, but the height of cute. A kind of kid's head on a prop-forward's body. Beautiful eyes, really trusting eyes.'

'When was this?' Jack asked.

'Summer ninety-five. He'd come up with some friends of my brother's, looking for some part-time action. And there was no doubt he was cut out for it. Real big, stocky, and willing, so very willing. Just ask Mikey to fetch, he'd be off before the words left your mouth.' There was a long pause. 'I loved him, Mr Latimer.'

'Tell me about your brother.'

'Martin's a shit,' Higgs replied bitterly.

'George Picket says he thinks Mikey was killed because he was singled out as a grass in a drugs gang.'

Higgs shook his head. 'Mikey wasn't a grass. No way. This

is going to sound bad but he didn't have the brains to be an informer. Believe me, he may have done a few bad things, but there wasn't a devious bone in his body. He was an innocent.'

'Simple, you mean?' Jack replied, recalling Picket's description of his son.

'Maybe. But not a mental case. Immature, I guess.'

'And people took advantage of that, I suppose?'

Higgs coloured slightly. 'I never did anything he didn't want to.'

'Because he was so desperate to please?'

'It was beautiful, what we had. Pure.'

'So how come he ends up a head on a mortuary table, Mr Higgs?'

'Oh, please!'

Jack apologized, aware he was the last person to criticize another's relationship. Yet something about the man irritated him, the demand for money, perhaps – or maybe something more, the genuine nature of the pained expression. If he was to be believed, then Higgs had loved and lost, really loved – but not enough to save the boy. A blind love, foolish, fatally flawed. Two men caught on the outskirts of a drugs ring, one dead, the other weeping crocodile tears laced with demands for money.

Higgs drained the last of his coffee, then took a deep breath. 'Martin had Mikey killed.'

'Your brother?'

Higgs nodded, spat the words. 'He's a ruthless bastard, always was. He heads up a coke ring in Ipswich. Twenty, thirty guys, from the boardroom down to the street. Made an absolute fortune from pushing Charlie for the last ten years.'

'What was your involvement?'

Higgs laughed. 'Me? Shit, take a look, honey. I'm a busted old queen who craps himself at the first sign of trouble. I had my uses, but handling, pushing and collection weren't amongst them. Martin used me like all the others, and I was too damn scared to split.'

'Used you?'

'Favours,' Higgs replied quietly. 'An operation like Martin's has many faculties, Mr Latimer, many potential leaks which have to be plugged.'

'And?'

He squirmed a little on his seat. 'Sometimes . . . Martin might ask me if I fancied someone. A copper, perhaps, who they thought might be useful to them.'

'Blackmail?'

'Some might call it that, yes.'

Jack sighed. 'And your end of the deal?'

'The flat, car, and as much nose candy as I could snort.'

'Kind of cheap, really.'

'We all have our price, Mr Latimer.'

'Go on.'

'Martin soon got word that Mikey was good at what he did.'

'Which was?'

'I think Martin would call it "company security". Mikey broke people's arms to order. Don't get me wrong, he didn't enjoy doing it.'

'Just wanted to please, right?' Jack replied cynically.

Higgs dropped his head. 'He was accepted, I suppose. Given nice things. I think he felt he was part of something, that he belonged, had friends.'

'Who subsequently killed him.'

'That was my fault.'

'Why?'

'Because I bottled it, Mr Latimer.' He took a moment to gather his thoughts, pressing his thumb down hard into his other palm. 'Martin had a big shipment coming in. Twenty k's packed into two holdalls, welded into a four-by-four arriving in Harwich on an overnight ferry from Oslo. Street value – close to two million.'

Jack's eyebrows raised a fraction.

'It was Martin's six-monthly order, took weeks to set up. Anyway, he thought the whole thing was safe, all the right palms had been greased, everyone was standing by. Then he gets word the police are planning a raid, intending to bust them with a couple of dozen armed pigs as the boys sat down to cut the coke for street sale. Martin panicked, sent someone round to my place with orders to stash the stuff somewhere until the heat was off.'

'He gave you two million quid's worth of cocaine?' Jack asked incredulously.

'He was freaking out,' Higgs explained. 'Didn't know who to trust. Picked me because I was family. Besides, it was hardly as if I was going to snort the lot. But I'll tell you this, I was terrified. I mean, there I was, suddenly taking care of two holdalls full of class-A drugs, knowing the cops could come knocking at the door at any moment.'

'And why didn't they?'

Another hollow laugh from Higgs. 'It was like something out of a Keystone Cops movie. Everything was happening so fast. The cops were down at the docks, tailing the four-by-four's every move as Martin and the boys set off in convoy. Somehow they managed to switch the holdalls, and forty minutes after it'd landed, I've got a cute kid in motorcycle leathers dumping it in my hallway. Next I get a coded call from Martin telling me to hide it real quick. They head back to a lock-up with the four-by-four, the cops charge in with guns and bulletproof vests to find Martin and the lads watching the footy, and laughing right back in their faces, as these furious little action men start ripping up everything in sight.'

'Guess they were none too pleased,' Jack said, visualizing the scene. 'You say someone tipped your brother off about the raid? Who?'

Higgs shrugged. 'Christ knows. Martin had a lot of sources. I really don't know, and frankly, I didn't want to know. I was happier not knowing. I had the flat, Mikey . . .'

'OK,' Jack pressed impatiently. 'So you're stuck with the holdalls. What happens next?'

Higgs sighed. 'I go to pieces. Literally, right there and then in the damn flat. I mean, I know Martin and the rest of the boys have most likely been pulled. Chances are it won't be long before I get size-twelve police boots come crashing through my front door. But it's like I'm paralysed, frozen. I can't think where the hell to drop the stuff. I'm way out of my depth, and going down for the third time. Whole thing's insane. It's a Friday night, and Mikey and I should've been out painting

221

the town bright pink, but instead we're facing ten to fifteen years for possession.'

'Let me guess,' Jack said. 'Good old dependable fall-guy Mikey fixes it for you?'

'It just happened so quickly,' Higgs replied, voice cracking slightly. 'One minute I'm there, talking to him, telling him how it's such a fucking mess – the next he's standing at the door with the bags, saying how everything's going to be all right, he knows the perfect place to stash the stuff. Then he's gone, out into the night.'

'The house wasn't being watched?'

'Not then,' Higgs replied sadly. 'And frankly, I was simply glad to have the coke gone. Ecstatic that Mikey had moved the damned stuff, not me. He'd taken the problem away, you see? Always trying to please.'

'And then?'

'Twenty minutes later, it's like they're reshooting *The Sweeney* in my apartment building. About six cars scream into the courtyard below, then there's all these pounding feet, before the front door's smashed in. In seconds I'm surrounded, staring into a dozen rifle muzzles, while others loot the place. After about half an hour of me telling them nothing, they take me to the nick, and I see Martin and the others for the first time.'

'And the police don't make the connection between the coke and the missing man – Mikey?'

Higgs smiled. 'Oh, they ask. Repeatedly. I tell them we've split up weeks ago, and I have no idea where the stupid shit is.'

'They accept this?'

'Had too, really. One of the officers grilling me knew Martin had some compromising video of him and me in a sauna that his wife wouldn't be too pleased about. Like I say, I had my uses. A porn pawn, I guess. I can see this copper starting to sweat a little nervously as I'm offering him sly winks, and surprise, surprise, he steers the interrogation right away from me. Beautiful, really.'

'Go on,' Jack said, trying to curb his own excitement. If Higgs was telling the truth, this was massive, a huge story.

'Martin had his legal man spring us, all eighteen of us. The cops looked sick as we left first thing Saturday morning. But what the fuck else could they do? The Charlie's nowhere to be seen, and without it, the case falls apart. Any suspicion they might have about Mikey is swiftly crushed when put into context.'

'Context?'

'Think of it from their side. What copper would honestly believe a major outfit like Martin's would entrust twenty kilos of Colombia's finest to a kid like Mikey? But, Jesus, that's how it happened, I swear.'

Jack nodded. 'You next see Mikey when?'

'Sunday night. He calls me from the car, and I'm terrified the cops have put a bug on the phone, or in the flat or something. So I'm using all the code words I can remember, praying something's going to get through to his lovely thick head. Which, of course, it doesn't. An hour later he walks through the door, and can't understand why I'm going mental, totally paranoid the police will come storming back any moment.'

'And do they?'

'No. I call Martin, who tells me that he's more or less sorted things out, and provided I've dropped the coke somewhere safe, everything's going to be OK. Inside sources say the police are getting their wrists slapped for the fuck-up, and as long as we all play good citizens, the heat will cool inside a month.'

'Did Mikey tell you what he'd done with the cocaine?'

'Wouldn't,' Higgs replied. 'God, I asked enough times, but those pretty little lips stayed shut tighter than a virgin's thighs. He wanted it that way, you see? Thought what I didn't know wouldn't hurt me. Stupid sod.'

Jack lit up, taking a moment to order events as he inhaled. 'And I suppose you were a little reluctant to tell big brother what had happened to his investment, right?'

Higgs followed suit, reached across the table for one of Jack's cigarettes without asking, then lit up from the most expensive-looking lighter Jack had ever seen.

'I was fast realizing,' Higgs continued, exhaling as he talked.

'That this old fag had gone out of the frying pan into the fire. I was terrified. Martin'd kill me if he knew. Literally. So I begged Mikey to let me know where he'd hidden it, frantically tried to work out a way we could sort it all out before Martin came looking for it.' A tear ran down an unshaven cheek. 'But Mikey wouldn't tell me. Said only he must know, that way it's safer for us both. And he's smiling all the time and trying to comfort me . . . and . . . oh God . . .'

Jack rummaged around in his pocket and handed the man a crumpled paper tissue. 'Another guess, Mr Higgs,' he said quietly. 'He brought it back to Chelmsford, and stashed it in his father's allotment shed?'

Higgs nodded, his shoulders shaking. 'That fucking shed. Jesus Christ.'

Jack gave him a minute to pull himself together, watching as Higgs fiddled with the empty coffee cup, tearing tiny pieces of white styrofoam as he spoke. 'Three weeks later, I get another coded call from Martin. They're coming round that night, and want the Charlie back. I've got the afternoon to fetch it. Only Mikey's not there, he's out with the other lads on a job, and I'm the silly tosser who's effectively lost two million, given the lot to a dumb blond.'

'You couldn't put Martin off until you'd spoken to Mikey?'

'No one puts Martin off, Mr Latimer. And besides, I knew then that it was all going to come out, because there's no way I'd have the time to coach Mikey into some convoluted lie that'd save our arses. Martin was going to know what I'd done, and I was history. He takes his business very seriously.'

'Oh, come on, Mr Hi –'

Higgs jumped in. 'Once, when I'd cocked up something or other, Martin told me it was my last chance. Next time, he'd have my arms broken, and he'd get Mikey to do it. Mikey was there, in the room at the time, and all he did was sort of blush, then nod. And I knew then that he'd do it. Mikey was just as afraid of Martin as I was.'

'Jesus.'

'So I split, got the fuck out of Dodge. Packed this rucksack, and ran. Shit, there was no way I was going to be there when Martin arrived. No way on earth.'

'But Mikey was, right?'

Higgs nodded, face crumpling again.

Jack played out an imagined version of the scene. 'Your brother asks for the cocaine, Mikey says he'll fetch it, Martin gets stroppy, wants to know where the hell you are, Mikey says he hid the drugs, not you. At which point . . .'

'From what I know, Mikey rang his father in Chelmsford,' Higgs moaned. 'Found out the fucking lot had gone up in a fire a week previously.'

'And then they kill him?' Jack asked, frowning. 'Right there in the flat?'

'I heard they took him to the garage.'

'The garage?'

'It's where . . . that sort of thing . . . happens.'

'Who told you this?'

'A friend.'

'One of the gang?'

Higgs nodded. 'Former lover. Said he owed it to me. Told me word was Mikey had told them this farcical tale about making the drop in his father's shed which was now ashes because some kids had burnt it to the ground. Martin was spitting blood, because he knew he'd be a laughing stock when the news got out. And believe me, Mr Latimer, gossip like that travels damn fast on the street. Other outfits would be pissing themselves laughing at him, and Martin simply isn't the type to lose face. After all, he'd just duped the cops, only to discover some brain-dead kid had lost the gear. So he had Mikey killed, by way of an example, a credibility restorer.' He began to chuckle, wiping away another tear. 'Imagine that, Mr Latimer. I mean, there's your news angle, eh? A couple of kids puffing away on a goddamned spliff just inches away from two million quid's worth of uncut coke. If they only knew.'

Jack passed him another tissue. 'Then you read my piece in the paper, right?'

'I was living rough, hostels and the like. Cut my hair, dyed it, that sort of shit. But in doing a runner, I'd forgotten all my credit cards. And there wasn't a chance in hell I'd go back for them. Chances were Martin thought Mikey's story was a crock of shit, and maybe I'd run off with the Charlie. It's a living fucking hell I'm in. I can't take a shit without worrying about the boys knocking on the cubicle door.'

'Which is why you need the money, for a plane ticket, presumably?'

'Give the man a gold star.'

'Why not sell the fancy lighter?'

Higgs's gaze dropped to his lap. 'Mikey gave it to me. It's all I have of him.'

'Chances are it'd be safer, Mr Higgs,' Jack replied. 'If your story checks out, and I can persuade an editor to take it, then there'll be a whole lot more people knowing about you, and your brother's business activities. From what you say, you'll be a hunted man for the rest of your days.'

'It's a risk I'll take.'

'Why, for God's sake?'

Higgs thought it over, his voice suddenly wistful, almost poetic. 'As an obituary, Mr Latimer. A fitting remembrance for Mikey. Jesus, if anyone deserved it, he did. He died for me. And I have to live with that. It's the least I can do to let the world know what a wonderful person he was. Please, just write it how it was. What I've told you. Then I'll take the risks.'

'I'll try,' Jack said, strangely unnerved and humbled by the sincerity, wondering if he had it in him to gamble with death if Amy's reputation was at stake. Maybe. Just maybe. Not before, but now. Perhaps he was beginning to see what love was capable of, what he'd lost, given up too quickly.

'Sometimes,' Higgs said quietly, 'we'd just sit and talk. Long, drifting conversations, and he'd tell me about the times he'd spent with his father as a boy, working that bloody allotment. Him and his dad, sitting in the shed, lazy-Sunday-afternoon stuff. He told me that he'd go there on his own if his father had beaten him, just sit in the evening quiet, soaking it all in. He loved it there, Mr Latimer, called that shed the safest place in the world.' Higgs stood, pulled his coat tight around him. 'Turned into his funeral pyre, didn't it?'

Jack found himself nodding, then turning off the micro-cassette.

34

With just over a week remaining until Christmas, Audrey Baxter had spent a miserable Thursday morning wandering Chelmsford's pedestrianized high street for presents. Not that she had a vast army of adoring friends and relatives to buy for, the list comprised just four – a brother in New Zealand, a cousin's daughter in Bristol, a little something for herself, and lastly, something for the Chairman. And it was the latter which had proved the most frustrating. What on earth could she get the man who reviled just about anything which could possibly improve his life? CDs, tapes, videos were all obvious non-starters. The same with clothes. She'd never seen George in any of the three woollen jumpers she'd spent so much time and effort choosing for him in previous years. Sometimes she even asked herself why she bothered buying for him at all, there was never any reciprocated gift, barely an acknowledgement from the great man. Indeed, she still remembered vividly the crushed embarrassment she felt when spending a considerable sum on a brand-new, shining, steel spade one year, only to be told it 'didn't have the right weight in the handle'.

Yet still she persisted, eventually settling on a smooth, white-iced Christmas cake from M & S, hoping perhaps the Chairman might invite her over to share a piece on the big day.

Next came the problem of when to deliver the gift, what to wear, whether to admit she knew of his son's death, offer the support she secretly fully feared might be flung straight back in her face? How would she react? Forgiveness? Make special allowances due to the appalling circumstances? Simply back away, give George the space William Kent had told her he needed?

Or perhaps another romantically optimistic tack entirely. Maybe, in the light of the tragedy, the way was lit for Audrey to take the emotional reins, bully her way into George Picket's heart, refuse to be shrugged off, stand her ground as his loyal supporter, encourage him to open up, share his pain, mourn the loss of his son together – take a few steps towards a new life for them both. Because Audrey sincerely believed there was a silver lining to every cloud, and that young Mikey's death, whilst undeniably tragic, could possibly also act as catalyst for a new beginning.

However, the initiative still lay with her. George wasn't the type to suddenly pop round and open up. Pride blocked the path, and although it formed part of his mysterious attraction, George's old-fashioned male sensibilities also walled him away, hid the inner man behind a sixty-year-barrier of traditional values and suppressed emotion. So Audrey trusted to her own reserves of feminine stamina to lure the real George from deep within. She would visit him because she cared, and stuff the consequences.

She took the bull by the horns that very afternoon, arriving in darkness after four, dressed smartly, carrying the lovingly wrapped cake.

Picket opened the door. 'Miss Baxter,' he said cordially, standing firm on the threshold.

Undaunted, she took a step closer, proffered the gift. 'Happy Christmas, George.'

He surveyed the neatly wrapped box. 'Christmas already, is it?'

'A week on Saturday,' she replied, shocked at his appearance. She'd never seen him so dishevelled, unshaven. Yet the eyes were keen, windowing a mind fiercely intent with some hidden purpose she was clearly interrupting.

'Another jumper, is it?'

'Have to open it and see.'

'Miss Baxter, I'm really very busy.'

'Can I come in?'

'You've heard about Mikey, I suppose?'

She nodded, flushed slightly. 'I'm really very, very sorry.'

'That old weasel Kent been shooting his mouth off, no doubt.'

She forgave him the slur. 'He's worried about you.'

'None of his damn business,' Picket replied. 'Or yours.'

Audrey found her willpower fast draining away. Perhaps the simplest thing would be to leave, take the ten-minute walk back to the comparative warmth of her own home, pour herself a large gin, forget the folly of her venture. But something kept her there, challenging the older man. 'I just wanted to see how you are,' she persisted.

'I'm fine.'

She practically thrust the cake into his plaster-flecked hands. 'Still hard at work on the house?'

He nodded, finally accepting the gift. Then gave her one of 'those looks', the penetrating kind which made her heart miss a beat. She watched his lips, entranced. 'You'd best come in, I suppose.'

Telling herself she was shivering with the cold rather than nerves, she stepped inside. 'I'll put the kettle on, shall I?'

'Suit yourself,' Picket replied, walking back upstairs.

'You might want to open your present, George.'

He stopped, looked at the box in his hands. 'Perhaps on Christmas Day, Miss Baxter. Never been one for early presents. Undermines the sentiment, destroys the tradition.' Another long, unsettling look. 'Don't you agree?'

'Yes, but in this case . . .'

'Then it'll wait, Miss Baxter,' he said tersely.

Audrey tried her best not to appear too crestfallen, her mind making massive allowances for the strange behaviour. She busied herself making tea in a kitchen piled high with dirty plates, pots and pans. She wondered if she should wash up, busy herself with domestic chores downstairs while he toiled away upstairs. Everywhere seemed coated in a fine layer of dust from the renovations, and she guessed the place hadn't been cleaned in weeks. William Kent's coded message rang in her ears – Picket needed a woman about the place, only he had too much pride to admit it.

In the end she decided against the predictable house-cleaning, realizing it would gain her no favours. Partly because she knew the Chairman would be arrogantly expecting her to set to with the rubber gloves and polish. And also, the unhealthy state of the place gave her another excuse to call back at a later date. Perhaps even on Christmas Day. She doubted he'd made any arrangements for the traditional lunch. Maybe she'd simply arrive early, bring over a bagful of cleaners and a boxful of food to celebrate the day in something approaching style. A bottle or two to mellow him, crackers. Audrey smiled as she poured the tea, preoccupied with the image of the Chairman in a paper hat.

She took both cups cautiously upstairs, realizing it was the first time she'd ever been so far into his domain. 'George?' she asked politely on the landing.

'In here,' came the intent reply. 'Watch yourself.'

Heart trembling, she walked carefully into the front bed-room to see a large bare space with just a sawdust-spotted rug dominating the middle of the floor. Picket wobbled unsteadily on a pair of creaking aluminium stepladders, working a hand-drill, frantically turning a hole into a large beam which ran the width of the room directly above his head.

'Put them down anywhere,' he said without turning, concentrating on the task. A trickle of sawdust ran from the swirling drill-bit on to his dirty overalls.

'Gosh,' Audrey said, watching him. 'You've been busy.'

'Ceiling joists were all rotten,' Picket explained, grimacing with the effort. 'Same as the floor. Had to cut them out, replace them. Chances are the water-tank would've fallen right through if I hadn't shorn it up.'

Audrey thought it proper to take an interest. 'And what are you making the hole for?'

'Drilling,' he corrected her sharply. 'One drills a hole.'

'Of course.'

'Going to run a cable for the lights through it. Run the new flex into the top electrical ring, drop it through, stick a new light fitting on the end.'

'I see,' Audrey replied, wondering why the existing bare bulb was inadequate, but reluctant to say something too easily misconstrued as foolish. At least his mind was occupied; therapy, no doubt, for the turmoil created by his son's death. 'I really was so very sorry to hear about your son.'

He stopped drilling and slowly turned to her. 'Know what the youngsters say, Miss Baxter? Shit happens.'

She blushed, seeking refuge behind her mug of tea.

He descended the ladder. 'But the point is, some of us get on, don't dwell on it. That's the difference between them and us, Miss Baxter, we survive, they crumple.'

'Them?' Audrey asked, preferring him up the ladder, out of visual range. His gaze was a little too personal – wild, almost.

'Youth of today,' he spat back bitterly, reaching for his tea. 'They all want the good times without the effort.'

She nodded, keen to appease.

'My son Mikey wasn't like them. A good boy, polite, respectful. Knew the value of manners, hard labour, effort for reward. Lived a short life, but died with a clear conscience, whatever people say.'

'I never met him,' Audrey said quietly, content to listen.

'Children are gifts, Miss Baxter, gifts from God. But if you don't come down on them hard, they run amok. Take your eye off them for a second, and the devil claims them for his own. Killed my son, they did. Killed my Mikey.' Picket took a sip of tea, lost in thought. Then smiled, turned to her again. 'We spend all our blasted lives buying things, yet never pay for anything. No one pays. No one. We growers understand that. Know why a carrot you grow on the allotment tastes better than the bright-orange fakes they sell you in the supermarket?'

'No chemicals?' Audrey suggested a little nervously.

'Because you've grown it, Miss Baxter. Put the effort in. Just the same with children. People think they can acquire them as simply as they pick up the groceries. There's simply no perspective any more. Nothing has any value. Not life, not anything.'

'Absolutely,' Audrey replied, keen to let him know she hung on his every word, regardless of the sense within. Right now, she considered it best to simply be a listener, accepting

231

whatever pain he disgorged. She found herself in the curious position of feeling deeply uncomfortable, yet wondering if she'd finally turned the corner and glimpsed a light at the end of her unfulfilled romantic tunnel.

Picket finished the tea, licked his lips. 'But I was brought up a little differently, Miss Baxter. You and I both were, taught to take life's knocks on the chin, put up, shut up and damn well get on with the business of living. Youngsters these days, they get away with murder. Literally. Well, not any more.'

'No. Not any more.' Audrey echoed hesitantly.

The Chairman suddenly turned on his doting fan, his voice a threatening sneer. 'Don't patronize me, Miss Baxter.'

'I'm sorry . . . I . . .'

His voice rose, eyes wild with fiery indignation. 'You walk all the way over here with some lame excuse about a present, when you're exactly like all the rest, sticking your god-damned nose into my business, then standing there like some love-sick puppy, pretending you agree with every damn word I say!'

'But, George, I . . .'

'Just get out!'

Audrey felt her throat begin to tighten, eyes mist over from the unexpected verbal assault. Her nerve was failing, and worse still she felt frightened, scared by the sudden change of mood. 'I'm sorry, really.'

He took a step towards her, stood far too close. 'Is that all you say, Miss Baxter? Sorry? That the best you can offer? Bloody women. You're all the same, you all want something for nothing, then when you're done, or dead, or off for the next poor dope, you leave a litter of abandoned little bastards behind you! Single mothers, divorces – it's all down to women wanting more. Women like you!'

Audrey's legs began to shake. She was acutely aware of the danger she'd stupidly placed herself in, alone with a ranting man closing in. Yet the closer his snarling face got to hers, the less she could move.

'I must be going,' she finally managed to blurt out.

'Don't let me stop you.'

'You're wrong, George,' Audrey said, hating herself for

crying, despising her naivety in coming to the house. 'Not every woman's the same.'

He laughed horribly, covering her face with foul breath. 'And you're going to prove otherwise, are you? Come on, then, show me, Miss Baxter. I've always thought you were a frustrated little slut.' He grabbed her, tried to kiss her on the lips. 'Still want me, do you, Miss Baxter?' he whispered into her ear as she struggled to avoid his mouth. 'Or would you rather we keep it as it always was – you go home and cry into your lilac pillow, and I'll spend the night thinking about the fuck we might have had.'

Audrey's head began to swim. He was too close, too obscene, pressing his body into hers, licking her hair, laughing. 'Let me go,' she stammered, somehow finding the strength to wriggle free.

Picket stepped back, still grinning. 'Best toddle off, then, Miss Baxter,' he said casually, before bowing and turning to the step ladders once more. 'There's no place for you here.'

Weeping, she stumbled from the room, then down the stairs two at a time, choking back the urge to vomit on to the threadbare carpet.

Seconds later, she was outside, taking down lungfuls of the cold night air, coughing and spluttering, the smell of the Chairman's breath foul on her face. Without turning to the upstairs window, she broke into a run, breaking the heel of a shoe in her frantic effort to get home.

35

The young couple walked side by side away from the town, huddled against the freezing night sky.

'Soon be Christmas,' Alex remarked as a succession of office workers drove back home on the crowded road beside them. 'Looking forward to it?'

'Not really,' came the unbearably quiet reply.

'Pardon?' said Alex above the roar of the traffic.

'I said "yes",' Eve Adams replied a little louder.

'I think it's overrated myself,' Alex announced, gaining confidence, enjoying the feeling of walking by her side. 'All that preparation, and no one has any real fun. Just like this whole millennium thing. It's all going to be a joke. The adults'll all get pissed and sing songs, while we sit in the corner eating crisps and feeling embarrassed.'

'My dad doesn't get drunk,' the girl replied. 'Or my mum.'

'Probably wait until you're in bed,' said Alex. 'They do that. Give you a massive guilt-trip about what a burden you are, blah, blah, blah – then the moment you're out the way start acting like kids themselves. I reckon it's all a jealousy thing. They can't stand the fact that we're young and they're old and boring.'

'How old are you, Alex?' she asked.

'Thirteen. And you?'

'Twelve,' she replied, then quickly added, 'nearly thirteen, though. Birthday's in January.

Alex smiled. He was enjoying himself, basking a little in the presence of the girl. Then realizing how good it felt to finally *be* himself. Not Zelda, not a bullied wimp at school – simply Alex. And the longer he strolled by her side, the more he found himself glancing across, watching the damp blonde ringlets bob in time to her stride, adjusting his pace to fit her own. A subconscious thing, natural almost. He really liked her, and maybe one day, if he was brave enough, he'd reach out and take her hand, squeeze her palm just a moment or two longer than mere reassurance demanded . . . then again, maybe not. What did he know about girls? Granted, he'd been as initially interested as everyone else when Sullivan brought in a porno mag he'd found at the back of his dad's cupboard, but just the one brief look at the open-legged gynaecological excesses had been enough to confirm that he had a long way to go before joining the baying mob in whooping appreciation of the fairer sex.

But with Eve, he knew it wasn't important, sensed she wasn't waiting for a smart chat-up line he didn't have. There was no pressure there, no expectation to be anyone other than himself. He felt accepted by her silence, revelled in the unspoken electricity crackling between them. There were no demands to be met, just reassurance to be gained. He felt as if he walked the familiar streets for the very first time, houses, cars, roads all blurring into an insignificant space – outside. Alex was inside – with Eve.

'You're really a lot cleverer than you let on to the others, aren't you?' she said suddenly.

He floated on the flattery. 'If I am, then I get it from my mum.'

'What does she do?'

He paused, unwilling to reveal his mother's job. What if it ruined everything?

He sighed. 'Typical mum, really. Spends her life telling everyone else what to do, only she gets paid a fortune for it.'

'And your dad?'

Another bout of mental shakes from Alex. 'He used to work in the media,' he said guardedly. 'Lost his job a while back.' No word of a lie, simply economical with the truth. But he knew, if he was serious about the girl, that sooner or later his dad's local notoriety would come out, that he'd have to cope with her admiration for the man, expectations for him to be more like Jack Latimer. But until the moment came, he wanted to smother his parents a little. Just spend a little more time with Eve liking him for him. Not whose son he might be.

'So he's unemployed, is he?' Eve asked.

'He keeps himself busy. And your parents?' Alex asked. 'What do they do?'

'Work. Mum-and-dad stuff.'

He noticed how she'd begun chewing at her bottom lip. 'What do they say, your mum and dad, about you bunking off school?'

'They get mad, I suppose.'

'You don't know?'

She stopped, looked at him, tapped the side of her head. 'When they start going into one, I switch off, vanish. I see their faces getting really serious, then it's like all in slow motion. They just sort of fade away. Then I can't hear them any more. I make it all go gold and purple, and no one's shouting at me.'

'Wow.'

'It helps.'

'Kind of a meditation thing?'

'S'pose.'

He smiled. 'You're not like Tracey and the others. What are you doing hanging out with them?'

'Same as you,' she said, reaching down to take his hand. 'Hiding.'

Alex stiffened, then relaxed, enjoying the feeling of her cold palm in his. 'Hiding? From what?'

'Stuff I can't take to the purple and gold place. Stuff that's always there.'

'Like what?' he asked, intrigued and concerned in equal measure.

She stopped walking, withdrew her hand from his. 'It doesn't matter.'

'Please,' Alex heard himself saying. 'Maybe I can . . . ?'

She shook her head. 'No. You can't. Nobody can do anything.'

Alex frowned, saw a sudden deep hurt in her eyes, wanted

so desperately to take it away. 'Listen, Eve, if you're in trouble, then my mum's a . . .'

'No. Nobody must know. Not you. No one. I'm fine, really. Fine.'

He reached out, took back her hand. 'I say that sort of thing, Eve. That everything's fine. Or OK. I tell my mum and dad that, just to get them off my back. But it isn't, really. It's just that I know they wouldn't understand. Or that it's something I've already talked to them about, only they didn't really listen.' Gingerly, he put an arm round her shoulder. 'I know you're not fine, Eve. I want to help.'

'Please,' she begged. 'He says terrible things will happen if I do . . .'

'Who says?'

'. . . and even though I don't believe him about dying any more – well, I can't be sure, you know?' Her eyes met his. 'What if he's right? What if something really shitty happens just because I told someone?'

'Dying?' was all Alex could echo. But she was walking away. He trotted back to her side.

'Just go away. I'm bad.'

'No. You're not.'

'Really. Leave me alone.'

Alex felt the calm confidence evaporate on the chill evening air. Buildings, houses, cars, flickering streetlamps all came back into focus. Something dark and black had stepped between them. A secret which held more of her than he ever could. He was floundering. Losing her, the silent world they had shared. His head tightened, and suddenly he couldn't bear the thought of whatever brief mental intimacy had passed between them simply shutting down, walking away.

'I want to tell someone, believe me,' she said, voice cracking. 'I want to tell the world. But what if it goes wrong? What if something awful happens to you? Because it could, couldn't it?'

'I . . . I don't know.'

She picked up her pace.

Alex matched it. 'But it's got to help to talk to someone.'

'Not if they die.'

237

He struggled to bend into her eyeline.

'No one's going to die, Eve. Not just for talking.' His mind struggled to find a solution. 'Got any brothers or sisters, mates at school?'

She shook her head. 'Mum says I'm enough trouble as it is. School lot think I'm weird.'

'I don't.'

'He says I've let them down. It's a sort of special school and costs a lot of money. He says if I keep truanting, he'll really make life difficult.'

'Who does?'

She choked back a tear. 'Dad.'

'All parents try that crap. The guilt thing . . .'

'He means it. He means everything he says.'

'Talk to your mum, Eve.'

'Can't. He won't let me.' She stopped, breathless, turned to him, eyes imploring. 'Look, I like you. But you don't understand.'

'Because you won't tell me,' Alex insisted.

'I hear them shouting at each other, and I know it's about me. Mum says Dad loves me too much. He gets mad and threatens her. She shuts up then, smiles like me.' She paused, looked away. 'Sometimes I wonder if she's got her own place to go to when he gets angry, and what colours hers is.'

She walked on, he followed, feeling useless, frustrated.

'It's just like you said, Alex. All grown-ups want to do is control us. It was Tracey who first got me to meet Mark and Damon; her mum does my mum's cleaning. It was really boring at first. Just boys doing silly stuff. Better than school, I suppose, but not much. Stupid games at the allotments in the summer, then coming home to find Dad shouting at me for not going to school. But then you arrived and said stuff which really made sense. You were different.'

They turned left into another street packed with well-to-do houses, home to double-garages, tidy front lawns bordered by established ferns.

'This your road?' Alex asked.

'Yes. We've lived here for about a year, now. Dad got lucky at work, so we moved from the other side of town.'

'New school, right?'

She nodded.

'And you were the new girl?'

'They hated me. Dad spent the summer trying to make me talk posher. Only I ended up speaking funny. Though not as stupid as the teachers. Miss Alward told me to take a plum out of my mouth, or something. Bitch, she is.'

Alex found his pace slowing, keen to quiz the girl further before they arrived at her house, wanting to delay the moment of their parting. 'And then you met Tracey?'

'No,' she sniffed, wiping away a rogue tear. 'I knew her from before, from the old school. Her mum started to bring her round ours while she cleaned. We got on. She wanted to know about what Mark was doing to her.'

'Mark?'

'Sex,' Eve replied, shuddering a little. 'She was less clued-up than I was, really naive. Used to call it "bed-kissing", and wanted to know all the ins and outs of it, if you'll pardon the expression.' A smile at last.

Which Alex returned, glad she was back with him, however embarrassing the subject matter. 'And she asked you?'

Eve nodded. 'But don't tell Tracey I told you; she'd flip.'

'You know about . . . that kind of stuff?'

'Don't you?'

Alex cleared his throat, unable to lie. 'Not a lot, actually, no.'

She squeezed his hand. 'Lots of people wouldn't have been so honest.'

He said nothing, hoping the blush wouldn't show under the orange streetlights.

'I knew enough to put her straight. The only reason Mark wears a condom is because I told her to make him.'

'I'm . . .'

'Shocked, yeah, I can tell.' She stood closer. 'I'm only telling you this because I want to be straight with you, too. I don't want you to have any ideas.'

He swallowed hard. 'Like what?'

'About me. You and I.'

'Oh, sure. Absolutely.'

'I want us to be friends.' She looked up into his darkened face. 'For the moment. That OK?'

He said nothing, dumbstruck by her proximity, the warm breath on his frozen cheek. His own was coming in short, tight bursts, riding a wild urge which rushed from somewhere deep and lonely inside. He held her close, suddenly cupped her face in both hands and kissed her quickly on the lips.

She struggled, broke away. 'Please. Don't.'

His heart sank. The stupidity of it! The crassness! Now she most likely thought of him as some sort of pervert. If only the pavement would dissolve, drag him under, bury him forever. 'I'm sorry,' he mumbled.

'No, *I'm* sorry,' she replied, taking his other hand. 'Listen. Whatever I had to give to you, he's already taken it.'

'Who's "he"? Your dad, is it? He's taken something from you?'

She fell silent.

A silence which suddenly unravelled a black and ghastly truth, flaunted it obscenely before them both. Alex had to ask. 'Have you been . . . you know . . . raped or something?'

She gave a short, hollow laugh. 'No. Rape's the sort of thing that happens in dark alleys, isn't it? Whereas with me . . .'

They'd stopped before a large detatched house covered in ivy. A light shone from inside. 'That's Clara,' she explained. 'She's from Brazil. Dad pays her a lot of money to look after me, but she's always on the phone, or watching the telly. I guess the school must have already rung and told her I wasn't there today. She doesn't mind because she doesn't have to pick me up.' Eve lowered her voice conspiratorially. 'Sometimes, we don't tell Dad I've bunked off. It's easier for everyone that way.'

She turned to leave. Alex stood, impotent, desperate for her to stay, feeling a wrench as she took the first step away up the path.

'Eve,' he asked quickly. 'Your dad? Does he . . . ?'

'What?'

This time he didn't care if she saw him blush. 'Do things?'

'What things?'

He couldn't work out if she was teasing him or not. He

opted for bluntness, stepping closer, then wrapping it in a suitably lowered voice. 'Sex and stuff?'

She screwed up her pretty young face in a frown, found a point somewhere beyond to talk to. 'Spelling practice, he calls it.'

Alex felt his stomach churn. 'Oh, Jesus.'

'But it's OK now, really. You mustn't worry.'

'He's stopped doing it?'

'No,' she replied, kissing him quickly on the cheek, and turning to run inside. 'But when he does, I think of you.'

36

Late Friday morning, with just eight days to Christmas, fifteen until the millennium itself, Jack found himself nursing a pint of Guinness in a quiet pub south of the town. The venue was his choice, partly because they kept a great pint, and also to seek out a little anonymity. Three other punters sat in silent corners, turning papers or simply staring into space. All men – crushed, somehow, Jack thought, as if this tawdry fag-fumed place was a sanctuary from whatever private hell they'd left behind. He hoped to God, that for all his woes and worries, he'd never end up a silent, solo drinker. The entire scene reeked of stale sadness, made worse somehow by the gaudy decorations and handwritten posters announcing tickets for the millennium party were now on sale behind the bar.

It was another long fifteen minutes before the furtive figure of DS Samson walked through the doors, spotted Jack and made his way over.   •

'This had better be good, Jack.'

'It's gold-dust.'

'Drink?'

'No, I'm driving. Your Uniform boys are going mental with the Breathalyzer these days.'

Samson fetched himself a bottle of LA, grimacing at the first sip. 'Wouldn't believe the trouble I had getting away. So what have you got, Jack?'

'The name Dave Higgs mean anything to you?'

Samson shook his head, tried another sip. 'Should it?'

'His brother's a Mr Big in the cocaine trade.'

Samson frowned, half remembering a face shown to George Picket up at police headquarters. 'Go on.'

'According to Dave, Ipswich CID had spent months planning a raid, timing it to catch the gang cutting a huge haul, street value – two million.'

'According to Dave? You've spoken to this bloke? Hang about, this is another George Picket-related fairy tale, isn't it? You're about to ask another one of your harmless little favours, which will leave me without gonads for the Christmas break.'

Jack held up a hand. 'Just hear me out. You were the one giving me the come-on about looking into stuff.'

'Only because I was in serious lumber following the last little favour.'

'Give me a minute, Kenny. Mrs Samson's still going to get her millennial nuptials, don't you worry.'

'I doubt it,' Samson replied. 'I'm working the big shift on the night. Top brass still haven't forgiven me for ringing Ipswich asking after Picket's son.'

'Picket's dead son,' Jack corrected him.

'Whatever.'

'You want to hear this?'

'Not particularly.'

'Trust me, none of this came from Picket . . .'

'Thank fuck for that.'

'Higgs turned up at the office yesterday, nervous as a pig in a butcher's. Wanted two grand upfront for his side of things.'

'Two thousand?'

Jack shrugged. 'I beat him down a bit.'

Samson sipped at his drink like it was pure lemon juice.

Jack continued. 'Anyway, this coke shipment was coming in to Harwich stashed in a Land Rover or something. Now here's where they screwed up. Instead of impounding the cocaine, they wait, follow Martin Higgs and his crew, intending to catch the lot in possession of a class-A substance. But the gang's one step ahead, tipped off.'

'By Picket's son,' Samson replied dryly. 'And then they did him for being a grass. Old news, Jack. Can I go back to the station, now? Only I've got a pile of paperwork taller than two giraffes piggy-backing.'

243

'Five minutes is all I ask.'

Samson took one of Jack's cigarettes, lit it, exhaled heavily.

'Somehow they manage to shake off the cops, bike the stuff round to Dave Higgs's place, telling him to stash it somewhere safe. He panics, goes to pieces. There's raids going off everywhere. Anyway, step forward his mentally retarded lover and part-time bully-boy for the mob – Mikey Picket.'

'He was queer?'

'Typical plod. Missing the point,' Jack sighed. 'According to Higgs, Mikey saves the day. Buggers off with these two hold-alls stuffed full of twenty kilos of triple-wrapped cocaine just before the armed cops pay the neurotic old queen a visit.'

A frown from Samson. 'Picket's kid had hold of all that Charlie? Bollocks.'

'Incredible, isn't it?'

'Wind-up, more like.'

'Should have seen the guy, Kenny. He was real enough, shaking like a leaf.'

'Wake up and smell the coffee, Jack,' Samson replied. 'This Higgs bloke, he was probably shitting himself that you'd tumble he was trying to take you for two large ones. Jesus, Jack, you're losing your touch.'

'No. He knew too much, told me too much. Higgs was the real deal, believe me. I know when people are bullshitting me. This guy wasn't.'

'Well, it ain't for me to tell folk how to flush their money down the toilet,' Samson said, crushing a yawn. 'But there's more, I suppose.'

Jack's eyes twinkled.

'Oh, God.'

'Here's the two-million-pound question, Kenny – guess where he stashed it?'

Samson faltered, shook his head.

'George Picket's allotment shed,' Jack said slowly.

A three-beat pause.

'Right, that's it,' Samson said. 'I'm off. This is Candid fucking Camera, right? Hidden videos everywhere in the bar. Mates back at the nick pissing themselves laughing.

244

What's next, Jack? A seven-foot parrot going to walk in and start juggling with the empties?'

'Two weeks later,' Jack persisted. 'The local fire brigade turn the place to sludge.'

Samson took a deep drag on the pilfered cigarette, exhaling high into the yellow ceiling. 'You really swallowed all this, didn't you?'

Jack nodded.

'Got to be crap, hasn't it?'

'Not necessarily.'

Samson scratched at the side of his face, played with an eyebrow.

'I think,' Jack told him, 'that it happened just as Higgs told me it did. I think Mikey Picket made the drop in the safest place he knew. His father's allotment shed.'

'Higgs. How did he find you?'

'He saw the piece in the *Observer*, put two and two together, sold me the story for his airline ticket out of here. Apparently his brother's some sort of psycho, been watching too many *Godfather* movies, reckons Higgs most likely did a runner with the lot.'

'It's insane, Jack,' Samson replied. 'Really mental. You mean to tell me those kids unknowingly burnt the biggest cocaine cache in Essex, all because they wanted a puff on a Marlboro?'

Jack said nothing, a grin spreading over his face.

Samson began to laugh. 'Straight up?'

Jack nodded, clinked his glass on Samson's, took a large pull.

The weather-beaten, rugby-playing face broadened into a wide grin. 'Oh, Jack, this is beautiful. Really fucking beautiful.'

'And the way I see it,' Jack continued. 'There's got to be a lot of shit flying around up at Ipswich CID. After all, they're the morons who let the cocaine into the country, then let it disappear right from under their noses. My betting is they – just like Higgs and his mobsters – are terrified word of their incompetence will leak out. And equally desperate to find the stuff. You're on a winner, Kenny.'

'Me?'

'Go see your guv'nor, tell him the real reason Ipswich are keen to slap D-notices on the whole farce. My guess is it's more about loss of public face rather than Mikey Picket's life. Should keep you out of uniform for a while.'

Samson squinted, piecing it together. 'If it's true, Jack. If it's true. This Higgs character, where's he now?'

'God knows. Fled the nest. Poor sod looked terrified out of his wits, desperate for the money he might make as whistle-blower.'

'But you paid him for the story, Jack. You know the rules. Any evidence he might have is inadmissible.'

Jack had expected this. 'So, if your guv'nor doesn't believe you, get a forensics team up to the allotments. My gut told me the man was real, and it also tells me you'll find a very interesting pile of ashes up there.'

'Or what's left of them. It was weeks ago.'

'Got to be worth a go, though, eh? Twenty kilos of grade-A's got to leave some sort of signature, hasn't it?'

'What's your bite on this?' Samson asked.

'You confirm Higgs's story, I get to do the follow-up to the original shed piece. Ipswich can't ban it, because it's an article about Chelmsford.'

'Aren't you forgetting someone? Picket'll flip.'

Jack drained his glass. 'I know. He's the stumbling block. Higgs wanted me to run the piece as a fitting obituary to his headless lover. Now I need Picket's permission to tell the country the apple of his eye was a thick gay cocaine trafficker.'

'Tough, being a reporter,' Samson smiled. He finished his own drink, then stood. 'Thanks, Jack. I appreciate this. Chances are you might well have saved my Christmas bonus.'

'I owed you one, for the computer.'

Samson's hands did a frantic aerial mime of a alien-blasting hand-console. 'How's it all going, then? The Zelda thing?'

'Kenny,' Jack replied. 'The locals are staring.'

37

George Picket listened impassively as the reporter unfolded his tale. It was late on a Friday afternoon and, quite frankly, he had better things to do than listen to the obscene imaginings of the wittering hack before him. Time was running out, and regardless of the hours he spent upstairs, there was still much to be done.

The main bedroom was nearly three-quarters completed, but the constant interruptions from bleating opportunists like Latimer, the idiot Kent and the Baxter woman had set him dangerously behind schedule. He still hadn't begun work on the separating wall, knowing he had to ration his strength for the heavy work ahead. The trips up and down the blasted stairs were enough to tax a man half his age, let alone carrying the rubble and mortar the connecting doorway would cause. Enough to fill another skip-load, for sure. Which meant more calls from the damn phone box to the robbing hire company – more time wasted.

And yet, curiously, the longer the deluded Latimer man droned on, the more Picket saw the hidden possibilities. The reporter was obviously building up to ask his permission to print the sad misconception he took for the truth – and Picket would grant it, gladly, realizing that there were far-reaching, unforeseen benefits.

For if the world was convinced that a bunch of layabout delinquent kids had unwittingly set his shed alight, then that would be an end to the matter. The identity of the fire-starter need never be revealed. A few thousand ignorant, newspaper-reading fools might stumble on the story – even less remember it after a fortnight. Only the local folk, other allotment holders would be shocked to hear of the sexual preferences and alleged criminal activities of their Chairman's former son. And he didn't give a stuff about their opinions. Because inevitably, the entire story would be small fry, once his own scheme had been fully realized. Mikey Picket's posthumous notoriety would pale by comparison to his father's claim to fame.

Thus the reporter would prove a useful part of the business, an ally to be tempted, flattered, beguiled with a promise to publish. And he had something that George wanted very badly, addresses which would save the hard-pressed Chairman a lot of leg-work.

'You're saying,' Picket said eventually. 'That my son was a homosexual?'

Jack coloured slightly. It had been a toe-curling ten minutes under the Chairman's tight-lipped scrutiny, hoping he'd adopted his most empathetic manner; sympathetic, yet keen for the truth. 'I think he was easily led, Mr Picket.'

'A lamb to the slaughter, perhaps? Corrupted by the beasts of Sodom for their own vile purpose?'

'The point is,' Jack continued, striving to offer a resolution, some kind of explanation for the grieving father. 'It makes sense as to why the police in Ipswich are so loath to make Mikey's death public, investigate it properly. They let a massive cocaine haul slip right out of their hands and could end up looking very incompetent indeed.'

'You'll appreciate, Mr Latimer,' Picket said deliberately. 'That it's an extraordinary tale.'

'I understand that, George.'

Picket flinched, hating the familiarity. 'And I would imagine that two million pounds' worth of drugs is a huge amount to hide in a humble garden shed.'

'I'm told it would have fitted into two holdalls,' Jack replied. 'Sports bags. Is there anywhere Mikey could have hidden them so you wouldn't have spotted it?'

Picket frowned, trying to concentrate, ignore the taunting voices from outside – Brian Feeling and his gang, John Shannon, Simon Ruddell, Karen Foster – back again, determined to ruin his concentration with disgusting secret screams they'd heightened and developed for his ears only.

But they'd pay. Every bastard one of them.

'George?'

'Just thinking,' he replied, frowning with the effort of reconnecting with reality. 'The shed. Trying to remember.'

Jack waited while the clock lazily counted the seconds.

'Right. Yes. I had a cupboard in there, an old dresser. Used it for all sorts, canes, twine, rooting compost. Spring stuff, mostly. I suppose he might have put some bags in there. But it all seems so unlikely.'

'You said he came to see you unexpectedly for the weekend in early October?'

Picket nodded.

'Friday night?'

'Saturday morning,' Picket replied. 'Knocked on the door about nineish.'

'Did you keep your shed locked, George?'

'What would be the point?' Picket scoffed. 'Gave up after the third lock was smashed by those vandals on bicycles. Buggered if I'd waste time and money fitting more damn locks.'

'You see,' Jack explained carefully, uncertain if the guy was really listening. The Chairman's eyes watched him, but didn't seem to focus. 'My take on this is that Mikey fled Ipswich on Friday evening, most likely spent the night in your shed. When I spoke to Higgs, he told me your son had special memories of it, called it "the safest place in the world".'

Picket rounded on the cautious reporter. 'On a freezing-cold October night? Don't be so ridiculous, man! If he did the preposterous thing you're alleging, then surely he'd have dumped these drugs, then come straight round here? It's only two hundred yards away.'

'I think he was protecting you,' Jack replied. 'For all he knew the police could have got the truth out of Higgs, then set off after him. Common sense told him they might well turn up knocking at your door looking for him. So he waited until the morning, hoping the coast was clear.'

'And I think we're entering the realms of fantasy, Mr Latimer. Clutching at straws.'

'How did he seem that weekend? Worried, nervous?'

'Mikey was always nervous. Life had kicked him hard many a time. People are largely animals at heart, Mr Latimer, and Mikey took a lot of vicious behaviour from many of them.'

Jack nodded. 'When you came to see me asking to find Mikey, you mentioned a phone call you'd had from him.'

The Chairman stared back. It pricked Jack's conscience. The stiff-backed man in grubby paint-splattered overalls looked suddenly vulnerable, smaller, somehow, fragile.

'He was scared, you said. People were after him. You had no idea why? He didn't mention any particular reason?'

'Couldn't get the slightest sense out of him.'

Jack took a long look round the dim, cluttered room. Then sighed. Was it right, he wondered, to put Picket back in the paper and let the public rake over his ashes as surely as the forensic guys would rake over his allotment?

He cleared his throat. 'George, I've got to tell you that chances are the police might get involved.'

'The police,' Picket gently reminded him. 'Are doing damn-all.'

'Our police. New Street.'

'Don't hold your breath.'

'They'll probably look into the whole business. Maybe even send over some officers to sift through the shed ashes, look for traces of the cocaine.'

'On the hearsay of a drug-taking homosexual who claims to know my son? Another idiotic waste of the taxpayers' money.'

Jack shifted slightly, popped the question. 'What I want to ask, George, is if this turns out to be true, then do I have your permission to write the story?'

Picket finished his tea. 'Gladly, Mr Latimer.'

Jack was shocked at the ease of it all.

The thin pursed lips slid into the tiniest of smiles. 'I only say that because I doubt there's a single shred of evidence to back up your absurd suggestion. Mikey's no more, and your so-called source has apparently fled the country on your wages. I suspect your story is as dead as my son is.'

'But even so . . .'

'What was it Wilde said? "Publish and be damned."'

'Then I have your permission?'

'To tell the truth, Mr Latimer,' Picket replied. 'And only the truth.'

Jack began walking slowly back to the front door. 'I just want to say, that from what I've heard, Mikey sounds like a good apple caught up in a rotten barrel. I want people to know that, together with everything you've suffered, too.'

'Naturally,' Picket replied, trying his best to look suitably downtrodden. On the whole he thought his performance had gone rather well so far. Now it was his turn to ask the question. 'There is something you can do for me, Mr Latimer, a favour for a favour.'

'Try me.'

'I've had a bit of a change of heart recently.'

'Oh?'

'Time to let bygones be bygones, all that nonsense.'

Jack returned the smile. 'What can I do for you, George? Bit of a hand with the DIY?'

'Much simpler,' Picket replied. 'I want to send some Christmas cards.'

Jack met the intent look with a puzzled expression. 'You want me to post them?'

'Addresses,' Picket replied. 'I want to try and make peace with the kids who burnt down the shed.'

'It's very noble of you, George.'

'Well, they've stayed out of our way for the last few weeks, and I just want to thank them for that. All this antagonism gets us nowhere, does it?'

'I'm surprised, really. After everything that's happened.'

'I'm moving on now, Mr Latimer. Trying to leave this godforsaken town, start afresh. It'd be nice to go with a clear conscience. And perhaps an olive branch in the form of a card might make these youngsters stop and think for a moment. Save them from Mikey's fate. Who knows, I might even invite them over, throw a party?' Picket paused, stared into space. 'I think Mikey would've wanted me to do that.'

Jack smiled, touched, doubtful. 'I'll see what I can do, George.'

251

'For Mikey's sake, Mr Latimer. And theirs. There has to be some good to come out of all of this.'

'Sure. I'll dig out the addresses I have.'

'I'd be grateful.'

''Bye, then, George.'

'Until the next time,' Picket replied, wiping his hand on his overalls and closing the front door.

He stood quietly for a moment, thinking hard. He was tired and hungry, but there wasn't time for food and sleep. Every waking second counted.

He wouldn't stop because Mikey's murderers didn't. And the louder they screamed, the harder Picket worked. It was his secret strategy, his edge. Their abuse merely served to bring their deaths closer and closer.

He went upstairs into the back bedroom, aware it was time for some more 'help'. He opened the top drawer on a small oak dresser, pulled out a white polythene parcel the size of a sugar bag, then sat on the creaking bed.

Seconds later, as he frantically rubbed at his gums, the cocaine began its way into his beleaguered system, revitalizing his vigour, re-energizing his aching limbs. It had been a good thing, a smart move of his to save this one bag from the shed. And if anything, Picket rather enjoyed the irony – that the very stuff which had led to Mikey's murder was now the chemical power supply for his killers' demise.

He set back to work, whistling happily, refusing to be beaten until every last one of them was dead by his own hands.

38

Jack's trip out to Chelmsford's crematorium rounded off a particularly stressful Christmas. And to cap it all he was late, walking into the fifteen-minute service just in time to watch the blood-red velvet curtains cover Anwar Patel's final trip to the waiting furnace beyond.

He stood at the back of the small chapel, trying to quell a coughing fit brought on by dashing the last hundred yards through freezing fog. Although he suspected Anwar would have seen the funny side, he doubted the mourning family of the deceased passive smoker would have been too impressed.

He surveyed the sea of covered heads, searching out C.F.'s, turning to look his way. He gave a discreet apologetic shrug, mouthed 'sorry' – then promptly broke into the dread coughing fit.

He'd received the distraught phone call late on the twenty-third, listening in shock as his secretary tearfully told him of her father's death. After he'd reached for a cigarette, then placed it silently back in the pack, he crumpled then tossed it into the wastebin, choking back the first real tears he'd shed in a long while. It was as if Anwar's death had finally changed things for real. He cried for Anwar, their times together, and the life he'd live without his friend. Cried, because more than ever, he felt so utterly, dreadfully alone. Made that way by death, the one story all his investigative skills would never be able to expose as an unscrupulous, unfeeling bastard on the trail of each and every one of us.

Sometime later, he turned out the light and wandered downstairs in a daze of guilt and sadness, through the heaving kebab shop and out on to Duke Street, now home to whooping tinsel-clad office revellers oblivious to the hunched figure who stared blankly ahead as they passed him by.

And it had been such a good day before the sad news. Samson had met Jack for a liquid lunch in the Cathedral Cellar Bar, detailing the forensic progress made with samples taken from what remained of George Picket's shed. Traces could be compounded to cocaine, the rejuvinated DS had announced, leading to the beginnings of a proper investigation into the whole business, most probably to start in earnest with interviews and statements shortly after the inevitable millennium furore. Higgs would have to be found for further verification, but Samson was hopeful that the scale of the alleged 'find' would persuade Interpol into the search, and with the offer of police protection and a new identity, Higgs would be cajoled into offering his services.

In the meantime, New Street CID wanted a copy of Jack's interview with Mikey Picket's former lover, which the satisfied journalist was happy to hand over on the proviso he got first bite out of the lucrative media apple which was sure to follow.

He returned home, cooked a curry in Anwar's honour, drank too much Johnny Walker, woke at three in the morning, sweating, cramped, and began to cry once more.

Jack went to his former home for Christmas Day bearing two presents and a home-made stuffing for the bird. The atmosphere was cordially festive yet improbably polite, both he and Amy over enthusing, then drifting into long silences. Once or twice, he caught her smirking knowingly, which only added to his discomfort. He tried hard for Alex's sake. Yet, inevitably, the boy made no real effort to catch the mood, preoccupied, Jack assumed, with other matters. He resolved to spend more time on the computer with him, get through to Alex as best he knew how, the image of Picket's strained, mourning face still strong in his mind.

At just past two, the doorbell went, sending Amy rushing

for it. Jack sat, wondering who would be so tactless to call on Christmas Day. Certainly, there were no visitors expected.

'Jack,' she said from behind the door. 'I'd like you to meet Luke. He's the new man in my life.'

His heart sank. He'd been set up, the knowing smile part giveaway to the charade. He sighed, stood, prepared to shake the hand of the lucky contender in the race for his former wife.

Amy walked slowly round the door holding a newborn baby. 'Isn't he gorgeous?' she whispered, as the weary, grinning parents followed behind. 'This is Pete and Naomi. From number thirty-one. Good friends. They've asked me to be Luke's godmother.'

Jack shook hands with the proud father, watching as the tiny, soft, pink hand gripped Amy's thumb. The relief was enormous. The baby began to cry. Amy handed him to his seated mother, then took Jack's hand. 'Weren't jealous, were you? Big strong man like you?'

Later, when Amy asked him to stay, he agreed, on the condition that there were to be no expectations, marital postmortems or recriminations. He told her about Anwar, and this time she simply listened, offered no solutions or emotional advice. He thanked her. Then they both lay awake, feigning sleep, each straining to catch the other's breath, the silence heavy with a thousand conversations missed along the way.

He left at seven the next morning, stepping out on to the cold, silent street, enjoying the isolation as he began walking back to the flat, trying to ignore the feeling that maybe he'd have liked to have stayed, woken up with her, but not trusting the confusion of feelings which had surfaced during the night. Still remembering the raw hurt he'd felt when she'd told him about the affair, undimmed by the passing years, yet also knowing he was angry because he still cared, still loved the damn woman. Learn to forgive – the priests always said. Three simple-sounding words made impossible by another – pride.

Much later, back at the flat, he called her. She sounded cool, wanted to know why he hadn't stuck around. He apologized, thanked her for the previous day. She made a joke about them getting back together. He laughed, a little too hard. They said good night. He was alone again.

Having finished the last of his bottled lager, he broke into his own Christmas present to himself, a discounted bottle of Bell's, pouring large measures as he silently ironed his white shirt and black tie for the following morning's service. He hit the sack at gone two after drinking close on to a third of the bottle, ensuring the late arrival at Anwar's final big day.

Undertakers with the next party were already shuffling in behind as Jack followed the last of the mourners out through the chapel side door to a covered patio area adorned with funeral bouquets, their natural colours made lifeless by the grey, foggy day.

He caught up with C.F., taking her arm, leading her slightly away from the hushed family group. 'Sorry, I'm late.'

She smiled gently. 'Dad would've expected nothing less from you, Jack.'

'Your mother seems to be taking it well,' he said, glancing towards the widow, who was bending down to inspect condolence messages, before reading them aloud to other relatives.

'She's glad for Dad that it's over. I'm glad for her, too.'

'And is anyone glad for you?' Jack asked.

She turned to him. 'I don't know, Uncle Jack. Are you?'

'I'm glad you're my friend. I'm glad you still want to work for me. I'm glad I can go into that crappy office and see your face beaming back at me every morning.'

'Are you trying to hit on me at my own dad's funeral?'

'Shit, no, C.F . . .' He saw she was smiling.

'You're so easy to wind up, you know that?'

'So Amy used to tell me,' he replied. 'Anyway, I just wanted to say that . . . you know . . . take your time, there's no hurry to get back to work.'

'I'm not about to malfunction, Jack,' she grinned. She pointed up to the sky. 'He's watching, you know. Dad would have a fit if I went to pieces over his death.'

'Even so, C.F . . .'

'I'll be in tomorrow. Any news on the news?'

'Slow news week, Christmas,' he said. 'The Semtex story's

gone cold again. Though I'm planning a trip to Ipswich in the New Year. Check out some of Dave Higgs's friends before plod and sundry start sticking their noses in.'

She reached into her coat pocket, pulling out a slim envelope with Jack's name written in a child-like scrawl on the front. 'He wanted me to give you this. You're honoured. He didn't write one for everyone.'

Jack took the envelope, turning it slowly in his hands. 'Christ, C.F. Now *I'm* about to go to pieces.'

'He said you would,' she replied, smiling. 'And that I'm to take good care of you.'

'*You* take care of me?'

She turned and began walking back towards the others. 'Nine-thirty tomorrow morning, Jack,' she called. 'I don't want you coming in late, either.'

Jack lifted his head, peered into the cold white fog and sighed. 'You did a great job with her, Anwar.'

He moved away, found himself a small bench amongst the evergreens, and gingerly opened the envelope.

Jack

We leave nothing behind but the best or worst of ourselves in our children.

Sorry to be blunt, but it's a dying man's prerogative. Look to your boy, shape him, then set him free.

your dear friend
Anwar
p.s. Bet you were late for the bonfire.

Ten minutes later, Jack walked slowly back out through the cast-iron gates towards his hired car, feeling a tight knot of tension coiling itself round his cold neck. He loosened his tie, telling himself it was time for a livener, a one-man wake to honour a great man turned to ashes as he'd sat contemplating Anwar's note.

However, upon reaching his car, a breathless middle-aged woman with short hair and glasses came rearing up urgently out of the fog.

'Mr Latimer?' she called from ten yards away.

Jack turned, nodded.

'My name's Audrey Baxter, and I simply have to speak to you!'

39

Picket beamed as he opened the front door. 'William, do come in. Bang on time. Great effort. Man could set his watch by a chap like you.'

William Kent followed the Chairman into the dusty hallway. 'Thanks, George,' he replied, offering a bottle of claret topped with a holly sprig. 'Merry Christmas and all that.'

'And the same to you, Bill. Have a good one, did you?'

'Quiet.'

'Same here. Damn thing went in a flash. Hardly knew where I was the last few weeks, truth be told. And Bill?'

'Yes?'

'About the other morning,' Picket went on. 'Lost my top a little. Poor you just a red rag to a bull, I'm afraid. Mind hasn't been too straight since Mikey . . . you know . . .'

'Are you feeling OK, George?' the older man asked. 'Only you seem a little . . .'

'Yes?'

'Well, agitated, I suppose.'

Picket thought it over, trying to find a mental definition of 'agitated', as the cocaine flashed a thousand unrelated images before his tired eyes. And God, was he tired. Shattered. But the joy of this stuff, the sheer crystalline beauty of it, was the eradication of the need for sleep. It didn't matter how weary his bones were, or how the muscles ached from the labour, his eyelids wouldn't close, his mind just ploughed on, churning and regurgitating plans, actions, wants, lusts and needs.

In less than three weeks, George Picket, Chairman of the Chelmsford Avenues Allotment Society, had gone from nervous first-timer, gently rubbing a tiny dab on to his upper gum – to snorting a line every four hours, convinced the very stuff that did it for Jules Verne, Sir Arthur Conan Doyle and Thomas Edison, would surely do it for him, too.

And George had been astonished at the results, with the effect that the renovations were completed two days ahead of schedule, allowing him a precious forty-eight hours to clean up, tidy, test devices and procedures before the idiot Kent was due to arrive.

So it was with some pride that he led his fellow allotment holder up the stairs on to the landing, pausing to wait outside what Kent presumed was a smaller bedroom next to the master bedroom.

'Got any plans for this goddamned millennium nonsense, Bill?' Picket asked, wondering if he was speaking too fast, if the old tosser could even hear him properly. Kent looked confused, baffled. Lord God, don't go senile on me now, Picket silently begged, suddenly aware the man was talking, but he hadn't heard a word. 'Sorry?'

'I think I'll most likely have a quiet one, George. I'm a bit too old for a knees-up.'

'Nonsense,' Picket shot back. 'Never say never and all that old cobblers, eh?'

'Yes, well. Even so . . .'

'I'm having a party, Bill,' Picket announced vigorously. 'And you're invited. In fact, you're essential. Can't back out if you wanted to . . . because . . . I'd kill you. No, no, just a joke. Mind's going wonky again. Can you hear them, Bill? Can you hear those bloody kids, can you? Can you?'

'Perhaps we should go back downstairs,' Kent suggested softly. 'Have a cuppa in the back room. All this standing –'

'Quite right,' Picket cut in. 'And we will, Bill. We damn well will. But first,' he said, opening the door with a flourish and turning on the light. 'Take a look.'

Kent stepped cautiously into the bare room, trying to fathom if, in his pain, the Chairman had turned to drink to dull the memory. And if so, then it was just as well he'd answered the note asking him to pop round and view the finished alterations when he did. Given a couple more hours, Kent suspected the man would have been passed out on the floor. He looked around. There were bars on the window, and a shiny steel bucket in one corner.

Picket stood by his shoulder. 'It's a slop bucket, Bill. You know, in case they need to go in the night.'

Kent wanted to sit down, but there wasn't an item of furniture in the room, just the barred window, freshly painted bare walls and a door to his left, set square into the middle of the wall adjoining the master bedroom at the front of the house. A door Picket marched proudly over to and opened just a tantalizing fraction.

'Pulled muscles I never thought I had getting this lot done in time. Cost a pretty penny, too. Still, I didn't buy rubbish.' Picket banged the door twice with his fist. 'Oak, bloody solid, Bill. Best hinges, cast-iron locks, galvanized-steel window bars, steel-mesh light fittings. It's about as authentic as it gets.'

'I'm not sure I . . .'

Picket beckoned Kent to the door. 'Now then,' he explained relentlessly. 'On my command, you'll open this door, lead one of them through, quick as you can, where I'll be waiting, ready with the cap.'

'George, I really think we should perhaps . . .'

Picket put a finger to his lips, silencing the confused visitor. And then slowly opened the door, studying Kent intently as the old man's eyes alighted on the suspended noose for the first time. Then the main beam. Finally the six-foot-square trap doors dominating the bare floorspace.

'My God,' Kent gasped. 'It's a gallows.'

Picket walked on to the centre of the trap door and stuck his head through the noose.

'George!' Kent squealed. 'What are you . . . !'

Picket smiled, slipped his head from the rope. 'Don't panic. I'm not about to top myself. It doesn't work. None of it does.' He jumped up and down three times on the trap doors, Kent flinching as the sound exploded off the bare walls. 'It's just for show. For my party.'

'Your party?'

'The one I'm inviting you to. You and a few others. Though I must say it's going to be quite a select gathering. Intimate is

261

the term I think my mother would have used.'

'Fancy-dress sort of thing, is it?' Kent asked, stepping cautiously forward and pressing a toe on to the join in the trap doors.

'More like a come-as-you-are.'

'It's very elaborate, George,' Kent said, examining the gleaming brass-eye Picket had spent close on two hours fitting into the rough hemp rope in order that the noose was authentically adjustable. 'Your father. He was in this . . . line, wasn't he?'

Picket nodded. 'Found part of a Home Office engineering blueprint in one of his old suitcases in the attic. All sorts of other stuff in there, too. Straps, tables, weights and measures for calculating the correct drop. There was even an old white hood in there, sort of like putting a heavy pillow case on. Used, possibly. Dark stain across the bottom of it, just where the rope would've been.'

Kent was still looking around the room, his gaze drifting from the noose through the doorway into the cell-like room beyond. 'You said I'd "lead them" through the door?'

'Proud to have you as my assistant,' Picket replied. 'Need a good man on board, someone who won't shrink from the task.'

'Er . . . who's "them", George?'

'Brian Feeling and his cohorts,' Picket replied to the uncomprehending Kent. 'Little sods that have been running riot over the allotments all damn summer. Finally managed to convince that dead-brained hack to give me a couple of names, addresses. I sent them each a Christmas card, inviting them over. We're going to teach them a lesson, Bill. One they'll never forget.'

'Those kids,' Kent replied, 'are coming here?'

'If all goes to plan.'

'You've invited them to your house? After all they've done?'

Picket nodded. 'I've told them it's tea and cakes and time to make up; but truth be told' – he dropped his voice to a teasing whisper – 'we're going to scare the living wits out of them.'

Kent took another look around the room, eyes rooted to the rope dangling menacingly from the main beam. 'I'm not sure that's such a good idea, George,' he said quietly.

Picket sighed, and leaned against the boarded-up window. 'Read a thing in the papers a while back, Bill,' he said. 'Some sort of police initiative to counteract juvenile crime. Apparently, they take these hooligans off the streets and stick them in a police cell for an hour, give them a taste of what to expect.'

'Sounds a good wheeze,' Kent cautiously replied.

'Thing was, none of these kids gave a bugger about it. All of them walked out laughing, saying it wasn't so bad, they could "handle it", or some other ridiculous phrase.'

'Probably bravado,' Kent said. 'You know, face-saving stuff.'

Picket shook his head, adopted his saddest tone. 'I think you're wrong, Bill. I think they genuinely didn't care. More needs to be done.'

'Like this?' Kent guessed, holding the rope at arm's-length.

'We're not going to hang them, Bill,' Picket laughed. 'Just scare the daylights out of them. Give them a new perspective. Simply hold them overnight . . .'

'Overnight?' Kent gasped.

'. . . put them through the routine. Charge them. sentence them, weigh them, let them stew, walk them out on to the trap, strap them, hood them, noose them.'

'Good God, George!' Kent burst out, letting go of the rope as though it was a spitting, venomous snake. 'You can't. Simply can't. Chances are they'll die of fright!'

'Faint, possibly,' Picket replied, nodding. 'But you have to remember who these vermin are, Bill. What they did to us. What they'll do to others unless we stand firm, teach them some respect.'

'It's too much, though. Far too much.'

'It's life, Bill.'

'And what about the police?'

'What about them?'

'George, you can't simply abduct a load of children. It's criminal, you'd be breaking the law.'

263

Picket smiled. 'We, Bill. We'd be arrested. And when we are, I know a money-hungry journalist who'll rush to tell the nation our side of things.'

'This is insane.'

'How many people, Bill, do you think will want to pillory us for standing up to these little runts, eh? For giving them the shock of their lives in order that they might finally start behaving like decent human beings?'

Kent stared blankly back. 'It just seems so extreme, George.'

'Perhaps it has to be. Perhaps it's the only thing that will finally get through to these kids, save them from a life in prison, the hurt they'll do to others. Innocent people, like you and me.'

'But we haven't seen them in weeks,' Kent protested weakly.

'They'll be back,' Picket replied grimly. 'Just waiting till the spring to start their little games again. We both know that.'

'But . . .'

Picket put a reassuring arm round the older man's sagging shoulders. 'Come on, Bill, think about it. It'll be a game, we'll simply be actors playing a part.' Picket flung the other arm out wide. 'And this will be our stage.'

'I'm really not sure . . .'

'Well, *be* sure, Bill. Be very sure. Be sure that if you dismissed the whining politicians and polled every law-abiding citizen in this country, they'd call for a return of the rope tomorrow. It's what we're crying out for, a return to decency, a penalty to rid ourselves of the flotsam which runs wild in every town, in every city. If you have a rotting limb, you cut it off, not pamper it with liberal understanding, social workers and head-in-the-sand ideology.'

'Yes, but . . .'

'And be sure that once these kids have been given a real taste of the people's justice, they'll never dare throw excrement through another person's property again.'

'I just don't . . .'

'And be very sure, Bill, be very sure that when we stand in court accused of abducting these youngsters, the very same nation of law-abiding men and women will rise to their feet,

264

applaud our efforts, because we actually did something. We took a step to apply a real solution. Our method worked.'

Kent stood stock-still on the trap, running his fingers slowly along the inside of the noosed hemp. For a long time he said nothing, simply listening to his own heart beat. Finally he said, 'And it's just a scare, right, George?'

Picket nodded.

'No one gets hurt?'

'A fainter at the most.'

'And we let them go straight after?'

'Absolutely.'

Kent scratched at his chin while Picket watched him like a hawk. 'We'll be arrested.'

'Let them come. Let them hear us. Let them see the children we've saved from themselves.'

'When are you planning this party for?'

Picket smiled, walked from the boarded window, ushered Kent back downstairs. 'Come on,' he said. 'Let's put the kettle on. I'll tell you all about it.'

40

It took a lot of nerve for Alex to return to the shabby front room of Cannon's house again. He had a lot to lose. Face, for one. There was no way the others were going to let him off lightly. But still the fact remained that, barring knocking on Eve Adams's door and hoping, Cannon's house was the most logical place to find her again. And after all she'd told him before Christmas, Cannon's place also seemed like a crèche compared with the potential lion's den of Eve's outwardly respectable home. The thought of meeting the girl's father filled him with a good deal more fear and repugnance than an encounter with Cannon and Co.

He'd spent a good deal of Christmas thinking about her, what she'd said. Then remembering her eyes, the damp softness of her hair, the very fragility of a girl who'd been subjected to horrors which had nevertheless failed to mar her beauty, failed to find her in the gold and purple place.

Thankfully, Alex's own parents hadn't noticed his demeanour, preoccupied, as always, with their own lives. He felt certain his dad had stayed over on Christmas night, hearing quiet voices downstairs, then two pairs of feet across the hallway beyond his bedroom. But in the morning he was gone again; his mother tight-lipped, snappy. He didn't ask why.

To his relief, Eve was at Cannon's. Sitting in the same corner, reading once more. He wondered how he should play it, cool, or straight? Simply walk over and sit by her side? Or take her hand, lead her gently back out into the street, away for a coffee, a film, perhaps? But what if she'd had second thoughts over the break? What if the whole thing was just some sort of massively cruel wind-up at his expense? And Cannon and the others were in on it?

When the time came, he opted for a small smile, which she returned, and he basked in while the warm relief crashed over.

Tony Minks had answered the door, saying nothing, running back into the fetid front room.

'Thought you'd be back, Posh,' Cannon sneered. Then pointed at Eve. 'Can't keep away from her, can you?'

The point at which he was rewarded with the smile.

'You two in love, or something?' the ginger-haired youth teased.

'Leave them alone,' Tracey said, wrapping both arms round his neck. 'Nothing wrong with love, is there?'

He pushed her away. Comment enough.

Alex went and sat by Eve. She put down the magazine, and he noticed the smell he'd been trying to remember for the last week; clean hair and the faintest trace of perfume.

Cannon continued to jeer and taunt, until suddenly he remembered something. He'd had a 'fucking shit' Christmas, but one thing was 'well weird'. A card. From Picket. He went to fetch it, returning with a cheap greetings card depicting an overweight Santa wedged in a toppling chimney pot.

'Old wanker's really lost it,' he announced. 'Fucking la-la. Wants to invite us over for jelly and fucking ice-cream.'

Damon Minks lazily scratched the back of his neck. 'What you on about?'

'It's a card, you pothead. From Picket.'

'The allotment guy?'

'Of course it's the fucking allotment guy! Jesus, how many Pickets do we know? Your brain's messed up with dope, Damon.'

'Oh, him,' Minks replied, squinting. 'He only sent me one an' all. Well, me and Giblet, like.'

Cannon frowned. 'What the fuck's he playing at?'

Alex quietly took the abandoned card and read it, before passing it to Eve. 'Wow,' he said. 'It's true. He's invited you round for tea – a party.'

Cannon gave a thin, sarcastic smile, pitched his voice into an enthusiastic squeak. 'Won't that be wonderful, eh?' Alex read the card aloud.

> Dear Mark, wishing you a very merry Christmas, and hopefully a more fruitful year for us all. How about you and your friends popping over for tea and cakes at around four on the 31st so we can all get to know one another better, and end all this silly nonsense between us?
> Yours hopefully, George Picket

Young Tony Minks immediately took up the chant. 'Picket's a wanker! Picket's a git!'

'Are you going to go?' Alex asked, then immediately regretted it. The very idea was preposterous. He coloured, wished he'd held his tongue.

'More your sort of mark, ain't it, Posh?' Cannon replied, milking the moment. 'You know, dossing round other people's houses, ripping them off for all their grub, then getting snotty about it, looking down your fucking nose at us.'

'No . . .' Alex stumbled. 'And listen, about what I said the other day . . .'

Cannon stood. '*You* go. You and Princess Butter-wouldn't-fucking-melt here. Bloody made for each other, you, her and Picket.'

Damon Minks began to giggle. 'I can just see it,' he managed. 'Thirty-first December, and while the world gets ready to party on down in the biggest knees-up in a thousand years, you and her will be kick-starting it eating cherry bakewells with a senile old git on Fourth Avenue!'

'Probably play pass the parcel,' Tracey added gleefully.

Cannon fished an opened pack of contraceptives from behind the sofa, hurled them at Alex. 'Here you are, Posh. Take some fucking balloons with you!'

Alex stood, held out a hand, which Eve took. Ignoring the cat calls and wolf whistles, he gently pulled her to her feet. Then turned to the expectant, grinning room. 'Strange thing was,' he said, voice trembling with rage and fear in equal measure. 'I first came here thinking you guys really were something.'

'We're more than you'll ever be,' Cannon growled.

'No,' said Alex a simply. 'You're just arseholes. All of you.'

'Like we're so scared, Posh.'

'Come on, Alex,' Eve whispered, tugging at his arm. 'Let's go.'

They left, and once away down the street, both vowed never to return. They'd meet at other places from now on, safe spots, as far away from Cannon's stinking front room as possible.

Over coffee, she asked him the question he knew she would. Would he consider going to Picket's, accepting the poor man's well-meaning invitation?

Alex wasn't sure.

She said she still felt guilty about what had happened the previous summer, being part of such mindless stupidity. She wanted to apologize, make things right. Maybe even offer to help Mr Picket with the allotment. Learn about growing stuff. Do something different, positive.

Alex thought long and hard, not wanting to go – yet not wanting to disappoint her, also. And wanting, more than ever, to spend as long as possible with the girl, regardless of where and when.

'Well, Alex?' she pressed.

His heart gave him no choice at all.

41

Jack chose the Waterfront on Whart Road because he knew Amy preferred it. The smell of gently roasting basil always made him want to heave, and the genteel decor was quite at odds with what he imagined a traditional Italian pizzeria should be – more chaotic, noisy, temperamental. But Amy liked it, appreciated the spartan design, expansive wine list and smartly dressed clientele.

He finished the last of his thin seafood special and refilled their glasses. 'Just think,' he said. 'Twenty-four hours from now this place will be packed to the gunwales. Whole town's going to be raving.'

She smiled. 'And you?'

'Not sure, to be honest.'

'I'm having a few friends round. Be nice to see you. Alex'd like that.'

Jack wished they'd gone for a table in the smoking section. 'We'll see. Who's sitting for him tonight?'

'Jack, he's thirteen. Quite capable of looking after himself for a few hours.'

'Right. Grow up too fast, don't they?'

She sipped at the wine. 'Do if you're not around to see it, Jack.'

He nodded, swallowed hard. 'Listen, it's like this . . .'

'Oh, God.'

He rubbed his palms on his thighs. 'Sometimes, I catch myself thinking about you, what we had, and I just think, "My God, Jack. What the fuck did you walk out on?" It's like I hear your voice on the radio, and all I want to do is be back home, pouring out a glass of red, waiting for you to come back.'

'When were you ever home?' she replied. 'Point was, you spent far too much time all over the place, digging around here, snooping over there. Christ, the thought of coming home to you and a Cabernet Sauvignon's deliriously good. But it wasn't like that, was it?'

He shrugged, tried to ward off the feeling of being exposed. 'Other times, I want to punish you, and I don't know how.'

She looked back, smiled. 'Like the other morning? Sneaking off before I woke up. You're doing a pretty good job on the punishment side of things, believe me.'

'Sorry. Guess I just couldn't face it.'

'Charming.'

'Not you. Me.'

'Cryptic as always.'

He took a sip of red. Sighed.

She reached over and took his hand. 'Let's go to a pub. I can tell you're dying for a fag. And anything's better than the heavy silence.'

'Sure. After you,' he said, catching the waiter's eye.

Back at the flat, Jack emptied the last of the Scotch into a glass and slowly closed his eyes. He couldn't remember feeling as tired. Ever.

The drink, he knew, was a temporary solution, a cruel diluter which would bide its time, come leering up in the harsh morning light to punish him with another godawful hangover when he was at his weakest. But that was several hours away.

But some thoughts couldn't be blocked or pushed away, drowned in drink. Presently, they meandered unsteadily towards George Picket – in particular the tale told him by Audrey Baxter, and the unwelcome light it had shed on the whole miserable business.

Somehow, as he'd listened to the prim, outraged woman outside the crematorium gates, nodding politely and making assurances that her side would also be told – Jack had known deep down that he was fooling the woman. Not that he disbelieved her. No – her version made a new and tragic sense of the whole sorry affair, the pieces fitting terribly neatly into place. A woman scorned . . .

271

Yet what was in it for him? Granted, the broadsheet editors would be quick with their cheque books, amazed at the sad truth behind an apparently trivial shed fire on an Essex allotment, but would money really make anything any better? And if so, how much? What price would soothe his conscience, his own professional ethics?

Crucially, how much money would it take to spare him from nightmares concerning another father struggling to do the best for his son, acting for his own benefits, perhaps out of love, even? For surely, that's how it had been. Everyone in the world loved someone, somewhere. Even George Picket. But not everyone unwittingly kills them. And while the full facts behind Picket's tale might make an interesting double-spread on a Sunday breakfast table in half a million homes, did Jack have the right to expose the old man's shame for money?

Or was it more the case, that if anyone should be so publicly vilified as duff-parent, it should be Jack himself, dad to a boy he hadn't the courage to face with his own inability to love as a father should? Because, for all Picket's misconceptions, Jack could follow the logic of what had happened, saw the real reason why the shed had burnt down that night.

As Jack now realized in the privacy of his own one-bedroomed gloomy hell – maybe the Chairman had loved his own son a good deal more than he'd ever loved his.

42

'Ah, children,' Picket enthused as he opened his front door. 'Do come in.'

Eve smiled, stepped smartly in, Alex following cautiously behind. He saw the look the tall man gave him, a cross between surprise, hunger and raw jubilation. As if Picket had never been so pleased to see anyone in his life.

Picket looked out into the Avenue. 'Just the two of you, is it?' he asked, closing the front door.

'The others . . .' Eve started, 'didn't want to come. I'm sorry.'

Picket smiled. 'Wonderful word, sorry. Covers a multitude of sins. The police kept telling me how "sorry" they were when they showed me my own son's dead head. But you'd know all about that already, eh?' He shot another look at Alex. 'Especially you, Brian. Comes as no surprise, I bet.'

Alex exchanged nervous glances with Eve, already beginning to wish they were anywhere else but here. The place was too dark, creepy and . . .

Eve screamed. A figure had appeared out of the gloom. An old man, pale-faced, rubbing his hands too fast.

'Say hello to Uncle Billy,' Picket said jovially, beaming at the startled girl. 'He's a very funny man. Knows lots of jokes.'

It was time to leave. Alex stood by Eve, taking her hand. 'Eve's got something she wants to say,' he said. 'Then we've got to go. Our mums and dads are waiting for us.'

Picket froze, frowned. Then laughed. 'But all this cake to eat?' he said. 'Pop to be guzzled. And I must thank you both so much for coming. Go? No, no, no. Can't go now, Brian. We're going to have such fun, believe you me.'

Alex turned to the older man, noticed how he couldn't meet his eye, knew instinctively this was suddenly getting very dangerous. He poked Eve in the ribs.

She said nothing, eyes widening, senses on overdrive.

'Miss Foster,' Picket prompted. 'You have something on your mind, perhaps?'

'Just that . . .' she began.

'Yes?'

'Sorry for what we did to your . . .'

'That word again.'

'I know, I'm sor –'

Picket's harsh voice erupted. 'Just can't help the empty platitudes, can you, Karen, eh?' He turned on Alex. 'Or you, Mr Brian bloody Feeling. Can't help yourselves, can you? Weaving your evil trails of devastation, without a fucking care for those you destroy along the way!'

'We've got to go,' Alex tried, his legs weak and empty, refusing to obey commands.

Picket shook his head slowly, eyes boring into the trembling boy. 'Not the same as when we last met, are we, Brian? Changed the haircut, lost a few pounds, shorter, on the whole. But then a lot of dirty water's gone under the old bridge, eh? And I suppose the devil comes in many guises.' He began climbing the stairs. 'Don't think I don't know *exactly* who you both are.'

'Come on, Eve,' Alex said, reaching for her cold, limp hand. 'This is a mistake. All of it. I'm not this Brian Feeling bloke, and she's Eve, not Karen.' He began moving her towards the front door.

'Uncle Billy!' Picket called from halfway up the stairs. 'Seems we have some reluctant guests.'

'Please, Mr Pic –' Alex began, but never finished, crumpling under a blow from a short cosh behind.

'Bastard!' Kent exploded, voice shaking. 'That's for my onions.' Then delivered another savage blow directly on to the skull.

Eve saw the body fall from her side, dumbstruck. She opened her mouth, but no scream came, just a short, empty breath.

Picket watched the old man bending and wheezing over the prone body. 'Uncle Billy's been getting in quite a state before you arrived,' he gently explained, cold eyes meeting Eve's once more. 'Used to be a commando, Karen. Still got those lightning reflexes.'

'My . . . name's . . . not . . . Karen.'

'Not so funny, is it, Karen?' Picket continued. 'Not so amusing to be on the receiving end, eh? Just like my poor Mikey was. You do remember that, don't you? You and your disgusting little boyfriend here terrorizing my boy, laughing at him, teasing him, turning him into your fool? Well, now it's come full circle, my dear.'

She started to cry as Bill Kent began pushing her firmly up the stairs. Then found the strength to scream.

And scream again.

'No one's going to hear you, Karen!' Picket excitedly joined in, bounding back down the stairs and taking her arm. 'Make as much of a din as you like! Oh, how I love a party! Up here, Mr Kent! Plenty more room inside!'

Eve twisted against Picket's grip, turning in horror to see Bill Kent struggling up the stairs with Alex's lifeless body slung limply over his shoulder.

On the landing, outside the newly converted former bedroom, Picket watched, impressed at his assistant's dogged tenacity. True, the cocaine he'd sugared Kent's tea with earlier had most probably helped, combined with a two-hour pep talk he himself had delivered, but it just went to show, Picket mused, you could never judge a book by its cover. Kent had changed from dubious participator into a full-blown psychopath in an afternoon, grunting from his efforts, almost manic to the cause. Good old Kent – man you could trust.

Halfway up, however, Picket noticed the boy's body begin to twitch. The bastard was coming round! He frantically dragged, then dumped, the awkwardly squirming girl into the austere barred room, then returned to help Kent with the boy.

Two long, clumsy, sometimes painful minutes later, both men had managed to rough-handle Eve and Alex into the cell, ignoring scratches, bites, pleas and insults. Hands had been tied behind backs, then gags applied. At which point, Picket realized he preferred it the way it was, all screams and sobs, a youthful duet of primal fear – simply too damn good on the ears to be gagged and smothered. And after all, hadn't he had to listen to their abuse year after year? He wanted to listen to something else. Their wailing swansong. His magnum opus.

So he removed the gags – chuckling all the while. Then turned the heavy deadlock on the door, feeling the surge of elation at a plan coming together, the first stages of a job well done.

For they were his now, Feeling and Foster – ringleaders, butchers of his son – trapped by their own stupidity, inside his house, the condemned awaiting execution.

Karen Foster, the little blonde tramp – she would be the first. Feeling next. How good of him to come. But then, Picket knew he wouldn't be able to stay away. They always returned, criminals to the crime. Always wanted to gloat, review the damage. But not any more. Not after midnight.

He walked slowly down to where Bill Kent sat morosely on the bottom stairs. 'There,' he said, wondering if the old man was crying. 'That's the worst of it over.'

'I . . . what happened, George?'

'You were pushed too far, Bill. We both were.'

Pale, watery eyes met Picket's. 'I hurt them, didn't I?'

'Cruel to be kind, Bill,' Picket replied, helping the trembling man to his feet. 'Just a small bruise here and there. Nothing to worry about.'

'I . . . just felt so angry. Couldn't help myself.'

An insistent pounding from upstairs. 'Listen,' Picket beamed. 'The little loves are fine. Making a din fit to wake the dead.'

'Didn't want any violence,' Kent insisted, being led away from the muted screams into the back room. 'Something just snapped. I . . .'

'There, there,' Picket cooed, sitting him down in a deep armchair by the fire. 'Neither of us wanted any violence, Bill. But needs must. You know that. We're saving these poor children from themselves, giving them a brighter future. And in a few short hours, believe me, they'll be the first ones to shake our hands, apologize, thank us for showing them our wisdom.'

'You really think so, George?' Kent pleaded. 'Only I –'

'Let's not have any more of this nonsense, eh?' Picket cut in. 'Plenty still left to do.' He walked to a shelf on the far side of the room, opening the small wooden box there and taking out two short leather straps. 'My father's,' he explained. 'One for the wrists, brought behind the back, then pinioned. Other's for the ankles, when they're on the trap. You need to dodge down, strap them double-quick, then leap clear.'

'Truth is, I feel a bit sick, George.'

'Need another brew, Bill, something to pull you together.'

'Who's "Feeling"?'

'The smug-looking one.'

'Upstairs . . . you said . . . you said he killed your son?'

Picket nodded.

'That little boy?'

The Chairman laughed. 'Is an illusion, Bill. That "little boy" commands the whole damn operation. Picked on my boy when he was a youngster, made Mikey's life hell. Don't be fooled by the appearance, Bill.'

Kent stared back, confused. 'But surely that was years ago, George?'

Picket said nothing, poured them both a fresh tea. 'It's two sugars, isn't it?' he asked, stirring the fine white crystals into the cracked china cup.

43

Twenty to nine on Millennium Eve, and the phone rang just as Jack reluctantly readied himself for Amy's party. 'Yes?' he answered.

'It's me.' Amy's voice, worried.

'Hi.'

'Is Alex with you?'

'Not unless he's perfected his invisible-man impersonation.'

'Shit!'

'What's wrong?'

'He's not here, Jack. I thought perhaps he was with you.'

'No. Haven't seen him all day.'

'Bloody typical, this is,' she said. 'I've got a houseful of guests arriving any moment, and a missing son!'

'What do you mean, missing?'

'Jack!' she hissed. 'He's not bloody here!'

'Slow down. Perhaps he's just out, or something. I mean, there's a lot going on tonight. Maybe he's out with friends. Didn't fancy the party. Can't blame the boy for wanting to spend some time with his mates.'

'What mates, Jack?'

A short pause, while Jack struggled to furnish his son with an army of obliging friends. 'Fair point.'

'Six o'clock, he said he'd be back. That's over two hours ago.'

'He's a kid. They're always late.'

'I made him promise!'

'And they always break their promises. Listen, chances are he'll come skulking in in the next half-hour. It's not like he's been gone all night, or anything.'

Amy's voice changed from anger to concern. 'It doesn't feel right, Jack. I'm worried.'

'OK. Where did he say he was going? Maybe I can go out, look for him or something?'

'Would you?'

'Sure,' Jack said, secretly glad to be given the chance to delay arriving for a while. A party with his ex-wife's friends wasn't the most appealing of nocturnal entertainments. Particularly as he suspected most eyes and unspoken conversation would be, as always, on and about the errant husband. 'He's probably decided to party with his pals.'

'It doesn't sound like him. He just went off on his bike sometime around three-ish.'

'Amy, he's a petulant, hormone-ridden teenager. The whole town's up for it tonight, and chances are he is, too.'

But it did nothing to soothe her angst. 'And you know as well as I do that town's going to be full of pissed-up morons, Jack. I don't want him wandering round out there.'

There was an audible commotion in the background, exchanged greetings, high spirits. 'They're beginning to arrive.'

'Leave it with me. I'll see what I can do.'

'Will you?'

'Sure. I'll take a look round. Like I say, he'll probably roll back drunk a little later. Just try and forget about it, eh?'

'Difficult, under the circumstances.'

'I'll bring him round when I find him.'

'OK. Thanks, Jack,' she replied. 'And Jack?'

'Yeah?'

'You be careful, too, huh?'

'Amy,' he said, grinning. 'I'm a grown man, going for a wander on the night of the biggest party in a thousand years. What could possibly happen to me?'

He replaced the phone.

44

There was a strong smell of urine when Picket and Kent entered the room. It was two minutes past ten, time to speed up procedures. Picket had spent the last few hours going through the drill with Kent, practising pinioning manoeuvres downstairs until the fumbling man managed the task with some sense of efficiency.

To his slight dismay, the distant screaming had stopped shortly after eight, giving way to an almost eerie silence, and twice he'd been tempted upstairs to check on the condemned, hoping they hadn't managed to prise the bars free, worm their little bastard bodies out through the windows and down into the night. It was an oversight, he conceded, not to install a peephole in the door, a deviation from Home Office blueprints. But with time at a premium, the Chairman had been forced to make the best job he could, and under the circumstances, felt he was to be wholly congratulated on both the condemned cell, and adjoining execution chamber, resplendent with its gleaming apparatus.

In quieter moments, he liked to think his late father would have approved, and that by following the traditional hangman's legacy to keep the craft in the family, perhaps the two of them might have acted together on the night, he assistant to the great man – father and son, united on the gallows, setting about the task with morally justified determination. Because Feeling and his rat-shit girlfriend hadn't merely robbed him of a son, but his father of a grandson, also.

And there was no other verdict in the Fourth Avenue People's Court. This wasn't to be a contentious Hanratty-type farrago. That Feeling *was* guilty had been proved, beyond all reasonable doubt. He'd lit the trail that ran to the powder keg of Mikey's destruction. His cruel jibes had pulled Mikey down, set him on the path to his murder. Feeling's pranks and wicked bullying had sapped the boy of his confidence, drained him of his ambition.

What else led a fine young boy like Mikey to end up associating himself with shameless criminals and rampant homosexuals? Certainly Picket wasn't to be blamed, devoting the best years of his life to Mikey in order to bring the boy up correctly, denying himself basic pleasures, modern conveniences, a lifestyle easily affordable if he hadn't had charge of his son.

It didn't matter to Picket who had physically killed his son, hacked off the head he once cradled so adoringly. Death was merely the endgame on a life set disastrously in motion by one boy – one youth who thought it funny to ridicule others who knew the meaning of the word 'manners'.

Further, it didn't matter what guise he came in, Picket knew Feeling would be back one day. The voices, they were proof enough that the evil boy had returned. The allotments, too. Hooligans tearing into ordinary people's lives – members of Feeling's new gang, eagerly following orders, worming their way back into Picket's life, gloating at Mikey's demise.

Fools! They hadn't reckoned that the Chairman would fight back – that he was always one step ahead. And that this time it was their turn to be bullied.

'You,' Picket barked at Eve, cowering with Alex in the far corner of the stinking room. 'Stand up!'

Gradually she stood. 'Can we go, now?'

'Please,' Alex begged, voice shot from shouting, chewing on a fingernail bloodied by endless futile attempts to dislodge the newly installed window bars.

Picket simply shook his head.

Alex began to cry.

Kent placed a set of bathroom scales on the floor. 'Stand on it,' he snapped at the trembling girl.

Picket watched, pen and clipboard in hand, amazed at how easy it was to brutalize. Eve stepped gingerly on to the scales.

Kent bent down to the weighing window. 'Six stone and three pounds,' he said, moving her back towards a wall where a height chart had been marked out. 'Five foot exactly.'

Picket noted it all down.

'Please.' Alex's voice again, veering between the octaves, choked by tears. 'We want to go. Our parents will be worried. Looking for us.'

Nothing from either man.

A gamble. 'We told them where we were going,' he said. 'They know the address. Please, just let us go. We haven't done anything wrong.'

'You've done plenty,' Picket quietly replied, nodding at Kent to place Alex on the scales.

'What's going on?' the boy asked, eyes wide with fear.

'Procedure,' Kent replied, mouth set.

'What for?'

'You'll find out.'

'Seven stone, two,' Kent barked, then pushed Alex roughly back towards the wall. Picket was again impressed at Kent's role-playing. The man really was putting his heart and soul into it. 'Height – five-four.'

Eve sat back in the far corner, drained by the sheer insanity of the situation, too weary to care. 'You're going to kill us, aren't you?' she said, finding strength in the startled look in the older man's eyes. Just the briefest flash – but she knew then that he was scared, too. Maybe more so than anyone. And tired, just like her, weakened by the madness.

She pressed on, gaze fixed on Kent as he half-heartedly pushed Alex back towards her. 'But you don't want to do this, do you?'

'Shut it,' Kent growled, becoming agitated.

'You know it's wrong, don't you?'

'Another word, and –'

'You'll hit me?' Eve said, seizing her chance, heart pounding. 'Just like Alex? A man, hitting a boy?'

'I said, shut up!' Kent yelled, feeling slightly nauseous, the amazing energy of the last few hours draining by the second. And why the hell was the girl looking at him that way? Fearlessly, almost? It just didn't make sense any more.

None of it did. He felt confused, trapped by her eyes, a deep, shining blue, like an adult's. Eyes which had seen things children should be spared from. Eyes which gave her strength to face him, the Chairman, the whole sick situation without turning away.

Eve slowly fixed her gaze on Picket, still making notes, oblivious to his assistant's hesitation. She was figuring it out, things becoming clearer, less terrifying, more comic, ridiculous. She began to laugh, tiny noises, totally alien in the otherwise starkly silent room.

Picket slowly raised his head, intrigued. Plucky, he thought, the girl Foster. Some spirit there, certainly more than Feeling, sobbing snottily behind her.

'Your dad did all of this, didn't he?' Eve said, fixing her gaze on Picket. 'Alex read it in the paper. It said he was a hangman or something.'

'Indeed he was,' Picket replied. 'And it's "Brian", my dear. Let's drop the pointless little "Alex" charade, eh?'

'They used to weigh them, didn't they, in the olden days? And measure them.'

Picket smiled. 'You're surprisingly knowledgeable.'

'Saw a film about it once. Thing about a man who'd shot a policeman on a roof.'

'Derek Bentley,' Picket replied. 'Good grief, there's a film about that, is there?'

Kent shrugged, unsure.

'They use measurements and stuff in order to work out how much of a drop to give the person they're hanging,' Eve said quite calmly.

Alex looked up, the situation becoming horrifically clear. 'You're going to hang us?' he squeaked, feeling himself start to pee involuntarily.

Picket consulted the clipboard. 'According to my father's old tables, you'll need a drop of . . . six foot seven, laddie.'

'Please, Mr Picket. Please . . .'

'Oh, do shut up, Feeling! This whining's really not you at all! Let's have a little defiance, eh?' he challenged. 'A quick chorus of "Picket's a wanker" at the very least.'

'We just want to go home.'

Picket sighed. 'I must say I'd expected something a little more acrimonious at this stage. All this blubbing is quite tedious.'

'Our mums and dads . . .' Alex started.

'Are nowhere to be seen or heard, Master Feeling. Six hours so far, and not a whisper from these so-called worried parents.' He wagged his finger, tutting. 'I don't think you told them where you were going for tea, did you, eh?' He turned to Kent. 'We all done, Uncle Billy?'

Kent nodded.

'Fine,' Picket said, allowing the older man to move swiftly past him out into the hallway, before quickly stepping out and slamming shut the cell door.

He stood silently outside for a moment, ear pressed to the freshly painted wood. 'Listen,' he whispered. 'You hear that? They're crying. I think it's both of them.'

Kent turned, nodded, took a huge lungful of unsullied air, then slowly headed downstairs for another cup of that delicious, reviving tea.

45

The third time he phoned Amy, Jack was beginning to worry. His mobile was down, and he searched for a phone box on the heaving high street, on which it seemed everyone else was very high indeed.

It was close to eleven yet still no sign of Alex.

Giggling girls in short skirts and long overcoats banged on the booth, drunken youths pressed their faces and other parts of their anatomy up against the glass. Jack buried his head into the receiver, a forefinger plugged firmly into his other ear, trying but failing to block out the near-constant audio-collage of whoops, yelps, breaking beer bottles, throbbing bass and car horns. If ever there was a living hell on earth, he thought, surely this came closest.

Failing, also, to get through to Amy, who although answering the phone, seemed less concerned about her son's whereabouts by the minute, or perhaps the glassful. During the final conversation, she was even drunk enough to insist Jack, 'Loosen up, stop being such a stuffy old bore. Alex will be fine. Tonight the world's in love, and he doesn't have to be here to feel mine.' A glowing testimony, Jack assumed, to one of her 'friend's' joint-rolling abilities.

For the second time in two hours, he headed home through the crowds, back past the heaving pubs, checking rear entrances for any glimpse of his son, passed out, perhaps, clutching a bottle of Scrumpy Jack, spittle running down his chin, hyperthermia setting in. Because, for all the warmth and jollity, the air was cold enough to kill a virgin drunk.

He walked on, up through Duke Street, passing pubs he sometimes stopped in for a swift pint or three at lunch, now temporary home to hundreds of merrymakers, bouncers perched at each doorway, sometimes taking the tens and twenties offered to slip lucky punters inside. The door of the kebab shop flashed by, Jack forced out into the street against the flow of human traffic. He crossed the road and tried the bus station one more time, walking past groups of yelling youths, studying faces without finding his son's.

By the time he returned to the flat, panic had set in. Rationalizing the feeling was hopeless, instinct driving a fast-growing knot of fear in his gut. He tried Amy once more. Still no sign of the boy.

He tried to think for a few minutes, ordering a mind which skimmed over everything yet focused on nothing. Outside, distant rhythmical thuds of fireworks began competing with the hooting of car horns.

It was too much. Yeah, he told himself, he was probably making a mountain out of the proverbial molehill, and chances were Alex was out with a bunch of mates having as much fun as the rest of the town . . . but he needed to know for sure. Needed to be told, by someone he respected, someone sober – an old friend working on this night of all nights, doing penance for a previous transgression.

The phone was answered on the third ring. 'DS Samson, how can I –?'

'Kenny,' Jack blurted. 'Thank God you're there.'

'Jack, you old sod!' Samson replied happily. 'Rung up to take the piss that I'm on the graveyard shift, have you? Listen, the amount I'm turning over tonight will get the wife and I a weekend in Paris . . .'

'No, Kenny. Listen . . .'

'No, you listen. I'm having the time of my life, sitting here doing bugger-all on triple pay, watching Uniform buzzing around like blue-arsed flies –'

'Kenny!' Jack exploded, aware he was speaking too fast, the words tumbling out in an incoherent mess. 'Please. I'm worried about Alex. He's not come back and he should've. I mean, he's not the type to stay out this late, Kenny. I've tried his mother's, but she's tripping off her bloody face, and all I can think about is –'

'Hang on, Jack,' Samson cut in, feeling the angst rip from the receiver. 'Deep breaths, take it calm and steady. Tell me from the top.'

Which Jack did, fighting the urge to drop the phone, walk back out of the door, begin the search again.

'Stay there,' Samson ordered. 'Just hold the line a minute.'

A minute which seemed like an hour . . .

'Jack, you still there?'

'Yeah.'

'All right. Your boy ever mention a young girl called Eve? Eve Adams?'

'No. Look –'

'Please, try and think about it.'

'No.'

'Certain?'

'Look . . . I don't know . . . I just want to find –'

'Cute-looking girl, blonde. Twelve years old. Only the desk got a call about four hours ago from her parents, too.'

'Yeah, fine,' Jack replied. 'Now, about Alex –'

'Jack!' Samson ordered. 'Calm down. Please. What I'm thinking is maybe the pair of them have gone off somewhere together.'

'Alex and a girl?' Jack didn't want the fairy tale, just his son. An uncomplicated reunion, nothing about missing girls.

'Hang on,' Samson said.

Jack felt the frustration rise intolerably as a muffled conversation took place between the DS and another officer.

'Look, Jack,' Samson said eventually. 'It's hell downstairs. Uniform are really stretched tonight, cell's are already heaving . . .'

'What about Alex and this girl?'

Samson sighed. 'The officer that took the call can't be sure, but he thinks the girl's mother mentioned that she was thinking of heading off to some sort of party. Swore she'd be back by six, never returned. I think an officer was dispatched to the home address earlier, but I'm buggered if I can find out what was said. The incident report looks like it's been written by a pissed dyslexic spider.

'What the fuck's this got to do with Alex?'

287

'Did he mention going to any party?'

'To his mother. Maybe. Look, I'm not sure,' Jack replied, heart racing.

'Thing is, Jack, this girl sometimes hangs around with Cannon and company.'

'Mark Cannon?'

'CCTV have spotted her several times. A group of them in the shopping centres. Nicking stuff, you know. Her and a girl called Tracey . . .'

'So what's the fucking point, Kenny?'

'CCTV have tape of your boy and this Tracey getting cosy outside McDonald's shortly before Christmas, while Cannon and his tealeaf buddies were screwing the Meadows for trinkets.'

'Fine. Can I go and look for my son now?'

'Jesus Christ, do I have to spell it out for you? Alex and this Eve kid obviously know one another. The girl tells her parents she's going over for tea and cakes at some old guy's house, then never –'

'An old guy?' Jack suddenly interrupted. 'Kenneth, you never said anything about an old guy!'

There was a pause which Jack took to be Samson looking through some notes. 'Says here on the report card . . . hang on, Jack, let me find it . . . oh yeah, here we are . . . shit, this writing's terrible . . .'

'Get on with it!'

'"Mrs Adams maintained Eve told her she was going to a party organized by an older relative of one of her friends. As it was early in the day, and the girl promised to be back by half-six at the latest, she consented. Her daughter left no note saying where she was going."'

A distant possibility was beginning to surface in Jack's mind, gradually ordering the mounting mental chaos of the previous few hours. A fleeting, innocent-sounding conversation with a kindly old man determined to right some wrongs, running with an unexpected change of heart.

'Picket,' Jack said softly.

'What's that?'

'Picket. Something he told me before Christmas. Said he

288

wanted Cannon's and the Minks brothers' addresses. Wanted to send them a Christmas card – turn over a new leaf.'

'And you gave them to him?'

'I didn't see the harm in it, Ken. He seemed genuine enough. Now I'm thinking he was the old guy the girl mentioned. Maybe he invited them over or something.'

Samson sighed. 'Jesus, won't this old scrote ever go away? I'll ring him. See if he knows what's happened. Chances are they all turned up for an hour, then buggered off somewhere to sniff glue in the park.'

'Alex doesn't do that shit, Ken. And you can't phone Picket. It's disconnected. Sod it, I'm going round there. I just get a bad feeling about all this.'

'About Picket?'

'He's not right in the head, Ken. I met someone the other day, a former lady admirer. She told me something very much at odds with the bumbling old fool we know.'

'Here we go. Such as?'

'According to her, he virtually raped her.'

'Picket? You sure?'

'*She* was. And knowing what I know about the bloke, I know who I believe.'

'Picket's a pervert?'

'And I know what happened in the shed. I know who started the fire, Ken. And why. Shit, I'm going over there. I'd appreciate it if you came, too.'

'Jesus, Jack,' Samson replied, 'I can't just walk out . . .'

'Something about the bloke I just can't trust. But maybe you're right. Maybe Alex and this girl stopped by earlier, and he knows where they've got to. Either way, I'm going. You coming?'

'Yet another Latimer-favour, eh?'

'For a favour. We'll stop by at Audrey Baxter's place. She'll give you the truth, Kenny. And nothing but.'

'Jack, all hell's going to break loose once Big Ben chimes us all in.'

'I'm begging you, Ken. Either that, or I go alone. But I can't just sit around here knowing Alex could be over there. Will you come?'

46

Inside the former bedroom, Alex and Eve sat with their backs to the cold smooth wall, having long since given up trying the barred window, inpenetrable with hard steel mesh. From outside came the distant sounds of a town in full celebration.

'That's fireworks, isn't it?' said Alex, trying once more to loosen the tight bonds round his wrists.

A half-smile from Eve. 'We're missing all the fun.'

'Wish Mark and Damon were here,' said Alex miserably. 'They'd have sorted Picket and his weird mate out.'

Eve yawned, shook her head. 'I think they were too well-prepared. We'd all have been in here, waiting. Can you imagine how Giblet would've been feeling?'

Alex tried, but couldn't, preoccupied with rescue, escape. He tried wriggling again – nothing. And where were his mum, Dad? Surely they must be coming soon? Then again, how did they know where to look? He hadn't told either of them where he was going, so innocently, just a few hours, yet a lifetime ago. The more he thought about it, the bleaker it became.

'What's going to happen?' he said at last.

'They're going to kill us,' Eve replied softly, sitting slumped against his shoulder.

'No. They're not. We mustn't think like that, Eve. Just don't. They're just trying to scare us, that's all. They're playing some sort of game with us. Did you hear them, calling us different names and stuff? They're just trying to scare us, Eve.'

'They're going to hang us,' she said softly. 'Both of us.'

'They won't,' Alex tried, feeling an ever tightening knot of nausea in his stomach.

'It's OK,' she replied, turning her head upwards towards his, managing the smallest of smiles. 'It's nice to be here with you. I'm not scared.'

He looked into her eyes, searching for any trace of fear, finding nothing but silent acceptance. 'We're going to get out of here,' he croaked. 'It's all a game, you'll see.'

'Sometimes,' she said quietly. 'Sometimes, it's like I'm already dead. Do you ever feel like that?'

'Eve, please,' he begged.

'I knew something like this would happen. He said it would – something terrible if I told anyone about what he does to me.'

'Your dad?'

She nodded. 'That night, when we walked home? I shouldn't have said anything. I'm sorry, it's all my fault.' She looked at him imploringly. 'You will forgive me, won't you?'

'We'll be fine,' he said. 'And Eve?'

'What?'

'That night – it was one of the best of my life.'

He rested his chin on her soft, blonde hair, wanting more of her, needing her closer, desperate she syphon his growing fear with her benign calm. He simply stared at the dark, heavy door, still in the midnight quiet, feeling the tears well steadily from the deepest place inside.

Twenty feet away, Picket and Kent went about their final silent preparations, the Chairman knotting a thin piece of twine round the looped rope, allowing the noose to hang at precisely the correct height from the trap doors below.

Kent laid out the white hood and leather ankle strap on a small low table just off the trap, noticing how two of the buckle holes in the pliant calf's leather had at some stage been torn into one; evidence, perhaps, of some horrendously futile struggle put up by a previous wearer.

The additional 'prop' had shocked him a little when the pair of them first stepped back into the mock-execution chamber. The Chairman, in his quest to build the perfect reproduction gallows, had since added a three-foot lever standing just off the trap, rising from the floor, bolted into a small box allowing it a graceful arc when pulled. Which was exactly what Picket allowed Kent to do – sensing the older man's nervous confusion at his latest piece of handiwork.

Silently signalling to Kent that the lever was 'all part of the act', Kent had gingerly moved the large wooden handle back and forth, supremely grateful that the trap hadn't opened.

Picket smiled back affably, then set about final adjustments to the noose, coiling then tying the spare to create a great loop next to the smaller one, just as his father's Home Office handbook had taught him.

And when at last it was ready, Picket checked his watch, finger to his lips, as the two men strained to catch the muffled conversation from the children just beyond the doorway dividing the two rooms. A sigh here, an occasional moan there, but largely both prisoners seemed reasonably subdued. Which pleased him. It was going to be a tricky operation, and he was prepared for more rough stuff if need be, especially from the Feeling boy.

But he wasn't so sure of Kent. He looked tired, drawn, simply going through the motions. He hoped his assistant's nerve wouldn't fail at the last.

Not now, not when he was so close.

Picket motioned that they should leave. The stage was set. Eight minutes till midnight. Perfect. Just time to change before the business began. He'd opted for one of his father's old suits, out of respect.

And a part of him just knew Daddy would finally be smiling.

47

Audrey Baxter hesitantly answered the door in her night-gown and slippers.

'I'm so sorry to disturb you, Miss Baxter,' Jack said as a particularly loud firework exploded close by. 'Have you got a minute?'

She stared back, confused.

'This is Detective Sergeant Samson,' he explained, pointing to the embarrassed-looking man behind his shoulder.

'Mr Latimer,' she replied curtly. 'I thought we'd agreed that I'd spoken to you about George in the utmost confidence. As it is, I must confess to feeling somewhat ashamed of the conversation, and indeed was considering contacting you in order that none of it made its way into another of your articles. I really didn't expect you to go running off to the police the moment my back was turned.'

'It's not about Mr Picket,' Jack replied. 'Well, not directly, anyway. It's concerning my son.'

'Your son?'

Samson took a step closer, flashed his warrant card. 'Have you spoken to Mr Picket in the last few days, Miss Baxter?'

'It's Audrey,' she smiled back sweetly. 'Do come in, you look perished with cold.'

'Very kind of you, ma'am,' Samson replied, stepping in and being led into a warm lounge, where there was a gently blazing coal-effect fire and a large colour television showing exuberant scenes from an expectant Trafalgar Square.

'I was about to pour myself a little livener,' she said, offering a glass of sherry to the slightly blushing policeman. 'Now, what was it you wanted to know?'

'Has Picket mentioned anything about throwing a party recently?' Jack asked, irritated at the delay.

'Not to me, Mr Latimer.' She laughed. 'Good grief, a party! The very idea seems utterly absurd. George . . . Mr Picket doesn't go in for that sort of thing.'

Samson discreetly placed his sherry on a well-polished nest oftables. 'We think he may have invited some of the children who were causing trouble up at the allotments round to his place this afternoon.'

Audrey's eyes widened in surprise. 'George? Are you sure?'

'He made no mention of this to you?'

'None whatsoever. Then again' – she looked away, studied the television – 'we haven't . . . seen eye to eye lately. He's been terribly stressed, you know. The loss of his son has . . .' She turned to face both men. 'And perhaps my interference provoked something in him. After all, we all have our breaking points, don't we? Our limits?'

Jack studied the imploring face, barely recognizable from the outraged woman who had told him so much just a few days previously. But now, it appeared she'd had time to think, mull over the implications, find excuses for Picket's behaviour, place herself at the centre of all blame. 'Audrey,' he said softly. 'Tell DS Samson what you told me about George and the shed. Remember, the phone call you overheard? The one his son made to him shortly before he died?'

Audrey's gaze darted between both men, their expectant faces. She stood quite still for a moment, then nodded her head, a tiny, delicate gesture, before sitting and cupping both hands around her own small sherry glass.

'George started the fire,' she said, voice barely above a whisper.

'Picket did?' Samson replied.

'He'd found something in there. "Stuff", he kept calling it. His son was coming to collect it. George got angry, then very sad. I heard him tell Mikey that the shed had been burnt down. This "stuff" had gone up in flames. And that he'd done it for the boy's own good.'

'Are you sure about this?'

'Absolutely. He kept saying how bad this "stuff" was, that

he'd found it in the shed, realized it was Mikey's, then destroyed it. In order that he wouldn't get into trouble.'

Samson stared back, puzzled. 'By burning down his own shed?'

'It was drugs, wasn't it?' Audrey asked sadly. 'Heroin or something. I saw the police going over the ashes the other day. They were looking for drugs, weren't they?'

Samson nodded.

'Picket burnt the shed down because he could blame the kids, Cannon and his gang,' Jack added. 'Sort of killing two birds with one stone – saving his boy, then framing the vandals who'd terrorized his precious allotment all summer.'

'And you kept all this to yourself?' Samson asked Audrey.

She nodded, face a mixture of shame and embarrassment. 'I just . . . felt for him, you know? He's a good man . . . by and large. It was only after I'd learned his son had been killed that I began to make sense of the phone call. George was so upset, trying to calm the boy . . . assuring him he wouldn't . . . you know, die. Then telling him to come home, he'd protect him. He loved him, more than anything. More than he'd ever love me.'

Jack tugged at Samson's sleeve. 'Ken,' he urged. 'I'm going round there. I've got to see if he knows anything about Alex and the girl.'

'Sure,' Samson replied, turning back to Audrey, surprised to see her standing also.

'I'll come with you,' she announced firmly. 'George isn't the easiest of men. I doubt he's even up. He's been working very hard on alterations to the house. And he won't take kindly to late visitors. Especially policemen.'

'You don't have to, Miss Baxter, really,' Samson replied, feeling a cold draft against the side of his neck as Jack headed back out into the night.

'Just let me get my coat and shoes,' she insisted, managing a smile. 'There's something I need to say to him too. Something I should have said years ago.'

'Can't it wait?' Samson asked, as the television began the final minute's countdown into the new millennium.

She took one last look at the screen before turning the set

off. 'We can spend our whole lives waiting for that one special moment,' she said. 'Then just like those people waiting for Big Ben, before they know it, it's gone. Over. Too late.'

She turned out the light and followed Samson into the bitter black.

48

Picket stood on the darkened landing, checking his watch one final time, half an ear on the distant sounds of the radio downstairs. Big Ben began its slow signature chimes heralding in the new millennium.

The moment had arrived.

He straightened his father's woollen tie, gave a last encouraging nod to Kent, then swiftly unlocked the door, flung it open, and stepped inside. Kent followed just behind, wrist strap in hand, as ordered.

He read the startled fear in their eyes, delighting as they cowered, tried pathetically to strike out, half-efforts, devoid of any real strength, of the passion which coarsed through *his* veins.

As agreed, he and Kent targeted the blonde girl first, pulling her roughly from Alex, striking out, slapping and cursing as they pulled her to her feet.

Picket held her tight as Kent untied her arms, then buckled the calf-skin strap around soft, yielding wrists.

Silence in the shocked room, save for great breaths, distant chimes from the radio, fireworks outside.

Kent stood, surprised at how easily the girl had complied. Maybe she knew, he thought, perhaps she realized the whole thing was just a game, a fantastically elaborate scare tactic. She certainly didn't have the terror resident in the boy's face, more a sense of dignified acceptance, giving herself up, making their job easier.

Picket moved smartly to the connecting doorway, unlocked it with a flourish, allowing Alex and Eve to see their fate for the first time.

The coiled noose hung silently, expectantly, just a few feet away.

'Leave her alone!' Alex wailed, terrified. 'Please, leave her alone!'

Then he watched in horror as Picket and Kent marched her away through the door, slamming it shut behind them.

'Go to the gold place, Eve,' he sobbed, curling himself into a ball. 'The gold and purple place! You're safe there. They can't touch you there!'

In the larger room, the two men marched Eve on to the trap, Kent's breathing heavy, the girl showing the first real signs of fear, struggling slightly, uselessly, in their stronger grasp.

Seconds away now. Big Ben still tolling . . .

. . . Boom . . . Boom . . . Boom . . .

Kent stopped Eve on the chalk-marked 'T', one patent-leather shoe either side, stooping to pinion her ankles, noticing a trickle of urine running between the closed legs.

Heart pounding, looking up, he saw Picket place the white bag over her head, followed an awful moment later by the noose, round to the front, slip-knot under the right-hand side of the lower jaw, just like the manual, hours of training on an old tailor's dummy paying off on the night.

. . . Boom . . . Boom . . .

Kent moved away from the trap, finally taking in the ghastly scene in its entirety. The girl, strapped, hooded, noosed, alone, white bag blowing with her rapid, constricting breaths.

He looked to Picket, desperately searching for the man's eyes, a signal to take the girl down. Surely he wasn't going to let her stand there any longer? She was almost certain to faint. Give the signal, man! he silently begged, keen to free the child.

But Picket never did.

Downstairs, Big Ben heralded in the new millennium, sending him lunging for the wooden lever. Kent watched in transfixed horror as the Chairman knelt before removing a hidden cotter-pin at the bottom of the mechanism . . .

Then pulled the handle sharply towards him.

As Kent fell in a faint, the last thing he saw was the centre of the room disappear, and with it the body of Eve Adams.

49

'Jesus!' Jack exclaimed, panting. 'That was a hell of a crash! What's going on in there?'

Samson rang the doorbell, a cold ear pressed against the wood. 'Don't think it works,' he said, trying the letterbox flap. A firework powered into the sky and burst nearby. 'Christ, look at us, Jack. The whole world's celebrating and we're trying to knock up an old man and ask him about your boy.'

'There's definitely lights on inside,' Jack said, backing up to take in more of the front of the house. 'Upstairs, at any rate. Looks like he's boarded the front bedroom up, and the lounge underneath. He's in there, I know he is. Probably working on his conversion.'

'What, at this time?' Samson asked, incredulous. A party spilt out a few doors away, disgorging a happy conga weaving its way noisily up the street.

'Something's happened in there,' Jack said above the noise. 'He was working on a new bedroom floor. Perhaps the silly sod's fallen right through.' He tried peering through the boarded up downstairs window. 'Can't see a thing. Or hear anything, either.'

Samson tried to ignore the streetlife, car horns, fireworks, and concentrate. 'Damn-all, Jack.'

Audrey Baxter returned from the side of the house, her face pale under the orange street-lights. 'About your party,' she said slowly. 'I think they're still here. That is, unless George is now repairing children's bikes as a hobby.'

Downstairs, in the lounge which now played the part of

execution pit, Picket sniffed another line of cocaine, then set about taking the girl down, lifting the lifeless body a little in order to free the hooded head from the noose.

Next he removed the white cap, noticing to his satisfaction that all was correct – a near perfect break between second and third neck vertebrae, instant death. The construction, planning, height and weight tables, had all come together remarkably smoothly. Even the idiot Kent hadn't faltered. Fainted, granted, but served his purpose well, played the part to his unwitting best.

Now came the difficult bit. Laying the body down, Picket began his way back upstairs, two at a time, back into the execution chamber, and set about hauling up the trap doors, readying the rope for the Feeling boy.

Pulse racing, he stopped to consult the tables, find the mark for the evil bastard. There it was – a drop of six-seven, eight inches shorter than the girl's.

What was that?

He froze, ears pricked.

A pounding from somewhere. Downstairs? The front door? Merrymakers? Or others – the rest of Feeling's hooligan tribe, out to rescue their beloved leader? He'd wondered when they'd show. But at least he'd got this far. Now to finish the job.

Heart racing, Picket fetched the stepladders from the hall-way, stood them under the beam and began making the adjustments for Alex's death, as all the while, the gently breathing figure of William Kent lay sprawled nearby.

'It's no good!' Jack shouted, pounding at the door. 'He's not going to answer it!'

'Calm down, Jack,' Samson replied, dragging his friend away. 'Perhaps there's another way.'

'He's got Alex in there! I know he has!'

Audrey piped up. 'The back door's locked, too. But there's a conservatory. Maybe we could break the glass, let ourselves in that way?'

Kent sat up to see the Chairman retying the noose. Everything was fuzzy, swirling, bright sparks dancing before his unfocused eyes. What had happened? His back ached from a stabbing pain caused by his collapse, whilst horrific images of the young girl falling rushed into his dazed mind.

'Where is she, George?' he mumbled, managing to slowly stand.

'Safe and sound, don't you worry,' Picket replied, tying off the twine. 'Had a bit of a funny turn, Bill. Thought I'd let you come to in your own time.'

'She . . .' Kent pointed to the closed trap.

'She's fine,' Picket repeated. 'Just a little shaken up, that's all.' He put the stepladders against the far wall. 'Right,' he said brightly. 'Time for the next one.'

'But she fell. The doors, they . . .'

'Eyes are playing up, Bill. She's downstairs drinking tea. Right as rain. Bit snively, but took it well, really.'

'I don't feel so good, George.'

'Plenty of time for rest later,' Picket replied, walking purposefully to the connecting door. 'Here's your strap. Same drill as before. You're doing fine, Bill. Top-draw, stuff.' He smiled. 'Knew I could count on my old friend Bill.'

'I need to sit down, George. Feel shaky all over. Just for five minutes. Is that banging I can hear downstairs?'

'Just the madding crowd, George. Celebrating the big moment.'

'I've got to rest.'

'After this one,' Picket quietly insisted. 'I promise.'

'Well, what are we waiting for?' Jack asked impatiently.

'It's not as simple as just smashing our way into a property, Jack,' Samson replied. 'I've got to have grounds.'

'And they're not grounds?' Jack shouted, pointing to the two abandoned bicycles on the black back lawn. 'One of those is Alex's, for God's sake!'

'And there could be any number of innocent explanations, Jack.'

'Those kids are in there, Kenny, I know they are.'

'Listen, I need more than just a hunch . . .'

Audrey Baxter pushed both men aside, before smashing a

small glass pane nearest the door handle with a large stone. 'There,' she said, turning to Samson. 'Looks like there's been a robbery. Is that grounds enough, Detective?'

Picket and Kent worked on, oblivious to the distant tinkle of breaking glass, the Chairman pulling Alex roughly by the hair through the connecting door into the chamber.

'His hands, Bill!' he gasped. 'Strap the bugger's hands.'

Kent brought one arm up, then the other, following the orders in a trance, smothering the urge to vomit that the hot and cold flushes brought with them.

Jack dashed through the small back room out into the dimly lit hallway, drawn by screams and voices from upstairs. 'Alex!' he cried, bounding up the stairs three at a time, adrenaline doubling every muscle.

Behind, Audrey Baxter stopped suddenly, eye caught by a small, slumped figure of a girl on the empty front-room floor. 'My God,' she said, walking slowly over, ignoring the terrible commotion directly above her head. 'What's he done to you?'

But the little figure didn't reply, already cold to the touch. Shock driving the basest emotions, Audrey knelt beside the body, reached over and cradled it in her arms.

'For God's sake, man, hold him still and upright!' Picket cursed, struggling to strap Alex's ankles. A bead of sweat fell from his forehead on to the scuffed, chalk-marked trap. His hands fumbled with the buckle as the boy wriggled like an eel. 'I said hold him still!'

Alex felt as if his head would explode. The speed, frantic activity, obliterating everything but the urge to kick out, flee this wretched place. A hand gagged his terror, and he bit deeply into it . . . down to the bone . . .

Kent let out an agonized yelp, then flung both hands round the boy's chest, feeling the madly pumping heart against his forearms. Picket hooded Alex from behind, then slipped and tightened the noose over the still-protesting head. Kent rushed clear from the trap.

Picket leant in close, breathing heavily, shattered by the effort. 'Brian Feeling,' he whispered. 'I sentence you to death for the wilful murder of my son. Die like the filth you are!'

Jack shoulder-barged the nearest door. Then again, ignoring the pain, driven on by Alex's audible struggles beyond. It was useless.

Samson came up swiftly behind, drawn by the racket, urgently radioing for help.

Jack turned in utter despair, to see Samson madly pointing at an open doorway further down, bright light spilling out on to the gloomy hallway. Jack was there in a second, rushing the empty room, turning to his left, speeding through the open connecting doorway . . . straight into a hell he'd never forget for the rest of his life.

Audrey Baxter looked at the deep red burn on the young girl's neck, then gradually lifted her gaze to the ceiling above, ignoring the din, eyes drawn to a thin beam of light flickering through a long, straight crack directly above her head.

'Oh, my poor child,' she whispered slowly, realizing the hideous significance of the two great panels above. 'My poor, poor child.'

Mind racing, she set the body gently down, moved quickly from the room to find Picket's deep armchair.

For an agonizing moment, Jack simply froze – taking it all in. Picket, standing over a huge lever. An old man slumped against the far wall, and Alex, hooded, strapped and noosed from a thick rope tied to a beam above his head.

Then he found his voice. 'Alex!'

A muffled reply. 'Dad!'

'Another step closer,' Picket warned, gripping the lever. 'And the boy goes the same way as the girl did.'

'What the fuck are you doing, Picket?' Jack gasped, as Samson finally managed to open the main doorway out on to the landing.

Picket turned to the shocked detective. 'Same to you,' he hissed. 'One step closer, and he drops!'

303

'Let him go, George,' Samson replied, struggling to control his breathing. 'Just let the boy go.'

'Oh, I will,' Picket replied, smiling. 'All the damn way to hell. But I must say it's very nice to have a gentleman of the press here to witness righteous justice carried out on my son's murderer.'

'That's my son, you sick fuck!' Jack exploded, throat dry with fear, hands shaking with rage. 'That's my boy – Alex Latimer.'

'Dad,' the voice called out weakly from under the hood.

'Just stay calm, Alex,' Jack shouted, watching as he began to sway slightly, legs twitching. 'Stand very still, Alex! Don't move now. Everything's going to be all right. I promise.'

'How touching,' Picket observed, hands tightening on the lever. 'But you see, once again the deluded reporter is labouring under a colossal misapprehension. This "boy" you know to be your son, is, in fact, Satan's child – Brian Feeling . . .'

'Picket!' Jack growled, unable to stand the sight any longer. 'Just let him go!'

'. . . a very naughty little boy indeed. A boy in need of a firm hand. A bit of a jolt, perhaps.'

'George,' Samson warned from the doorway. 'The police are on their way. It's all over, George. Move over to me now, slowly.'

'Can't do that, I'm afraid.'

'Now, George.'

'No,' said Picket simply, pulling the lever quickly towards him.

'Alex!' Jack screamed, watching in terror as the floor became a gaping mouth which greedily swallowed his son.

Audrey Baxter had worked feverishly, shifting whatever furniture she could find to form a crude pile below the closed trap doors. Then urgently scoured the downstairs for cushions, towels, tea-towels, coats, anything soft to lay on the ungainly heap, praying to every God in her heaven for precious time – just a few seconds more.

She was breathlessly throwing on a pile of unwashed

seat covers when the ceiling opened, and the boy dropped through, crashing on to the pile, screaming in agony, but alive . . .

Jack rushed to the edge, peered down, saw Audrey clamouring to hold Alex, struggling to remove the white hood, calm the hysterical boy, relief flooding over him that the rope wasn't straight, Alex wasn't dead at the end of it.

Picket stood quite silently, smile evaporating, staring disbelievingly at the rope's floppy slack which betrayed his carelessness.

The boy Feeling still lived – Impossible!

The devil had once more protected his own! The 'father', the vile reporter man – he'd been the one to ruin it, in cahoots with the whore Baxter woman. And now he'd die, then her, and the cringing policeman – they'd all die – then Feeling would be brought back up again . . .

Roaring, Picket leapt across the edge of the open trap, crashing Jack against the wall, fingers round his throat, squeezing . . . squeezing . . .

Samson moved in fast, kidney-punching the man twice, shocked at Picket's strength, his resistance to the blows, the unfailing grip on Jack's neck.

'Die, you bastard!' Picket roared, showering Jack in white flecks of warm spittle.

And from somewhere deep inside, as the world began to dim, and reality started to slip and slide, Jack found a tiny nugget of unused strength, saw it gleaming gold in the palm of an old friend. He reached out, took it, and Anwar's smiling face disappeared from his mind.

Jack's final effort was a crushing knee to the testicles which, many years ago, had once spawned a simple boy who would do anything to please.

Picket gagged, stared back in shock, then utter disbelief. The grip began to falter. He took a step back. Then another as Samson tried in vain to stop him, the heavy woollen jacket slipping through his grasp.

Still frowning, eyes boring into Jack's, Picket fell through the open trap, turning horribly. Except the Chairman didn't fall feet-first like his victims. George Picket's head collided brutally with a corner of an old dresser inadvertently put there by the only woman who had ever really loved him.

From inside the pit, Audrey Baxter screamed and screamed.

50

At ten past four on the morning of the first of January, 2000, Jack Latimer walked slowly out of Broomfield Hospital's A and E department. A familiar figure beckoned from a bench opposite. He wandered over, pulling his coat tighter round his bandaged neck, then sat, gazing at the stars in the clear night sky.

'Didn't know you smoked cigars,' he croaked, using painfully swollen vocal cords.

Kenneth Samson drew on the crumpled panatella. 'Found it in my top pocket,' he replied. 'Jenny must have put it there for the big moment. Fancy a pull?'

Jack took it, watching the tip burn fiery red as he inhaled. 'Good woman, your Jenny.'

'A diamond. How's Alex?'

'Sedated,' Jack replied, feeling the hot smoke rip at his raw throat. 'Amy's still with him up there. Broken shoulder, neck burns, busted ankle, shock, trauma . . . seen the millennium in in some style, hasn't he? Hopefully, he'll pull through.'

'Kids,' Samson sighed. 'Indomitable, aren't they?'

'Eve Adams wasn't.'

Samson took back the cigar. 'Just spent the best part of an hour with her parents.'

'Shit job, yours, isn't it?'

'Doesn't seem right, does it? Not tonight of all nights. I mean, three-quarters of the western world's going to wake up with a hangover, and Mr and Mrs Adams are going to start 2000 without a daughter.' He paused. 'Were they close, her and Alex?'

Jack shook his head sadly. 'Never seen her before in my

307

life. Alex has called out her name three times so far. God knows what we're going to tell him.'

'Shit job being a parent, too, sometimes.'

A lone car sounded its horn somewhere in the melancholy distance. Jack stood. 'I suppose Picket's house is crawling with your mob?'

Samson nodded. 'Uniform sealed it all off, special team from HQ arrived to take over. Same old story, Jack. We'll get all the paperwork, they'll get the glory.' He inhaled deeply. 'Still, you've got the exclusive you've always dreamt about.'

Jack stood, looked around slowly. 'I don't know, Kenny,' he replied. 'Maybe I'll leave it to the boys from the tabloids. Place will be crawling with them this time tomorrow.'

'But you've got the inside story,' Samson insisted. ' "I grappled on the trap with a madman" – by Jack Latimer. It's the big one, Jack.'

The tired reporter managed a half-laugh, swallowing back a burning cough. 'Joke, isn't it? All these years I've prayed for something like this to happen, but now it has . . .'

'Don't bottle out, Jack. Not now.'

He turned to his friend. 'Something in Picket's eyes, Kenny. Just before he went over. Something that will haunt me till my dying day.'

'What?'

'Recognition.'

'Come again?'

'Know what he was doing in that room, for all his insanity?'

'Murdering innocent kids.'

'No,' Jack replied. 'He was doing exactly the same thing as I was – trying to kill the person he thought had murdered his son. Madness, yeah, but born from the loss of the thing he loved most in this world. Maybe the only thing, Kenny.'

'You're going soft on me, Jack.'

'Perhaps I'm no better than he was, because I'll tell you this, God knows where I found the strength from, but I wanted to kill that evil bastard so badly.'

'Jack, listen to me . . .'

'And for all the conversations we had, all the times we

ever met, that last look was the only time we ever really communicated.'

'You're talking bull, Jack. It's the shock.'

'It wasn't fear I saw, or anger, or madness – but something else. Sadness, Kenny. Sadness that he failed to avenge his boy.'

'You'll feel different when you've slept on it, Jack.'

'I doubt it. I really do.'

Samson yawned, stretched, then stubbed out the cigar. 'How about you doing me a favour?'

'Name it.'

'Go back in there, get Amy, go home – together.'

'No. She wants to stay by Alex. So do I.'

'You've already asked?'

'An educated guess.'

'Yeah, and to assume makes an ass out of you and me,' Samson replied. 'Just ask her. I'm fed up of your miserable face whenever you talk about her latest boyfriend, or whoever.

Jack thought about it. 'Maybe.'

Samson hugged his friend. 'Let's do this again sometime, eh? What do you say, about once every thousand years?'

'Book me in,' Jack replied, allowing himself his first small smile in hours. 'See you around, Kenny.'

'With you, Jack, it's inevitable.'

'And thanks. I couldn't have done it without you.'

'I know,' Samson replied. 'Now either get in that hospital and make it up with Amy, or get home and start writing the story. You want to make it up to me? Make me a hero, a one-day broadsheet wonder. Sergeant Kenneth Samson, ably assisted by Miss Audrey Baxter – suburban crime-fighters!'

'Maybe I could do both.'

'Ta-ra, Jack.'

Jack watched as Samson headed slowly back towards the car park, eventually disappearing into the gloom. He turned his head painfully to the bright blazing lights of the hospital, let out the biggest sigh his throat would allow, then began walking slowly back towards it.